TEACHER'S EDITION

Progress™
Mathematics

1

**For additional online resources, go to www.SadlierConnect.com
and enter the Teacher's Access Code:**

State	Access Code	State	Access Code
Alabama	SBIP01AL1X	Missouri	SBIP29MOQW
Arizona	SBIP04AZ1L	New Jersey	SBIP34NJL6
Arkansas	SBIP05AR1C	New York	SBIP36NY9Y
California	SBIP06CA89	North Carolina	SBIP37NCT6
Colorado	SBIP08CO1P	Ohio	SBIP39OHPT
Connecticut	SBIP09CT17	Oklahoma	SBIP40OKL1
Florida	SBIP12FL1L	Pennsylvania	SBIP42PA39
Georgia	SBIP13GA18	South Carolina	SBIP45SC9Y
Illinois	SBIP17IL1S	Tennessee	SBIP47TN1V
Kentucky	SBIP21KY1J	Texas	SBIP48TXR4
Louisiana	SBIP22LA23	Virginia	SBIP51VIPK
Massachusetts	SBIP25MA1R	Wisconsin	SBIP55WI2K
Michigan	SBIP26MIPR	All Other States	SBIPNA13AX
Mississippi	SBIP28MS11		

S® Sadlier School

TEACHER'S EDITION

Cover: *Series Design:* Studio Montage; *Title design:* Quarasan, Inc. **Photo Credits:** Cover: Corbis/Scott Speakes: *top left*. Getty Images/Jill Buschlen: *bottom left*; Tim Hall: *bottom right*; Purestock: *top right*. Used under license from Shutterstock.com/ RoboLab: *background*. Interior: Blend Images/Jose Luis Pelaez Inc: T3; Corbis/Ocean /2/Dave J. Anthony: T15; Ocean/2/Siede Preis: T15 computer *inset*. Dreamstime.com/Nyul: T17; Yobro10: T9. Masterfile (Royalty Free Division): T12; Alamy/PhotosIndia.com LLC: 8 *top*. Corbis/Scott Speakes: vi *center*. Dreamstime.com/Viktor Gladkov: vi *top right*. Getty Images/Asia Images: 160 *top*; Dorling Kindersley: 161; Maskot: 206 *top*; Mint Images - Frans Lanting: 9; Tetra Images: 94 *top*. Punchstock/Photographer's Choice: 95. Used under license from Shutterstock.com/axz700: 207 *bottom*; Elenamiv: 207 *background*; elisekurenbina: vi *bottom left*; FocusDzign: vi *top left*; Jana Guothova: 8 *bottom*, 94 *bottom*, 160 *bottom*, 206 *bottom*; Ian 2010: vi *bottom right*; Frank L Junior: 207 *top*; pjhpix: 207 *center*; RoboLab: 1, vi *background*. **Text Credits:** Common Core State Standards Copyright © 2010. National Governors Association Center for Best Practices and Council of Chief State School Officers. National Mathematics Advisory Panel. *Foundations for Success: The Final Report of the National Mathematics Advisory Panel*, U.S. Department of Education: Washington, DC, 2008. All rights reserved. **Illustrator Credit:** Bob Holt

William H. Sadlier, Inc.
9 Pine Street
New York, NY 10005-4700

Printed in the United States of America.
ISBN: 978-1-4217-3161-2
1 2 3 4 5 6 7 8 9 WEBC 18 17 16 15 14

Contents

Access Your Digital Resources

Get Started

1. Go to www.SadlierConnect.com.

2. Log in

Don't have a username and password? Self register! Teachers click "Get Started!" in the Teacher Registration section.

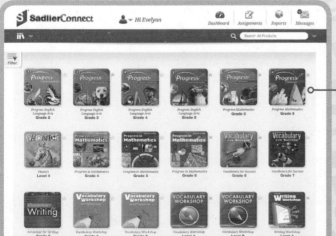

3. Select your program to begin accessing content.

With one username and password, you now have access to all your Sadlier Mathematics and English Language Arts content.

Contents

continued next page

Contents

continued next page

Contents

Program Overview

Progress Mathematics is a streamlined, yet comprehensive K–8 supplemental mathematics program that provides standards-based instruction, scaffolded practice, and assessment for the critical skills and concepts of each grade level.

In *Progress Mathematics*, students will:

- Build understanding of key mathematical concepts using multiple representations of a skill.

- Model mathematics with real-world problems to make sense of math and apply their knowledge.

- Share their thinking and reason mathematically while developing academic vocabulary.

- Use higher-level thinking skills and apply levels of Webb's Depth of Knowledge (DOK) with rigorous, cognitively-demanding independent practice items.

- Regularly apply the National Council of Teachers of Mathematics (NCTM) Process Standards—communication, reasoning, representation, connections, and problem solving—in all aspects of learning mathematics.

With the support of a comprehensive Teacher's Edition, teachers will be able to:

- Scaffold student learning with easy-to-use, comprehensive lesson plans.

- Use student assessment data, both observational and formal, to inform and redirect instruction.

- Understand the progression of skills and concepts and how they unfold within a grade level and across the grade levels to help students make connections.

- Support diverse learners, including English language learners, struggling learners, and those needing extended learning opportunities.

- Access online and professional development resources to enhance instruction.

Built to Support the National Mathematics Advisory Panel (NMAP) Report

The instructional and programmatic features of *Progress Mathematics* were built to support the findings and recommendations of the National Mathematics Advisory Panel (NMAP) in the areas of **Curricular Content**, **Learning Process**, **Instructional Practices**, and **Assessment of Mathematics Learning**.

NMAP Findings & Recommendations		How Addressed in *Progress Mathematics*
Curricular Content	Focused, coherent progression of mathematics learning, with an emphasis on proficiency with key topics, should become the norm in elementary and middle school mathematics curricula. (p. xvi) The mathematics curriculum in Grades PreK–8 should be streamlined and should emphasize a well-defined set of the most critical topics in the early grades. (p. xiii)	The table of contents of each grade level is organized around a focused, coherent group of mathematical topics to help build students' understanding of key skills and concepts. Lessons at each grade level focus on the Benchmarks for the Critical Foundations of the grade levels as defined by NMAP and the NCTM Curriculum Focal Points. *Learning Progression* charts at the beginning of each Unit in both the Student Worktexts and the Teacher's Editions describe how skills and concepts are developed within and across grade levels.
Learning Process	To prepare students for Algebra, the curriculum must simultaneously develop conceptual understanding, computational fluency, and problem-solving skills. (p. xix) Use should be made of what is clearly known from rigorous research about how children learn, especially by recognizing the mutually reinforcing benefits of conceptual understanding, procedural fluency, and automatic (i.e., quick and effortless) recall of facts. (p. xiv)	Skills and concepts are taught through a consistent lesson design (Guided Instruction, Guided Practice, Independent Practice), which provides routine opportunities with fluency practice, concept development, application problems, and daily formative assessment opportunities. The Guided Instruction section focuses on developing conceptual understanding of mathematical skills/concepts through Understand-Connect instructional presentations, often using models to help students visualize math and make connections. The Guided Practice offers students an opportunity to practice their newly learned skills with teacher support and to collaborate with other students. The Independent Practice section provides intentionally sequenced and scaffolded exercises so that students build knowledge to reach the expectation of the learning objective. Application problems require students to apply the four-step problem-solving model (Read-Plan-Solve-Check) to efficiently and accurately solve problems. Daily ongoing review in terms of **fluency practice** is available online at **www.SadlierConnect.com** and is identified at point of use in each lesson of the Teacher's Edition.

NMAP Findings & Recommendations		How Addressed in *Progress Mathematics*
Instructional Practices	High-quality research does not support the contention that instruction should be either entirely "student centered" or "teacher directed." Research indicates that some forms of particular instructional practices can have a positive impact under specified conditions. (p. xiv) High-quality research does not support the exclusive use of either approach. (p. xxii)	*Progress Mathematics* was built on the Gradual Release of Responsibility instructional model (Pearson and Gallagher, 1983). Each lesson incorporates all three steps of the Gradual Release of Responsibility model beginning with direct and guided instruction (I do it.), guided practice (We do it.), peer collaboration (You do it together.), and concludes with independent practice (You do it independently.).
Assessment	Teachers' regular use of formative assessments improves their students' learning, especially if teachers have additional guidance on using the assessment results to design and individualize instruction. (p. 47)	*Progress Mathematics* provides a range of formative and summative assessment opportunities to help guide students to mathematical proficiency. Observational Assessment suggestions in the Guided Practice section of each lesson in the Teacher's Edition offer formative assessment opportunities to gauge students' conceptual knowledge. Each unit introduction includes a *Progress Check* that allows students to focus on the unit's key skills and concepts, self-assess before the learning, and reflect on progress at the end of the unit. It also provides data for teachers to determine if students need additional instruction on precursor content in order to successfully master new content introduced in that unit. *Unit Reviews* and *Unit Performance Tasks* also support teachers in determining students' level of mastery.

Flexible Program Use

Progress Mathematics lessons focus on the grade-level key skills and concepts and combine solid content with a pedagogically-sound lesson design that simplifies the instructional process.

Progress Mathematics can be used as:

- Supplemental lessons in a core Mathematics program.
- Targeted preparation materials for state standardized assessments.
- Support for individual or small group instruction on a particular skill or concept.

Diverse Grouping Models

The *Progress Mathematics* program employs diverse grouping and instructional models to help teachers provide effective instruction in key mathematical skills/concepts.

Guided Instruction The program uses **whole-class** instruction to provide direct skill instruction and think-aloud modeling while the students follow along with the teacher, helping students conceptualize skills and concepts through modeling and reasoning.

Guided Practice Students work through scaffolded-practice problems of increasing complexity, independently or in small groups, as the teacher circulates around the classroom to gauge understanding of the concepts and skill being learned.

Independent Practice Lessons offer independent application practice requiring students to use their critical-thinking skills and apply their math knowledge.

Foundational Skill Support and Fluency Practice

Foundational skills lessons and fluency practice are provided in the following ways in *Progress Mathematics*.

- A comprehensive Foundational Skills Handbook, located in the back of this guide as well as in the Student Worktext, provides a review of *all* prerequisite mathematics needed to understand the grade-level concepts and skills.
- Fluency practice is available online providing students with the opportunity to build their skills of performing calculations and solving problems quickly and accurately in order to meet the grade level fluency expectations.
- Problem-Solving Model offers students a four-step model as an approach to solving problems.

Student Worktext

(in print and eBook formats)
Organized around a focused, coherent group of mathematical topics, the standards-based instruction includes clearly-stated models, multiple representations of skills, a focus on the critical areas of each grade level, and connections between topics. ▶

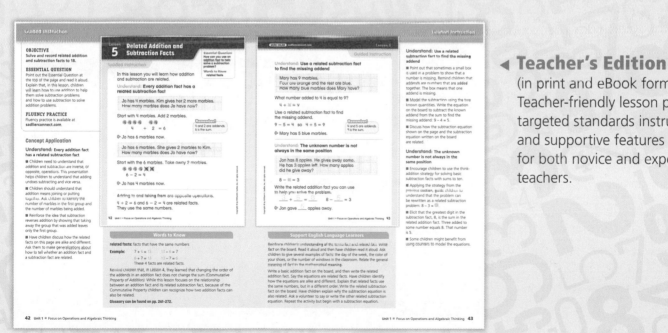

Grade 1 Pages 42–43

Grade 1 Teacher's Edition Pages 42–43

◀ Teacher's Edition

(in print and eBook formats)
Teacher-friendly lesson plans with targeted standards instruction and supportive features suitable for both novice and experienced teachers.

Progress Monitor*
(Optional Purchase)

Four comprehensive Benchmark Assessments to identify instructional needs as benchmarked against grade level mathematical skills and concepts. ▶

*Items are mapped to CCSS.

28. 9 + 2 = ■

Write a related subtraction fact to find the sum.

_____ − _____ = _____

29. Nick draws 6 stars.
Tess draws 8 more stars than Nick.

How many stars does Tess draw?

Tess draws _____ stars.

Explain how you solved the problem.

_____

_____

12. Which show the same number?
A twenty-six and 60 + 2
B 60 + 2 and 20 + 6
C twenty-six, 26, and 60 + 2
D twenty-six, 26, and 20 + 6

13. Which shape has exactly 5 angles?

A △   B ◇

C ⬠   D ⬡

14. Which equation shows the total number of circles in this array?

A 4 + 4 + 4 = 12
B 3 + 3 + 3 = 9
C 3 + 4 = 7
D 4 + 4 + 4 + 4 = 16

39. How many tens are there in 100?
A 1
B 10
C 100
D 1,000

40. How many centimeters longer is the truck than the car?

A 9 centimeters
B 5 centimeters
C 4 centimeters
D 1 centimeter

Grade 1 Progress Monitor

Grade 2 Progress Monitor

Grade 2 Progress Monitor

Online Digital Resources

A rich array of online resources at **www.SadlierConnect.com** supports program implementation and extends learning.

Home Connect Activities support family member involvement and help create associations with math in real-world situations. ▼

HOME CONNECT... UNIT 1

Conversation Starter

Make up an addition word problem that can be solved using models, drawings, and equations. For example, *I have 4 pennies in my pocket. There are 9 pennies on the table. How many pennies are there in all?* Work with your child to model the problem using pennies or drawings. Then have your child write an equation to solve the problem. Make up a subtraction word problem. For example, *I had 12 marbles. I gave 4 marbles to my friend. How many marbles do I have left?* Help your child model the problem and write an equation to solve it. Continue to create other word problems that involve addition or subtraction with numbers 20 or less.

Problem 1
Make a drawing to model the problem.

Write and solve an equation.

_____ + _____ = _____

Problem 2
Make a drawing to model the problem.

Write and solve an equation.

_____ − _____ = _____

Problem 3
Make a drawing to model the problem.

Write and solve an equation.

_____ _____ _____ = _____

Grade 2 ▪ Unit 1 ▪ Focus on Operati

Grade 2 Home Connect

HOME CONNECT... UNIT 2

Conversation Starter

Count by 5s with your child. Start at 5 and count up to 50 (5, 10, 15, 20, 25, 30, 35, 40, 45, 50). Then count by 10s with your child. Start at 10 and count up to 100 (10, 20, 30, 40, 50, 60, 70, 80, 90, 100). Then have your child count by 5s or 10s to complete the dot pictures.

Count by 5s to make a picture.

15
20
10   25
            • 30
Start 5
50
    45   40   35

Count by 10s to make a picture.

30
20   50
Start 10   40
            • 60
100
    90   80   70

Grade 2 ▪ Unit 2 ▪ Focus on Number and Operations in Base Ten

Grade 2 Home Connect

HOME CONNECT... UNIT 3

Activity

Work with your child to use an inch ruler to measure the lengths of various objects, such as a book, a phone, or a pen, etc. Have them record the length of each object they measure in the table in the Length in inches column. Then measure the same objects to the nearest whole centimeter, using a centimeter ruler. Record those measurements in the Length in centimeters column. Discuss with your child the pattern they see in the table. Point out that for each object, it took more centimeters to measure the length than it did inches.

Object	Length in inches	Length in centimeters
	about 5 inches	about 14 centimeters

Grade 2 ▪ Unit 3 ▪ Focus on Measurement and Data

Grade 2 Home Connect

Print and Digital Resources

Unit Performance Tasks

provide practice opportunities for Performance Tasks related to the content of each unit. ▶

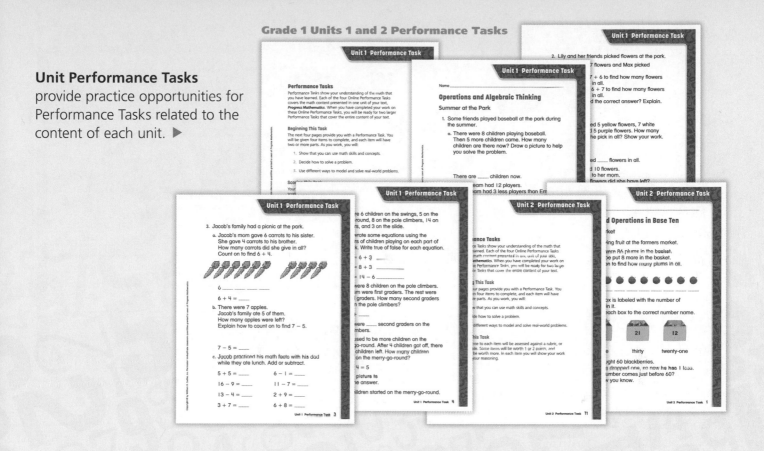

Grade 1 Units 1 and 2 Performance Tasks

Performance Tasks 1 and 2

allow students to apply their learning and provide teachers with robust evaluation support. These tasks can be used for mid-year and end-of-year assessment purposes. ▼

Grades 1 and 2 Performance Task 2

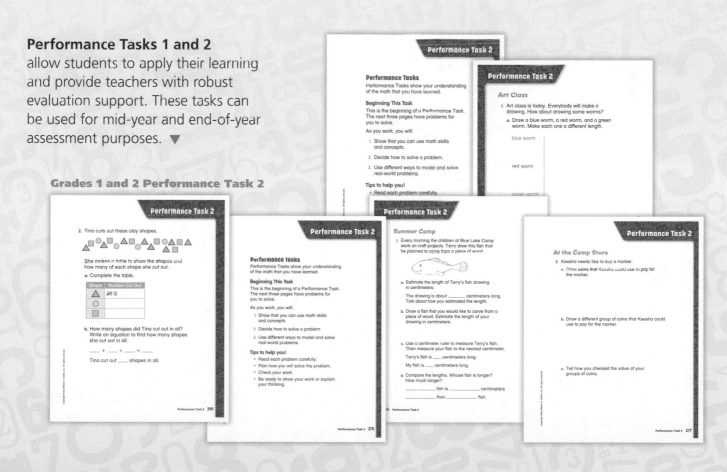

Print and Digital Resources

Additional Practice offers opportunities to augment program practice. ▼

LESSON 6 **Additional Practice**

Name _____

Count on to solve.

1. 5 + 3 = ____

5 ⟶ ____

2. 7 − 6 = ____

6 ⟶ ____

3. 8 + 3 = ____   4. 12 − 4 = ____

Lesson 6 ▪ Relate Counting to Addition and Subtraction   1

Grade 1 Additional Practice

LESSON 11 **Additional Practice**

Name _____

**Start at the number shown.
Write the next 5 numbers.**

1. 38, ____, ____, ____, ____, ____

2. 66, ____, ____, ____, ____, ____

Fill in the missing numbers.

3.

82	83	84	85	86		88	89	
91	92	93		95	96	97	98	99	100
101	102	103	104	105		107	108	109	110

4.

51	52		54	55	56	57		59	60
	62	63		65	66	67	68	69	
71	72	73	74		76	77	78	79	80

Lesson 11 ▪ Count to 120   1

Grade 1 Additional Practice

LESSON 19 **Additional Practice**

Name _____

How long is each object?

____ paper clips

____ cubes

____ paper clips

Lesson 19 ▪ Measure with Same-Size Length Units   1

Grade 1 Additional Practice

Fluency Practice provides opportunities for students to improve speed and accuracy with simple calculations. ▼

Fluency Practice

Name _____

Addition: Sums to 12

1 + 9 = ____   5 + 4 = ____   4 + 8 = ____

6 + 5 = ____   8 + 1 = ____   2 + 9 = ____

2 + 8 = ____   6 + 3 = ____   5 + 5 = ____

7 + 2 = ____   6 + 6 = ____   4 + 7 = ____

```
  4     3     3     7
+ 8   + 5   + 4   + 3
```

```
  4     3     4     9
+ 6   + 8   + 7   + 3
```

```
  7     3     2     6
+ 5   + 7   + 9   + 2
```

```
  3     2     5     6
+ 9   + 5   + 7   + 4
```

Grade 2 Fluency Practice

Fluency Practice

Name _____

Subtraction: Sums to 20

13 − 5 = ____   15 − 8 = ____   12 − 3 = ____

11 − 6 = ____   9 − 0 = ____   18 − 9 = ____

16 − 8 = ____   14 − 9 = ____   10 − 8 = ____

14 − 6 = ____   8 − 8 = ____   13 − 7 = ____

```
  11    14    15    13    16
 − 4   − 5   − 9   − 6   − 9
```

```
  11    13    17    15    10
 − 8   − 8   − 9   − 7   − 7
```

```
  16    15    14    13    12
 − 7   − 6   − 8   − 4   − 9
```

```
  12    13    17    14     8
 − 8   − 9   − 8   − 7   − 6
```

Grade 2 Fluency Practice

Fluency Practice

Name _____

Addition and Subtraction

```
  76    52    28    67    36
+  4  − 15  + 11  −  4  +  8
```

```
  85    16    68    85    43
− 14  + 26  + 15  −  9  − 26
```

```
  59    17    62    24    37
+ 15  −  5  − 34  + 39  +  8
```

73 − 23 = ____   48 + 15 = ____   27 + 43 = ____

63 + 9 = ____   51 − 8 = ____   46 − 28 = ____

90 − 41 = ____   33 + 54 = ____   34 − 27 = ____

Grade 2 Fluency Practice

iProgress Monitor* (Optional Purchase)

This dynamic online assessment system is available to help monitor student progress on grade-level mathematical skills and concepts in real time and customize assignments based on individual needs through its built-in test generator feature. See page T17 for more information about this online assessment system.

*Items are mapped to CCSS.

eBooks (Optional Purchase)

Student Worktext eBook The eBook provides the same quality content as the print Student Worktext. Delivered via Sadlier's one-stop platform at **www.SadlierConnect.com**, the eBook format also provides access to robust tools that allow students to:

- Read Text
- Make notes and highlight important information
- Search for key words
- Zoom in on specific content

Teacher's Edition eBook The eBook provides the same quality content as the print Teacher's Edition. Delivered via Sadlier's one-stop platform at **www.SadlierConnect.com**, the eBook format also provides access to robust tools that allow teachers to:

- Toggle between the Student and Teacher's Edition
- Use Full-screen Mode to project the Student Edition onto a whiteboard to focus on instruction
- Assign lessons to an entire class or a specific group of students to take offline (in PDF format)
- View digital resources at point of use
- Make notes and highlight important information
- Search for key words
- Zoom in on specific content

Progress Mathematics Grade 1 eBook

Progress Mathematics contains many formative and summative assessment opportunities to help teachers gather evidence of students' progress toward mastering grade-level skills and concepts and prepare for the new state-standardized assessments.

Integrated, Ongoing Assessment Opportunities

Observational Assessment opportunities are a routine part of each Lesson Plan in the Teacher's Edition. Common Errors and Teaching Tips features at point of use help teachers identify student misconceptions and provide strategies for solutions. ▶

Teaching Tips

Item 16

Students may have difficulty solving the problem because they do not draw the array correctly. Provide grid paper for those who have difficulty aligning rows and columns.

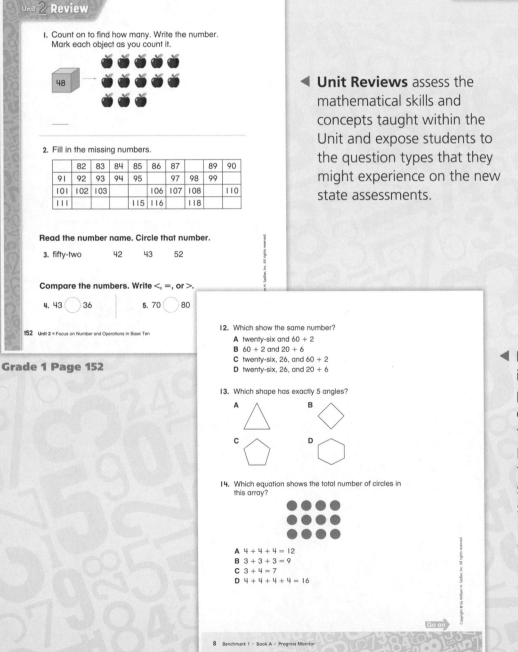

Grade 1 Page 152

◀ **Unit Reviews** assess the mathematical skills and concepts taught within the Unit and expose students to the question types that they might experience on the new state assessments.

◀ **Benchmark Assessments*** in Progresss Monitor (optional purchase) provide four comprehensive assessments that can be administered periodically throughout the school year to evaluate students' knowledge and skill level relative to grade-level mathematical skills and concepts.

*Items are mapped to CCSS.

Grade 2 Progress Monitor

Correlating Assessment and Instruction

Unit Performance Tasks, available online at **www.SadlierConnect.com**, provide practice opportunities for students to solve real-world problems that integrate the skills and concepts within each unit, and often require students to explain and justify their solutions.

Performance Tasks 1 and 2 ▶ provide tasks that parallel those in standardized assessments. The tasks assess students' conceptual understanding of grade-level skills and concepts and require them to show evidence through application, modeling, and written arguments. Performance Tasks 1 and 2 are also available online at **www.SadlierConnect.com**. They can be used for mid-year and end-of-year assessment purposes. These Performance Tasks play a vital role in helping you determine if students are able to integrate the skills and concepts being taught and to apply them in solving real-world problems.

Grade 1 Pages 156–157

iProgress Monitor* (Optional Purchase)

Augment your assesment resources with customized assignments and test-building power!

With the **iProgress Monitor**, teachers can:

- Assign, evaluate, and monitor student progress with preformatted program assessments in an interactive format.
- Build custom assessments with a built-in test generator.
- Track students' progress and guide instruction with real-time data.

*Items are mapped to CCSS.

Student Worktext

With a full-color, engaging design the Student Worktext provides students with the opportunity to:

- Develop proficiency in mathematics through the integration of skills and concepts
- Build conceptual understanding of mathematical content following a gradual release of responsibility model of instruction
- Reason and communicate mathematically
- Develop mathematical arguments and model real-world problems

Organized around a focused, coherent group of mathematical topics, the lessons in the Student Worktext focus on developing conceptual understanding, computational fluency, and problem-solving skills.

A Unit Introduction That Focuses on Standards

Grade 1 Page 7

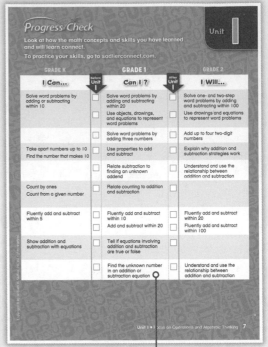

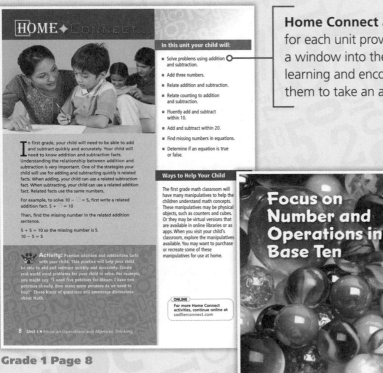

Grade 1 Page 8

Grade 2 Page 55

Home Connect activities for each unit provide families a window into their child's learning and encourage them to take an active role.

Progress Check at the beginning of each unit allows students to focus on the unit's key skills and concepts, self-assess before learning, and reflect on progress at the end of the unit.

An **Essential Question** sets the focus and identifies the big idea for each unit, enhanced with vivid images featuring engaging and relevant content that helps students make connections between math and the real world.

Gradual Release of Responsibility

Each standard is taught using a gradual release of responsibility instructional model. By gradually decreasing the level of support within each lesson, students can develop the conceptual understanding necessary for solving complex problems and tasks independently.

This gradual release of responsibility instructional model starts with **Guided Instruction**, helping students conceptualize skills and concepts through modeling and reasoning.

Guided Instruction

Grade 1 Page 42

Each lesson begins with an **Essential Question** to prompt students' thinking and classroom discussion to help define the lesson objective.

Key **academic vocabulary** is highlighted and used strategically when teaching the lesson.

The **Understand** instructional presentations break down the mathematical skills and concepts into simpler chunks of content to help students build their knowledge of the complete standard being addressed.

Grade 1 Page 43

The **Connect** and **Understand** presentations, together, help build knowledge to answer the lesson's Essential Question.

Opportunities for classroom discussion build student confidence with the new material being learned.

Notes provided throughout the instruction provide scaffolding of concepts so students can go back and review each step.

Grade 1 Page 44

Overview of the Student Worktext

Gradual Release of Responsibility

The structure of the lesson continues the gradual release of responsibility model with **Guided Practice**, which allows the opportunity for students to work through problems with the teacher's supervision and assistance.

Guided Practice

Scaffolding is gradually removed as students work through the problems on the page(s). This allows students more independence in applying and developing strategies and skills necessary to solve the problems.

Think-Pair-Share opportunities encourage students to think independently about mathematics and then discuss, model, and explain their reasoning while learning from one another.

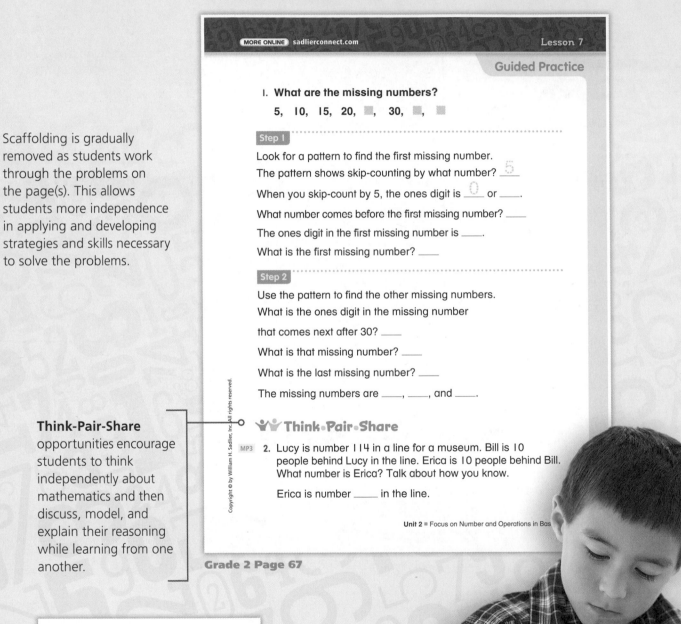

MORE ONLINE sadlierconnect.com

Lesson 7

Guided Practice

1. **What are the missing numbers?**

   5, 10, 15, 20, ▪, 30, ▪, ▪

   Step 1

   Look for a pattern to find the first missing number.
   The pattern shows skip-counting by what number? 5
   When you skip-count by 5, the ones digit is 0 or ____.
   What number comes before the first missing number? ____
   The ones digit in the first missing number is ____.
   What is the first missing number? ____

   Step 2

   Use the pattern to find the other missing numbers.
   What is the ones digit in the missing number
   that comes next after 30? ____
   What is that missing number? ____
   What is the last missing number? ____
   The missing numbers are ____, ____, and ____.

   Think·Pair·Share

   MP3 2. Lucy is number 114 in a line for a museum. Bill is 10 people behind Lucy in the line. Erica is 10 people behind Bill. What number is Erica? Talk about how you know.

   Erica is number ____ in the line.

   Unit 2 ■ Focus on Number and Operations in Bas

Grade 2 Page 67

Think·Pair·Share

Gradual Release of Responsibility

The gradual release of responsibility model culminates with **Independent Practice**, which requires students to use their critical-thinking skills, apply their math knowledge, and respond to problems leveled to Webb's Depth of Knowledge. These independent practice pages can be used independently at home or in class.

Independent Practice

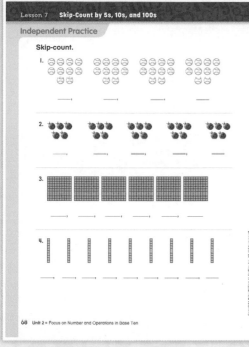

As the level of scaffolding decreases and students' knowledge and confidence with the material increases, the exercises become more difficult and require higher-order thinking as well as justification of answers.

Grade 2 Page 68

Grade 2 Page 69

Students have ample opportunities to model, reason, and justify their answers.

Grade 2 Page 70

Grade 2 Page 71

Built-In Assessment Practice

Every unit concludes with a **Unit Review** that provides practice with items similar to those students will encounter on state standardized assessments. Covering all of the skills and concepts taught in the unit, the reviews allow teachers to monitor student progress and understanding of each skill/concept.

Unit Review (Grade 2 Page 50)

Write a related subtraction fact.

1. $8 + 6 = 14$

____ − ____ = ____

2. $4 + 9 = 13$

____ − ____ = ____

Circle the correct answers.

3. Circle all the even numbers.

12   13   15   17   18

4. Circle all the odd numbers.

4   6   7   8   9

Add or subtract.

5. $16 − 9 =$ ____

6. $8 +$ ____ $= 11$

7. ____ $− 5 = 8$

8. ____ $+ 9 = 17$

9. $15 − 6 =$ ____

10. $14 −$ ____ $= 7$

11. ____ $+ 8 = 15$

12. $9 + 9 =$ ____

Grade 2 Page 50

Unit Review (Grade 2 Page 51)

13. Circle the correct equation to solve the problem.

Brady has 32 fewer marbles than Emma.
Emma has 63 marbles.
How many marbles does Brady have?

$63 + 32 = 95$ $63 − 32 = 31$ $95 − 32 = 63$

14. Draw a picture to model the problem.
Write a subtraction equation. Then solve the problem.

There were 29 acorns.
Molly took some of them.
Now there are 14 acorns.
How many acorns did Molly take?

____ − ____ = ____

Molly took ____ acorns.

Write and solve an addition equation to solve the problem.

15. Antonio collects 16 pinecones on Friday and 20 on Saturday. How many pinecones does he collect in all?

____ + ____ = ▨

Antonio collects ____ pinecones in all.

16. Noah has 19 shells. Gia has some shells too. Together Noah and Gia have 31 shells. How many shells does Gia have?

____ + ▨ = ____

Gia has ____ shells.

Grade 2 Page 51

Unit Review (Grade 2 Page 52)

17. Circle the even number. Draw 2 equal groups ... k that you are correct. Then write an ... equation to show your work.

11   10   9

____ = ____

... the rows. Complete the equation to tell ... any hearts in all.

$4 + 4 + 4 =$ ____

... the array. Circle the equation that shows ... any flowers.

$5 + 5 + 5 = 15$
$4 + 4 + 4 + 4 = 16$
$5 + 5 + 5 + 5 = 20$

... array with 2 rows and 3 counters in ... w. Write two equations for the array. ... at each equation shows.

Grade 2 Page 52

Performance Task I

Sticker Books

3. Hector and Jess collect stickers.
Hector has 20 stickers.
Jess has 40 stickers.

a. Compare the number of stickers each child has. Use <, =, or >.

____ ◯ ____

b. Hector gets 10 more stickers.
How many stickers does Hector have now?

____ stickers

c. Jess gives away 20 of her stickers.
How many stickers does Jess have left?
Draw a picture to check your answer.

____ stickers

Grade 1 Page 158

Performance Task 2

2. Tina cuts out these clay shapes.

She makes a table to show the shapes and how many of each shape she cut out.

a. Complete the table.

Shape	Number Cut Out
△	Ⅷ III
◯	
▢	

b. How many shapes did Tina cut out in all?
Write an equation to find how many shapes she cut out in all.

____ + ____ + ____ = ____

Tina cut out ____ shapes in all.

Grade 1 Page 245

Performance Tasks in a real-world setting provide opportunities for students to demonstrate their mathematical understanding through application, modeling, and written arguments.

Teacher's Edition

Teacher-friendly, easy-to-use lesson plans support teachers in providing systematic instruction, practice, and application of mathematical skills and concepts. *Progress Mathematics* Teacher's Edition is also available in an eBook format.

At-a-Glance Unit Introduction Pages

Unit introduction pages, featuring a student self-assessment, a home connection, a planner for understanding key concepts, and learning progressions provide an at-a-glance reference for busy educators!

Each unit begins with support for student self-assessment and connecting to home. The **Progress Check** provides students with a visual roadmap identifying how the skills and concepts are developed and linked across grade levels, emphasizing coherence.

Home Connect activities for each unit encourage families to take an active role in their child's learning and connect math to real-world situations.

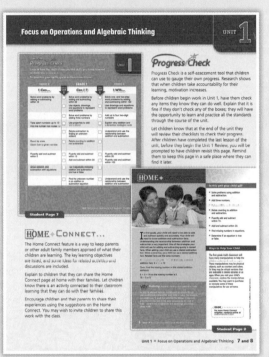

Grade 1 Teacher's Edition Pages 7 and 8

Unit Planner

The **Unit Planner** outlines everything a teacher needs to know to gather unit resources, and identify all lesson objectives, essential questions, and vocabulary.

	Lesson	Objective	Essential Question	Words to Know
1	Problem Solving: Addition	Use objects, drawings, and equations to solve word problems that involve addition.	How can you use addition to solve word problems?	add
2	Problem Solving: Subtraction	Use objects, drawings, and equations to solve word problems that involve taking from, taking apart, and comparing to subtract.	How can you use subtraction to solve word problems?	subtract
3	Problem Solving: Addition of Three Numbers	Use models and equations to solve word problems that add three whole numbers and have a sum within 20.	How do you use addition of three numbers to solve a word problem?	addend, sum
4	Apply Properties of Operations	Use the Commutative and Associative Properties of Addition.	How can the properties of operations help you add?	
5	Related Addition and Subtraction Facts	Solve and record related addition and subtraction facts to 18.	How can you use an addition fact to help solve a subtraction problem?	related facts
6	Relate Counting to Addition and Subtraction	Use counting on to add or to subtract.	How can you use counting on to add or subtract?	count on
7	Addition and Subtraction Facts to 10 (Fluency)	Use strategies to build fluency in adding and subtracting within 10.	What strategies can you use to add and subtract quickly?	doubles, doubles plus 1
8	Addition and Subtraction Facts to 20	Use making 10 and other strategies to add and subtract within 20.	What different strategies can help you learn addition and subtraction facts to 20?	
9	Addition and Subtraction Equations	Use models and equation symbols to tell whether an equation is true or false.	How do you know if an equation is true or false?	equal sign, equation
10	Finding Missing Numbers in Equations	Use counting on or the relationship between addition and subtraction to find the missing number in an equation.	How can you find the missing number in an addition or subtraction equation?	

Grade 1 Teacher's Edition Pages 9A and 9B

Learning Progressions

Learning Progressions provide context and background knowledge of the critical skills and skills progression across the years by showing what students learned in the previous grade and connections to what they will learn in the next grade, building coherence within and across grade levels.

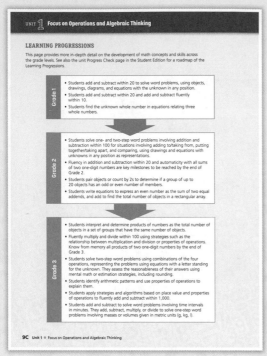

Grade 2 Teacher's Edition Page 9C

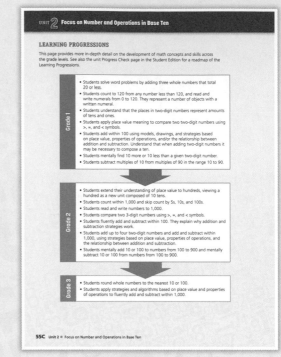

Grade 2 Teacher's Edition Page 55C

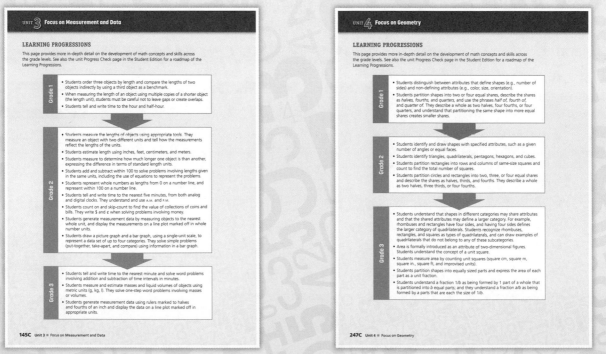

Grade 2 Teacher's Edition Page 145C

Grade 2 Teacher's Edition Page 247C

On-the-Spot Lesson Support Makes Teachers Mathematical Experts!

Teacher-friendly Lesson Plans provide targeted standards-based instruction and supportive features suitable for both novice and experienced teachers.

Guided Instruction

Clearly stated objectives provide the focus for each lesson.

Fluence Practice, a daily ongoing review, is listed at point-of-use.

Support/Strategies for effectively teaching the lesson's skills/concepts and engaging students in productive learning are provided in the **Concept Development**. Skills and concepts are broken down to help students build knowledge and gain full understanding.

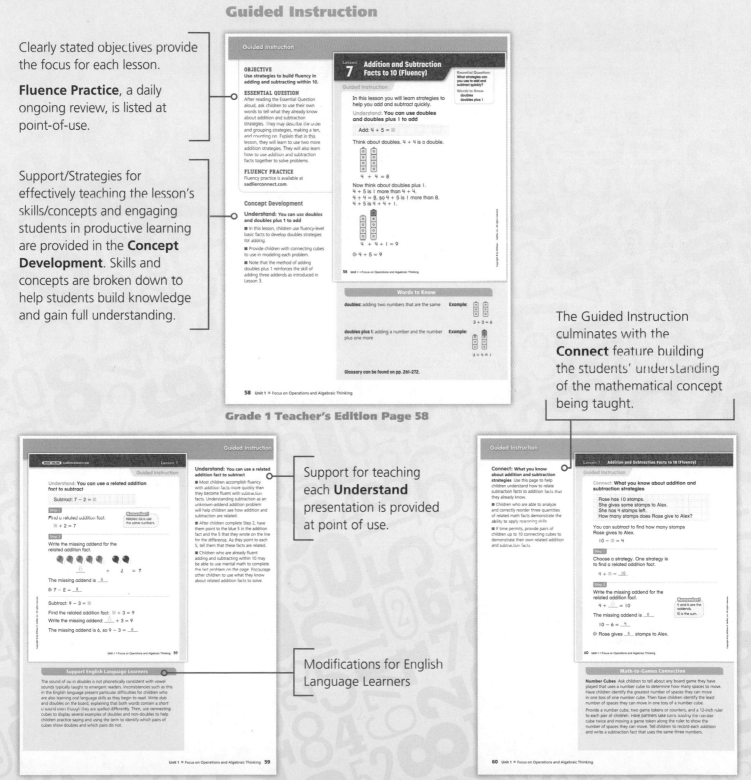

The Guided Instruction culminates with the **Connect** feature building the students' understanding of the mathematical concept being taught.

Grade 1 Teacher's Edition Page 58

Support for teaching each **Understand** presentation is provided at point of use.

Modifications for English Language Learners

Grade 1 Teacher's Edition Page 59

Grade 1 Teacher's Edition Page 60

Successive Increase of Student Responsibility Leads to Success

Guided Practice

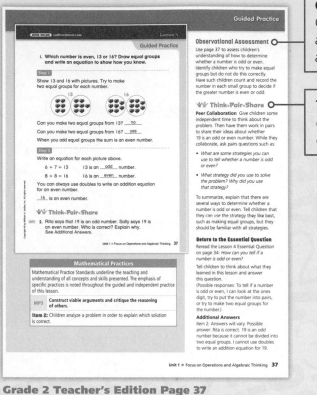

Grade 2 Teacher's Edition Page 37

Observational Assessment The Guided Practice pages offer teachers an opportunity for formative assessment to gauge student progress.

Think-Pair-Share Support for this peer collaboration activity helps teachers to encourage students to work together.

Return to the Essential Question In order to help solidify understanding before students begin to work independently, teachers encourage them to return to the Essential Question of the lesson, allowing the students to explain what they have learned in their own words.

Grade 2 Teacher's Edition Page 91

Scaffolded Practice Makes Independent Application of Skills Accessible

Progress Mathematics provides ample opportunity for rigorous independent practice, allowing students to develop procedural fluency together with conceptual understanding.

Teaching Tip Point-of-use teaching strategies and Common Error analyses provide help to identify potential areas of confusion or misconceptions.

Independent Practice

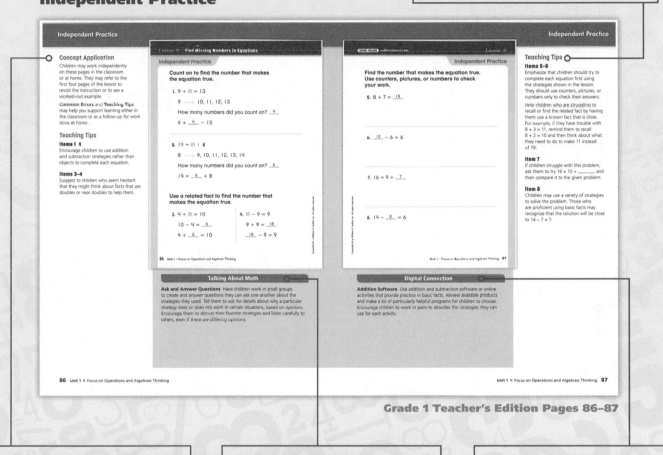

Grade 1 Teacher's Edition Pages 86–87

Concept Application Teachers direct students to work independently on increasingly cognitive demanding exercises and tasks.

Talking About Math Teacher-directed suggestions for helping students to make connections between concepts and to integrate ELA skills in their math lessons.

Digital Connections give suggestions for helping students find online resources to enhance their understanding of mathematical concepts.

Assessment Tools Make Grading Simple

Progress Mathematics supports busy teachers by offering easy-to-use rubrics for grading and results charts that outline next steps after grading or assessing.

Grade 2 Teacher's Edition Pages 136–137

A correlation is provided for each item in the Unit Review, identifying the lesson in which the concepts or skills are presented providing teachers with a quick reference should students require a review of the concepts/skills.

Each item is identified by the DOK level, allowing teachers to quickly identify the level of understanding of each student.

Grade 2 Teacher's Edition Page 141

The reviews culminate with higher-order thinking problems and require students to justify their answers in writing.

Additional Assessment options are referenced at point-of-use.

Performance Task Rubrics provide clear and thorough guidance on how to evaluate the assessment.

Suggested Planning and Pacing Guide

Weeks	Student Worktext	Online Resources to Enrich, Support, and Assess
1–10	Unit 1: Focus on Operations and Algebraic Thinking Lessons 1–10; pp. 7–89	Unit 1 Performance Task; Additional Practice; Fluency Practice; Teacher Resources Optional purchase: iProgress Monitor
11–17	Unit 2: Focus on Number and Operations in Base Ten Lessons 11–17; pp. 96–151	Unit 2 Performance Task; Additional Practice; Fluency Practice; Teacher Resources Optional purchase: iProgress Monitor
18–22	Performance Task 1 pp. 155–158	Performance Task 1
23	Unit 3: Focus on Measurement and Data Lessons 18–22; pp. 162–201	Unit 3 Performance Task; Additional Practice; Fluency Practice; Teacher Resources Optional purchase: iProgress Monitor
24–27	Unit 4: Focus on Geometry Lessons: 23–26; pp. 208–239	Unit 4 Performance Task; Additional Practice; Fluency Practice; Teacher Resources Optional purchase: iProgress Monitor
28	Performance Task 2 pp. 243–246	Performance Task 2

Suggested Pacing

To achieve optimum student results, it is suggested that *Progress Mathematics* become an integral part of your math instruction. The multi-part lesson structure provides you with the flexibility you need in order to focus on a particular math skill/concept each day.

Suggested Timeline	Day 1	Day 2	Day 3	Day 4	Day 5
Lesson Structure	Guided Instruction	Guided Practice	Independent Practice	Independent Practice	• Additional Practice Online • iProgress Monitor (optional purchase) Customized Assignments

Progress Monitor Student Benchmark Assessments, an optional purchase, contains four comprehensive Benchmark Assessments that you may administer throughout the school year to track and assess students' mastery of grade-level skills/concepts.

Successful students use the following mathematical practices as they approach their study of mathematics. Using these mathematical practices instills in students the reasoning and problem-solving skills they need to be confident in their ability to learn and use mathematics both in school and in their everyday lives. These Mathematical Practices are fully embedded within the instruction and practice, labeled as MP , and encourage students to develop the habit of reliance on the practices when approaching problems.

Mathematical Practices in *Progress Mathematics*

The National Council of Teachers of Mathematics (NCTM) Process Standards—communication, reasoning, representation, connections, and problem solving—are integrated in these mathematical practices.

1. **Make sense of problems and persevere in solving them.**
   The Guided Instruction provided in the program offers stepped out approaches to solving problems, helping students develop strategies to use when approaching new problems.

2. **Reason abstractly and quantitatively.**
   Concepts are introduced using the Understand and Connect structure to help students break down the components of the standard and develop the reasoning skills necessary for deep conceptual understanding.

3. **Construct viable arguments and critique the reasoning of others.**
   Whether justifying their reasoning in writing or participating in group discussions about a Think-Pair-Share exercise, there are opportunities in every lesson for students to practice the skills of developing and defending mathematical arguments and communicating their ideas clearly.

4. **Model with mathematics.**
   In addition to the models of real-world situations presented to the students throughout the program to introduce new concepts, students are encouraged to develop their own models when working through the exercises.

5. **Use appropriate tools strategically.**
   Having a solid understanding of the tools available and practicing with those tools during Guided Instruction and Guided Practice, fosters familiarity and fluency using the tools when working independently.

6. **Attend to precision.**
   Students are encouraged to be precise and accurate during each stage of the problem solving process, from using the correct vocabulary to communicate ideas to attending to the units used to express their answers.

7. **Look for and make use of structure.**
   Presenting concepts and skills in a way that reveals mathematical structures, allows students to seek out these patterns on their own.

8. **Look for and express regularity in repeated reasoning.**
   As students work through cognitively-demanding exercises they develop an awareness of repeated reasoning which promotes their ability to apply similar reasoning in real-world situations.

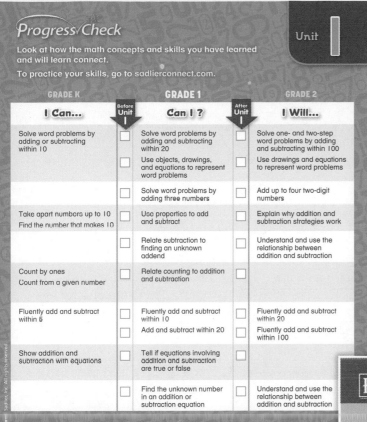

Progress Check

Look at how the math concepts and skills you have learned and will learn connect.

To practice your skills, go to sadlierconnect.com.

Unit 1

GRADE K I Can...	Before Unit 1	GRADE 1 Can I ?	After Unit 1	GRADE 2 I Will...
Solve word problems by adding or subtracting within 10	☐	Solve word problems by adding and subtracting within 20	☐	Solve one- and two-step word problems by adding and subtracting within 100
	☐	Use objects, drawings, and equations to represent word problems	☐	Use drawings and equations to represent word problems
	☐	Solve word problems by adding three numbers	☐	Add up to four two-digit numbers
Take apart numbers up to 10 Find the number that makes 10	☐	Use properties to add and subtract	☐	Explain why addition and subtraction strategies work
	☐	Relate subtraction to finding an unknown addend	☐	Understand and use the relationship between addition and subtraction
Count by ones Count from a given number	☐	Relate counting to addition and subtraction	☐	
Fluently add and subtract within 5	☐	Fluently add and subtract within 10	☐	Fluently add and subtract within 20
	☐	Add and subtract within 20	☐	Fluently add and subtract within 100
Show addition and subtraction with equations	☐	Tell if equations involving addition and subtraction are true or false	☐	
	☐	Find the unknown number in an addition or subtraction equation	☐	Understand and use the relationship between addition and subtraction

Unit 1 ■ Focus on Operations and Algebraic Thinking

Student Page 7

Progress Check

Progress Check is a self-assessment tool that children can use to gauge their own progress. Research shows that when children take accountability for their learning, motivation increases.

Before children begin work in Unit 1, have them check any items they know they can do well. Explain that it is fine if they don't check any of the boxes; they will have the opportunity to learn and practice all the standards through the course of the unit.

Let children know that at the end of the unit they will review their checklists to check their progress. After children have completed the last lesson of the unit, before they begin the Unit 1 Review, you will be prompted to have children revisit this page. Remind them to keep this page in a safe place where they can find it later.

HOME ✦ CONNECT...

The Home Connect feature is a way to keep parents or other adult family members apprised of what their children are learning. The key learning objectives are listed, and some ideas for related activities and discussions are included.

Explain to children that they can share the Home Connect page at home with their families. Let children know there is an activity connected to their classroom learning that they can do with their families.

Encourage children and their parents to share their experiences using the suggestions on the Home Connect. You may wish to invite children to share this work with the class.

HOME ✦ CONNECT...

In first grade, your child will need to be able to add and subtract quickly and accurately. Your child will need to know addition and subtraction facts. Understanding the relationship between addition and subtraction is very important. One of the strategies your child will use for adding and subtracting quickly is related facts. When adding, your child can use a related subtraction fact. When subtracting, your child can use a related addition fact. Related facts use the same numbers.

For example, to solve 10 − ☐ = 5, first write a related addition fact. 5 + ☐ = 10

Then, find the missing number in the related addition sentence.

5 + 5 = 10 so the missing number is 5.
10 − 5 = 5

Activity: Practice addition and subtraction facts with your child. This practice will help your child be able to add and subtract quickly and accurately. Create real-world word problems for your child to solve. For example, you might say, "I need five potatoes for dinner. I have two potatoes already. How many more potatoes do we need to buy?" These kinds of questions will encourage discussions about Math.

In this unit your child will:

- Solve problems using addition and subtraction.
- Add three numbers.
- Relate addition and subtraction.
- Relate counting to addition and subtraction.
- Fluently add and subtract within 10.
- Add and subtract within 20.
- Find missing numbers in equations.
- Determine if an equation is true or false.

Ways to Help Your Child

The first grade math classroom will have many manipulatives to help the children understand math concepts. These manipulatives may be physical objects, such as counters and cubes. Or they may be virtual versions that are available in online libraries or as apps. When you visit your child's classroom, explore the manipulatives available. You may want to purchase or recreate some of these manipulatives for use at home.

ONLINE
For more Home Connect activities, continue online at sadlierconnect.com

8 Unit 1 ■ Focus on Operations and Algebraic Thinking

Student Page 8

UNIT PLANNER

	Lesson	Objective
1	Problem Solving: Addition	Use objects, drawings, and equations to solve word problems that involve addition.
2	Problem Solving: Subtraction	Use objects, drawings, and equations to solve word problems that involve taking from, taking apart, and comparing to subtract.
3	Problem Solving: Addition of Three Numbers	Use models and equations to solve word problems that add three whole numbers and have a sum within 20.
4	Apply Properties of Operations	Use the Commutative and Associative Properties of Addition.
5	Related Addition and Subtraction Facts	Solve and record related addition and subtraction facts to 18.
6	Relate Counting to Addition and Subtraction	Use counting on to add or to subtract.
7	Addition and Subtraction Facts to 10 (Fluency)	Use strategies to build fluency in adding and subtracting within 10.
8	Addition and Subtraction Facts to 20	Use making 10 and other strategies to add and subtract within 20.
9	Addition and Subtraction Equations	Use models and equation symbols to tell whether an equation is true or false.
10	Finding Missing Numbers in Equations	Use counting on or the relationship between addition and subtraction to find the missing number in an equation.

Essential Question	Words to Know
How can you use addition to solve word problems?	add
How can you use subtraction to solve word problems?	subtract
How do you use addition of three numbers to solve a word problem?	addend sum
How can the properties of operations help you add?	
How can you use an addition fact to help solve a subtraction problem?	related facts
How can you use counting on to add or subtract?	count on
What strategies can you use to add and subtract quickly?	doubles doubles plus 1
What different strategies can help you learn addition and subtraction facts to 20?	
How do you know if an equation is true or false?	equal sign equation
How can you find the missing number in an addition or subtraction equation?	

Unit Assessment

- Unit 1 Review, *pp. 90–92*
- Unit 1 Performance Task ONLINE

Additional Assessment Options

Optional Purchase:
- iProgress Monitor ONLINE
- Progress Monitor Student Benchmark Assessment Booklet

ONLINE Digital Resources

- Home Connect Activities
- Unit Performance Tasks
- Additional Practice
- Fluency Practice
- Teacher Resources
- iProgress Monitor (optional purchase)

Go to SadlierConnect.com to access your Digital Resources.

For more detailed instructions see page T3.

LEARNING PROGRESSIONS

This page provides more in-depth detail on the development of math concepts and skills across the grade levels. See also the unit Progress Check page in the Student Edition for a roadmap of the Learning Progressions.

Grade K

- Students count by ones and count on from a given number by ones, and apply counting on by ones to find the answers to addition and subtraction problems.
- Students represent addition and subtraction using objects, fingers, drawings, expressions, equations, and other representations. They use these representations to solve addition and subtraction word problems and add and subtract within 10.
- Students decompose numbers within 10 into different pairs of addends and find the number that makes 10 when added to a number from 1 to 9.
- Students fluently add and subtract within 5.

Grade 1

- Students add and subtract within 20 to solve word problems involving adding to and taking away, putting together and taking apart, and comparing, using objects, drawings, diagrams, and equations with the unknown in any position. They solve word problems by adding three numbers whose sum is less than 20.
- Students apply properties of operations as strategies to aid in addition and subtraction; e.g., by rearranging three addends to make a ten.
- Students understand subtraction as finding an unknown addend, and apply this to transforming equations from one form to another to solve problems.
- Students relate counting on to addition and subtraction.
- Students add and subtract within 20 using a variety of strategies, and add and subtract fluently within 10.
- Students understand the meaning of the equal sign in an equation and determine if addition and subtraction equations are true or false. Students find the unknown whole number in equations relating three whole numbers.

Grade 2

- Add and subtract fluently with 20, and add and subtract within 100 to solve one- and two-step word problems. Equations with unknowns in any position are used to represent and solve problems.
- Fluently add and subtract within 100.
- Add up to four two-digit numbers and add and subtract within 1,000.
- Explain why addition and subtraction strategies work.

Focus on Operations and Algebraic Thinking

Unit **1**

Essential Question:
How are addition and subtraction related?

Unit 1 ■ Focus on Operations and Algebraic Thinking **9**

As children become involved with the Essential Question they will use properties of addition and the inverse relationship between addition and subtraction to develop a deep understanding of the two operations.

Conversation Starters

Encourage children to examine the picture of the birds by asking questions such as: *What kind of birds are on the branch?* (parrots) *How many parrots have mostly yellow feathers?* (1) *How many have mostly red feathers?* (4)

Then use the picture to evaluate children's knowledge of addition and subtraction.

To determine whether children can count with understanding and perhaps recognize amounts by sight, ask questions such as: *What could you do to find out how many parrots are on the branch altogether?*
(I could count them starting with the yellow and then the reds: 1, 2, 3, 4, 5.)
Suppose you counted the red parrots first and then the yellow. Then how many parrots would there be in all? (5)
How else could you find the number of parrots in all? (I could add the 1 yellow and the 4 reds to get 5 in all. When I saw 1 yellow parrot and 4 red ones, I just could tell that there were 5 altogether.)

Activity

Materials: drawing paper, yellow and red connecting cubes or yellow/red two-color counters

Tell children that they will use the materials to model the picture of the parrots on the branch. Have children draw one line across the paper. The line will be the "branch" that the "parrots" will perch on. Have children model the parrots in the picture by placing the matching numbers of yellow and reds on the branch. Have them look at their models as you repeat the Conversation Starters questions. Now, challenge children to show another group of 5 parrots using different numbers of yellows and reds. Have them talk about the numbers of yellows and reds they chose. Record their choices as addition sentences on the board.

OBJECTIVE
Use objects, drawings, and equations to solve word problems that involve addition.

ESSENTIAL QUESTION
Make sure children understand that a word problem tells a story or describes a situation. Relate that an addition word problem involves joining numbers of objects or finding the number of objects in all.

PREREQUISITE SKILLS
Use Foundational Skills Handbook page 247, *Number Names and Counting,* to review counting the number of objects in a group.

FLUENCY PRACTICE
Fluency practice is available at **sadlierconnect.com**.

Concept Development

Understand: Add to find how many in all

■ In kindergarten, children learned how to use numbers to represent quantities and model simple joining situations. Children will now relate the model of joining situations to simple equations.

■ Provide children with concrete objects for modeling the word problems. Explain that they can model the problem by counting the number given for each group. Then they can put the groups together and count the total to add.

■ Be sure children can identify why the given word problems indicate addition. Guide them to use words such as *join* or *put together* as they explain.

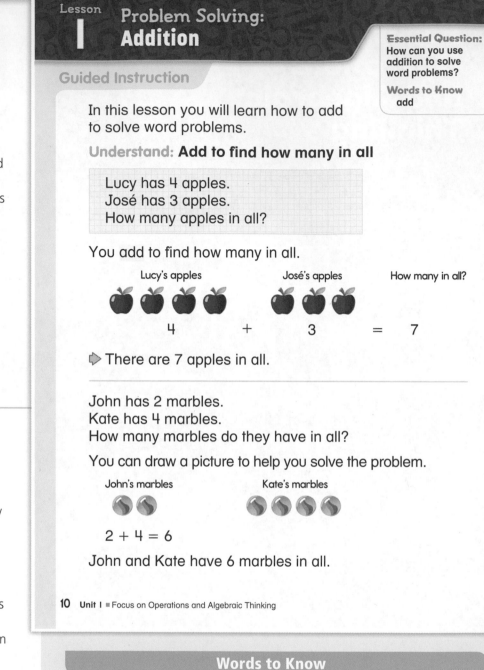

Lesson 1

Problem Solving: Addition

Essential Question: How can you use addition to solve word problems?

Words to Know
add

In this lesson you will learn how to add to solve word problems.

Understand: Add to find how many in all

Lucy has 4 apples.
José has 3 apples.
How many apples in all?

You add to find how many in all.

Lucy's apples   José's apples   How many in all?

$$4 \quad + \quad 3 \quad = \quad 7$$

▷ There are 7 apples in all.

John has 2 marbles.
Kate has 4 marbles.
How many marbles do they have in all?

You can draw a picture to help you solve the problem.

John's marbles   Kate's marbles

$$2 + 4 = 6$$

John and Kate have 6 marbles in all.

10   Unit 1 ■ Focus on Operations and Algebraic Thinking

Words to Know

add: to find how many in all

Example:

$$2 \qquad + \qquad 3 \qquad = 5$$

Glossary can be found on pp. 261–272.

Lesson 1

Guided Instruction

Understand: Sometimes you need to find how many in one of the groups

There are 6 butterflies in the garden.
Some more butterflies flew in.
Now there are 9 butterflies.
How many more butterflies flew into the garden?

6 butterflies   some more flew in   9 butterflies in all

$+$ ▇ $=$ 9

6 plus how many more will make 9?

6 and 3 more make 9.

$6 + 3 = 9$

➡ __3__ more butterflies flew into the garden.

Ken has 6 blocks.
His friend Joe gives him some more blocks.
Now Ken has 10 blocks.
How many blocks did Joe give Ken?
Draw a picture to help you solve the problem.

blocks Ken had   blocks Joe gave Ken

$6 + ▇ = 10$ $6 + \underline{} = 10$

Joe gave Ken 4 blocks.

Understand: Sometimes you need to find how many in one of the groups

■ Be sure children understand that if they can put together two groups of objects to find the number in all, when they know the number in all and the number for one of the groups being joined, they can find the unknown number for the other group.

■ Help children identify such key words as *how many more* in addition situations that involve a missing addend.

■ Some children may need to use counters to model the number in all, and the number for the groups being joined, before they can make a drawing to represent a word problem.

Support English Language Learners

Vowel sounds in many languages tend to be consistent, unlike the variations found in English. For example, the sound made by the letter *a* in *add* and *aid* are significantly different. Further, the letter *a* in many languages is pronounced as an *ah* sound, such as in *papa* or *padre*. This can be very confusing to children who are learning English terms. Display the word *add* and ask volunteers to read the word aloud. Then have children practice saying the word in pairs so they can become accustomed to variations in pronunciation. Accept a pronunciation that sounds more like the word *odd* from children whose primary language is not English, but model the common English pronunciation. This activity will help to avoid confusion about the word used as children discuss the concepts of the lesson.

Connect: What you know about adding to solve word problems Use this page to help children strengthen their understanding of how to use groups and the number in all to identify unknown quantities.

■ Children analyze a story situation to identify what they know, what information is unknown, and what the problem is asking them to find. Make sure children read the word problem carefully before they begin.

■ Children who are already fluent in addition and subtraction of basic facts may express the problem as a subtraction situation. Although this is another way to answer the problem, the emphasis here is to recognize the addition equation that contains an unknown quantity.

Connect: **What you know about adding to solve word problems**

There are 12 children on the swings.
Some are girls and 7 are boys.
How many girls are on the swings?

Step I

How many children in all? __12__

How many boys? __7__

Use ■ for the number of girls.

■ + 7 = 12

Step 2

You can use connecting cubes to help you find the missing number.

How many plus 7 equals 12?

5 plus 7 equals 12.

5 + 7 = 12

▷ There are __5__ girls on the swings.

Math-to-Physical Education Connection

Hopscotch Game Use a Hopscotch game mat or use tape or chalk to outline a hopscotch pattern on the floor. Have children take turns jumping to a specific block and then naming how many blocks they have landed on and how many more blocks there are to go. Provide scenarios that include missing addends such as: *There are 10 blocks in the pattern. A player jumps on 7 blocks. How many blocks plus 7 equals 10?*

As each child takes a turn, have the other children use connecting cubes and a game token to model each addition. After each turn, be sure children can describe the addition scenario as a number jumped, a number to go, and the total number. A standard Hopscotch game has ten blocks, but more or fewer may be used to match the needs of the learners.

MORE ONLINE sadlierconnect.com

Lesson 1

Guided Practice

1. **Ryan has 8 balloons.**
   Some are red and some are blue.
   How many of each color can Ryan have?

   Step 1

   To solve this problem you need to find
   two numbers that make 8.

   Decide on how many red balloons he has.
   Color 4 balloons red.

   Step 2

   Color the rest of the balloons blue.

   How many balloons are blue? ____

   $$\underline{} + \underline{} = 8$$
   red   blue

   ⇨ Ryan has __4__ red balloons and __4__ blue balloons.

♕ Think•Pair•Share

MP4   2. Draw a picture to show another way to solve the
   balloon problem. Then use addition to solve it.

   Answers may vary. Check children's work.

   ____ + ____ = ____ balloons

Unit 1 ■ Focus on Operations and Algebraic Thinking   **13**

Observational Assessment

Use page 13 to assess whether children
have an understanding of how to put
together groups of objects to equal a
specific number in all. Observe whether
children have the organizational skill
to keep like-colored balloons together
rather than creating an alternating or
random pattern. Take note of those
children who have difficulty drawing
the picture for problem 2 or recording
their results.

♕ Think•Pair•Share

Peer Collaboration Have children
work in pairs to find another way to add
the balloons. Ask each pair questions
such as:

• *How many balloons did you color red?*

• *How did you find the number of
  balloons that should be blue?*

• *How does your work show that
  putting together the groups makes
  8 in all?*

Encourage children to compare their
pictures to see whether others chose the
same or different groupings of balloons.

Return to the Essential Question

Reread the Lesson 1 Essential Question
on page 10: *How can you use addition
to solve word problems?*

Tell children to think about what they
learned in this lesson to answer this
question.
(Possible response: I can use groups of
objects or drawings to model the
problem. I can put together two groups
to find how many in all. I can also find
how many are in one group when I know
how many there are in all and how many
are in the other group.)

Mathematical Practices

Mathematical Practice Standards underline the teaching and
understanding of all concepts and skills presented. The emphasis of
specific practices is noted throughout the guided and independent practice
of this lesson.

MP4   **Model with mathematics.**

Item 2: Children apply what they know about numbers by drawing a
model and completing an equation to represent a real-world situation.

Concept Application

Children may work independently on these pages in the classroom or at home. They may refer to the first four pages of the lesson to revisit the instruction or to see a worked-out example.

Common Errors and **Teaching Tips** may help you support learning either in the classroom or as a follow-up for work done at home.

Common Errors

Item 2

Children may identify the given numbers and add them rather than carefully reading the mathematical situation. Have them check their work by substituting their answers into the word problem in order to see whether the story still makes sense.

Teaching Tips

Items 1–2

Point out to children that some of the information in each problem is given in number words rather than in numerals. Have children underline the number words, if needed, and identify the numerals that name the same amount.

Draw a picture to help you solve each problem.

1. Five boys are on the bus.
   Two more boys get on.
   How many boys are on the bus now?

   How many boys are on the bus at the start? __5__

   How many more get on? __2__
   How many boys are on the bus now?

   $5 + 2 = $ __7__

   There are __7__ boys on the bus now.

---

2. Three girls are at the park.
   Some more girls come to the park.
   Now there are 10 girls at the park.
   How many more girls came to the park?

   $3 + $ __7__ $ = 10$

   __7__ more girls came to the park.

Talking About Math

Retell Stories Have children work in pairs to retell each problem scenario. Have each child use counters to demonstrate the details. Tell children to include whether each item asks them to put together groups or to identify the number in one group.

Have pairs of children create their own math stories that can be modeled with drawings or counters. Ask for volunteers to share their math stories with the class.

Lesson I

Independent Practice

Draw a picture to help you solve each problem.

3. Six players are on the field.
   Three more players come onto the field.
   How many players are on the field now?

   6 + 3 = ___9___

   There are ___9___ players on the field now.

4. Some birds were in the tree.
   Five more birds flew over.
   Then there were 13 birds in the tree.
   How many birds were in the tree before?

   ___8___ + 5 = 13

   ___8___ birds were in the tree before.

5. There are 15 crayons on the table.
   Eight of them are red.
   The rest are yellow.
   How many crayons are yellow?

   8 + ___7___ = 15

   There are ___7___ yellow crayons.

Unit I ■ Focus on Operations and Algebraic Thinking **15**

Common Errors

Item 4

This item is the first one in the lesson that places the missing information at the beginning of the problem. Some children may state that the problem does not contain enough information to find a solution, or they may try to add 5 and 13. Have them analyze each sentence to identify the place where the unknown quantity is given.

Teaching Tips

Items 3–5

Children may need more than the available space on the page to draw their pictures. Provide extra art paper or plain paper as needed.

Children who have difficulty making the drawings may benefit from modeling the items with counters and then drawing their models.

Digital Connection

Addition Games Search the Internet for games and activities that involve addition to 10. Within these resources, select those games and activities that use objects to model putting together groups or identifying missing addends. You might make a list of videos for children to use after you have reviewed them.

Common Errors

Items 6-8

Children may not understand that the sum belongs on the right side of the equal sign in these problems. Be sure children understand the meanings of the plus and equal sign if the placement of the numbers are not in the correct order.

Draw a picture to help you solve each problem.

6. Nine toys were in the toy box.
   Max puts some more toys in the box.
   Now there are 18 toys in the box.
   How many toys did Max put in the box?

   $\underline{\hphantom{9}9\hphantom{9}} + \underline{\hphantom{9}9\hphantom{9}} = \underline{\hphantom{9}18\hphantom{9}}$

   Max put __9__ toys in the box.

7. Some cars were parked in the garage.
   Seven more cars drove in.
   Now there are 11 cars parked there.
   How many cars were parked there before?

   $\underline{\hphantom{4}4\hphantom{4}} + \underline{\hphantom{7}7\hphantom{7}} = \underline{\hphantom{11}11\hphantom{11}}$

   __4__ cars were parked there before.

8. Twelve fruits are in the basket.
   Some of the fruits are oranges.
   Eight of the fruits are apples.
   How many oranges are in the basket?

   $\underline{\hphantom{4}4\hphantom{4}} + \underline{\hphantom{8}8\hphantom{8}} = \underline{\hphantom{12}12\hphantom{12}}$

   There are __8__ oranges in the basket.

Math-to Reading Connection

Addition Stories Use math storybooks to help children practice counting and combining groups of objects. Provide books that use basic addition to tell a story.

Have pairs of children identify one of the addition scenarios in the book that they select, make drawings to model the groups, and explain their drawings to the class.

Lesson 1

Independent Practice

Draw a picture to help you solve each problem.

9. Some ducks are in the pond.
   Six more ducks fly to the pond.
   Now there are 11 ducks in the pond.
   How many ducks were in the pond before?

   __5__ ducks were in the pond before.

10. There are 7 black sheep and 8 white sheep
    in the barn. How many sheep are there in all?

    There are __15__ sheep in all.

MP1 11. Kim has five books.
    Some are old and some are new.
    How many can be old and how many
    can be new?

    ____ + ____ = ____ books
    old   new

    Talk about other possible answers.
    Answers may vary. Check children's work.
    Possible answers: 0 old, 5 new; 1 old, 4 new;
    2 old, 3 new; 3 old, 2 new; 4 old, 1 new; 5 old, 0 new

Unit 1 ■ Focus on Operations and Algebraic Thinking **17**

Common Errors

Item 9

Children who write 0 as the solution may have misunderstood the use of the word *before* in the question. Be sure they understand that *before* refers to the number of ducks in the first sentence of the item rather than the number of ducks before any were in the pond.

Teaching Tips

Item 11

Children do not have to list every possible combination to complete the problem. If they struggle to select a starting number, suggest that they write numbers 1 to 5 on five small pieces of paper, place the numbers into a paper bag, and randomly draw one of the numbers out of the bag. Have children designate that number as the number of old books and then find how many more will make 5 in all to name the number of new books.

Mathematical Practices
MP1 **Make sense of problems and persevere in solving them.**

Item 11: Children use concrete objects or pictures to analyze, plan a solution to, and solve an addition word problem.

OBJECTIVE

Use objects, drawings, and equations to solve word problems that involve taking from, taking apart, and comparing to subtract.

ESSENTIAL QUESTION

Remind children that a word problem tells a story or describes a situation. Relate that a subtraction word problem involves taking from, taking apart, or comparing.

PREREQUISITE SKILLS

Use Foundational Skills Handbook page 250, *Subtraction,* to review subtracting.

FLUENCY PRACTICE

Fluency practice is available at **sadlierconnect.com**.

Concept Development

Understand: Sometimes you need to find how many are left

■ In this lesson, children use taking from, taking apart, and comparing with drawings, pictures, and numbers to solve subtraction word problems. Children relate these actions to simple equations.

■ Provide children with concrete objects to show the action in subtraction word problems: In subtraction, the starting number stands for a larger group. After *taking from* a larger group of objects, a smaller group of objects is *left.*

■ Be sure children can identify why the problems indicate subtraction. Guide them to use words such as *take away, give away, take apart,* and *left* as they explain.

Lesson 2 Problem Solving: Subtraction

Essential Question: How can you use subtraction to solve word problems?

Words to Know subtract

Guided Instruction

In this lesson you will use subtraction to solve word problems.

Understand: Sometimes you need to find how many are left

> Robin has 6 bananas.
> She gives 4 of them to her friends.
> How many bananas does she have now?

You can subtract to find how many are left.

$$6 \quad - \quad 4 \quad = \quad \blacksquare$$

6 take away 4 is 2.

$$6 - 4 = 2$$

▷ Robin has 2 bananas now.

Sam has 7 stickers. He gives 3 stickers to Juan. How many stickers does Sam have left? Draw a picture to help you solve the problem.

○ ○ ○ ○ ⊗ ⊗ ⊗

$$7 - 3 = 4$$

Sam has 4 stickers left.

Words to Know

subtract: to find how many are left

Example:

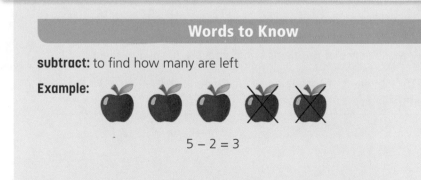

$$5 - 2 = 3$$

Glossary can be found on pp. 261-272.

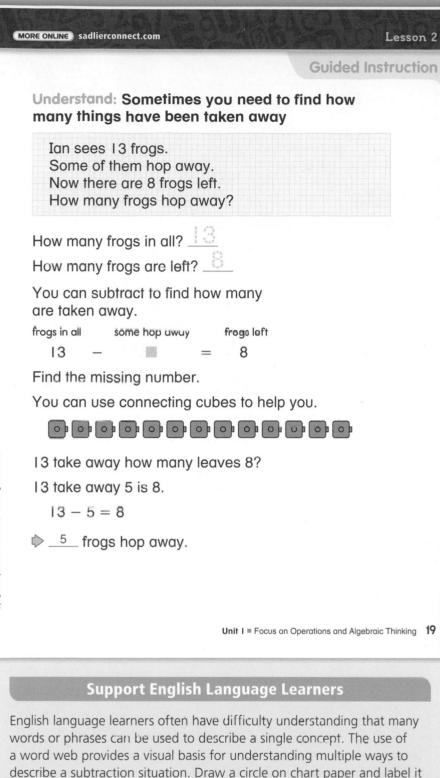

MORE ONLINE sadlierconnect.com   Lesson 2

Guided Instruction

Understand: **Sometimes you need to find how many things have been taken away**

Ian sees 13 frogs.
Some of them hop away.
Now there are 8 frogs left.
How many frogs hop away?

How many frogs in all? __13__

How many frogs are left? __8__

You can subtract to find how many are taken away.

frogs in all   some hop away   frogs left

13   —   ■   =   8

Find the missing number.

You can use connecting cubes to help you.

13 take away how many leaves 8?

13 take away 5 is 8.

$13 - 5 = 8$

▷ __5__ frogs hop away.

Unit 1 ■ Focus on Operations and Algebraic Thinking   **19**

Understand: Sometimes you need to find how many things have been taken away

■ Be sure children understand that the number they need to find can be in any position in the equation that tells about the problem situation. Sometimes the unknown number is how many objects are left, but not always. Sometimes the unknown number is the number being taken away. Emphasize that it is very important to read the question carefully.

■ Provide connecting cubes or other counters for children to act out the problem.

Support English Language Learners

English language learners often have difficulty understanding that many words or phrases can be used to describe a single concept. The use of a word web provides a visual basis for understanding multiple ways to describe a subtraction situation. Draw a circle on chart paper and label it *subtract*. Ask children to name some of the ways they can tell someone to subtract a number without using the word *subtract*. As each word or phrase is given, write it on a spoke around the center circle. Possible responses may include *give away, take away, take from, remove, hide, go away, fly away, hop away, take apart, separate,* or *compare.* Some children may also suggest terms that describe the result of subtraction, such as *the number left.*

Guided Instruction

Connect: Use subtraction to compare Use this page to help children understand that subtraction can be used to find *how many more* or *how many fewer* objects are in compared groups.

■ This presentation guides children through a thinking process for problem solving. Be sure that children understand that starting with *what you know* is essential for solving various types of word problems.

■ Comparing sets of objects using one-to-one correspondence is a critical area of mathematics instruction in kindergarten. Be sure children are able to explain how the objects that do not match up indicate which group is larger and how much larger.

■ Provide additional comparison situations for children who demonstrate confusion or hesitancy about when to describe one set as containing *how many more or how many fewer* objects.

Connect: **Use subtraction to compare**

There are 5 yellow flowers and 8 red flowers. How many more red flowers are there than yellow flowers?

Step 1

Start with what you know.

How many red flowers are there? __8__

How many yellow flowers are there? __5__

Step 2

Match each yellow flower with a red flower.

How many did you match? __5__

Subtract to find how many more red flowers.

$8 - 5 = 3$

▷ There are __3__ more red flowers than yellow flowers.

You can also say there are __3__ fewer yellow flowers than red flowers.

20   Unit 1 ■ Focus on Operations and Algebraic Thinking

Math-to-Science Connection

Flower Petals Collect several wildflowers or take a nature walk with children and gather flowers. Have children work individually or in pairs to compare the number of petals on at least two different types of flowers. Encourage them to describe the comparisons using terms such as *more, fewer,* and *same.* Be sure children can identify *how many more* and *how many fewer.*

If time allows, have children draw two flower stems on art paper and glue cutouts of petals on each stem to show the comparisons that they made.

Guided Practice

1. **Bapi has 6 fewer baseball cards than Dan.**
   Dan has 11 baseball cards.
   How many cards does Bapi have?

Step 1

Start with the cards Dan has.
How many cards does Dan have? __11__
Draw Dan's cards.

☐ ☐ ☐ ☐ ☐ ☐ ☐ ☐ ☐ ☐ ☐

Step 2

How many fewer cards does Bapi have? __6__
Cross off 6 cards.

☐ ☐ ☐ ☐ ☐ ☒ ☒ ☒ ☒ ☒ ☒

Use subtraction to solve the problem.

$$11 - 6 = \underline{5}$$

Bapi has __5__ cards.

☆ Think•Pair•Share

MP1 2. Make up a problem you can solve using
   subtraction. Draw a picture to show
   your problem. Then solve the problem.
   Check children's work.

Mathematical Practices

Mathematical Practice Standards underline the teaching and
understanding of all concepts and skills presented. The emphasis of
specific practices is noted throughout the guided and independent practice
of this lesson.

MP1	Make sense of problems and persevere in solving them.

Item 2: Children create and model their own real-world subtraction
problems and check their solutions.

Observational Assessment

Use page 21 to assess whether
children understand what constitutes
a subtraction word problem. Observe
whether children have difficulty
making the transition between using
the drawings and completing a
subtraction equation.

☆ Think•Pair•Share

Peer Collaboration Have pairs
of children present their created
subtraction stories to the class. Ask each
pair questions such as:

- *Did you make up a problem that
  compares groups or one that takes
  away a number?*

- *How does your picture show the
  problem that you created?*

- *Did you match objects to compare the
  numbers, or draw one whole group
  and cross off some of the objects?*

Encourage groups to compare their
pictures to see whether others
chose the same or different types of
subtraction situations.

Return to the Essential Question

Reread the Lesson 2 Essential Question
on page 18: *How can you use
subtraction to solve word problems?*

Tell children to think about what they
learned in this lesson to answer
this question.
(Possible response: I can use objects or
drawings to model a group of objects and
take some away. I can match objects in
two groups and see how many objects do
not match to find out how many more or
how many fewer objects one group has
than the other.)

Concept Application

Children may work independently on these pages in the classroom or at home. They may refer to the first four pages of the lesson to revisit the instruction or to see a worked-out example.

Common Errors and **Teaching Tips** may help you support learning either in the classroom or as a follow-up for work done at home.

Common Errors

Items 1-2

Children may choose an incorrect operation for solving the problems. If they add the given numbers, have them read the question again and analyze whether the solution to the problem makes sense. For example, if children answer *12* for the first exercise, ask if it makes sense for more than nine children to be left after some children leave.

Teaching Tips

Item 1

Direct children to first determine what is being taken away. Most children will find this type of word problem easy to interpret as a subtraction situation. Provide extra paper for children to make a model, if needed.

Item 2

Remind children that they can use counters or a drawing to help them solve this problem. Encourage them to show the starting number, 11, and then cover up or cross out all except for 8 objects. Lead a discussion about what each group of objects represents.

Draw a picture to help you solve each problem.

1. Nine children are in class. Then 3 children leave. How many children are left in the class?

How many children started in class? ___9___

How many children leave? ___3___

Subtract to find how many children are left.

$9 - 3 = $ ___6___

There are ___6___ children left in the class.

---

2. Eleven apples were on the tree. Some fell off. Now there are 8 apples on the tree. How many apples fell off the tree?

How many apples were on the tree to start? ___11___

How many apples are on the tree now? ___8___

Subtract to find how many apples fell off the tree.

$11 - $ ___3___ $ = 8$

___3___ apples fell off the tree.

Talking About Math

Compare and Contrast Experiences Lead an introductory discussion about pets with the class. Then ask children to work in small groups to talk about their pets. Have children make at least two comparisons, such as the number of group members who do and do not have a pet, or the number of cats and dogs. Point out to children that zero can also be used as a comparison, such as the number of dogs as pets and the number of pets that none of them have, for example, giraffes as pets.

Have each group of children share two comparisons with the class.

MORE ONLINE sadlierconnect.com

Independent Practice

Draw a picture to help you solve each problem.

3. There are 10 plates on the table.
   Meg takes away 5 plates.
   How many plates are left on the table?

   $10 - 5 = \underline{5}$

   $\underline{5}$ plates are left on the table.

4. Tony has 15 crayons.
   Sue has 8 crayons.
   How many more crayons
   does Tony have than Sue?

   $15 - 8 = \underline{7}$

   Tony has $\underline{7}$ more crayons than Sue.

5. There are 9 more oranges than apples.
   There are 16 oranges.
   How many apples are there?

   $16 - 9 = \underline{7}$

   There are $\underline{7}$ apples.

Unit 1 ■ Focus on Operations and Algebraic Thinking **23**

Common Errors

Items 4–5

As children move from subtractions within 12 to subtractions within 20, computation errors become more likely. Have children use objects or drawings to check their work as needed.

Teaching Tips

Items 3–5

Children may need more than the available space on the page to draw their pictures. Provide extra paper as needed.

Each of these word problems is different in the type of subtraction situation given. Help children break down each situation by asking them *what they know* and *what they are asked to find out.* If necessary, allow children to use counters to model each problem before drawing a picture.

Item 5

Some children may have difficulty analyzing problem 5 due to the order of the first two sentences. Have children read the sentences in reverse order to help clarify the problem. Remind children to compare as well. If further help is needed, provide 2-color counters for children. Have them show 16 of the same color and turn over 9 of them and count the ones that are left.

Digital Connection

Math Games Use classroom videos or games that involve one-to-one correspondence at the first grade or foundation level. Free games and activities can also be found online by searching for *one to one correspondence math activities.* After you review the activities, allow children to use the appropriate ones to practice comparing sets of objects and recording the comparisons. Encourage children to work in pairs to describe *how many more* or *how many fewer* objects are shown in one group than in another.

Common Errors

Item 6

Children often assume that the number to the right of the equal sign is the answer to the problem. Make sure children can identify what is being asked before they complete the sentence. Have children reread the problem while they point to the numbers in their equations.

Draw a picture to help you solve each problem.

6. There are 7 books on a shelf.
   Anna takes some books off.
   Now there are 3 books on the shelf.
   How many books does Anna take off?

   $$\underline{7} - \underline{4} = \underline{3}$$

   Anna takes __4__ books off the shelf.

---

7. David has 6 pencils. Selene has 10 pencils.
   How many fewer pencils does
   David have than Selene?

   $$\underline{10} - \underline{6} = \underline{4}$$

   David has __4__ fewer pencils than Selene.

---

8. Al has 5 more cars than Mike. Al has 14 cars.
   How many cars does Mike have?

   $$\underline{14} - \underline{5} = \underline{9}$$

   Mike has __9__ cars.

Math-to-Music Connection

Subtraction Songs Use common children's songs to practice subtraction skills. Provide words to songs that involve taking away or making comparisons. If you cannot find songs, or they are not readily available, use the Internet to find audio and video subtraction songs.

Have children sing together as a class or have groups of children demonstrate different songs to one another.

Independent Practice

Draw a picture to help you solve each problem.

9. There were 9 bikes on a bike rack.
Children rode 4 bikes away.
How many bikes are on the rack now?

$\underline{9} - \underline{4} = \underline{5}$

There are __5__ bikes on the rack now.

10. Some children were playing.
Then 9 children leave.
Now there are 8 children playing.
How many children were playing at the start?

$\underline{17} - \underline{9} = \underline{8}$

__17__ children were playing at the start.

MP4 11. Nikki has 14 stickers. Jason has 8 stickers.
How many fewer stickers does
Jason have than Nikki? Check children's work.

$\underline{14} - \underline{8} = \underline{6}$

Jason has __6__ fewer stickers than Nikki.

Talk about how you can use the word *more*
to compare Nikki's and Jason's stickers.

Answers may vary. Possible answer: Nikki has more stickers than Jason.

Unit 1 ■ Focus on Operations and Algebraic Thinking   **25**

Common Errors

Items 9-11
Children may mix up the order of the numbers in the equations if they do not read carefully. Help children focus on identifying what is being asked in each instance and determine the meaning of the first blank in each equation. In problem 10, point out that the first blank represents the unknown number. It may help for children to write the subtrahend and the difference first, and then find the minuend. Using this approach, they can more easily identify the relationship between the numbers.

Mathematical Practices	
MP4	**Model with mathematics.**

Item 11: Children use concrete objects or drawings to explain the relationship between quantities.

OBJECTIVE

Use models and equations to solve word problems that add three whole numbers and have a sum within 20.

ESSENTIAL QUESTION

Read aloud the Essential Question and ask children to tell what they think it means. Explain that the lesson will help them understand how to put together three numbers to solve a problem.

FLUENCY PRACTICE

Fluency practice is available at **sadlierconnect.com**.

Concept Development

Understand: What numbers and operation help you find how many in all

■ In this lesson, children use counting and pictures to solve addition word problems within 20 that involve three addends.

■ Use this lesson as a way to review crucial terms pertaining to addition, such as *how many in all*. Children will also begin using terms such as *addends* and *sum*.

■ Ask children to explain how they know that they need to add more than once.

Lesson 3 Problem Solving: **Addition of Three Numbers**

Guided Instruction

Essential Question:
How do you use addition of three numbers to solve a word problem?

Words to Know
addend
sum

In this lesson you will learn how to solve word problems by adding three numbers.

Understand: What numbers and operation help you find how many in all

> Hannah has 6 oranges.
> Jack has 3 apples.
> Angela has 5 pears.
> How many fruits do they have in all?

You can add to find how many in all.

| Hannah's oranges | Jack's apples | Angela's pears | fruits in all |

Which numbers should you add? __6__, __3__, __5__

$6 + 3 + 5 = $ ▪

The three numbers you add are called addends. You want to find the total, or sum.

First add the addends 6 and 3. $6 + 3 = 9$

Then start with 9 and add the 5. $9 + 5 = 14$

$6 + 3 + 5 = 14$ The sum is 14.

▷ They have 14 fruits in all.

Words to Know

addend: the numbers you add

Example:

$4 + 1 = 5$

addends

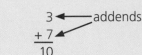

$$\begin{array}{r} 3 \\ + 7 \\ \hline 10 \end{array}$$ addends

sum: the answer in addition

Example: $4 + 3 = 7$ ◀— sum

Glossary can be found on pp. 261-272.

Understand: **Solve word problems by adding three numbers**

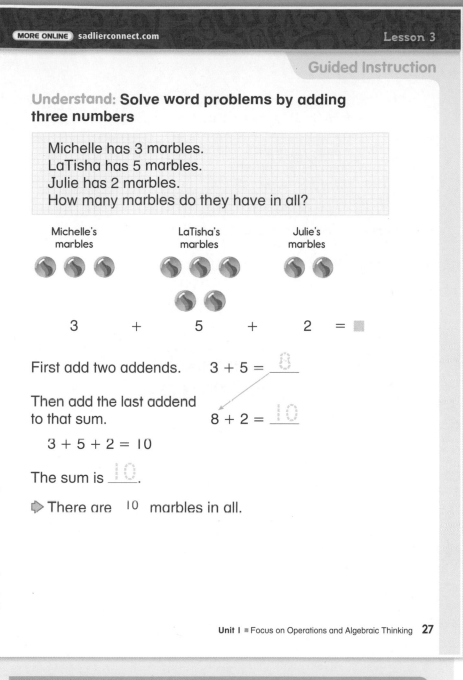

Michelle has 3 marbles.
LaTisha has 5 marbles.
Julie has 2 marbles.
How many marbles do they have in all?

Michelle's marbles   LaTisha's marbles   Julie's marbles

3   +   5   +   2   = ▪

First add two addends. $3 + 5 = \_\_$

Then add the last addend
to that sum. $8 + 2 = \_10\_$

$3 + 5 + 2 = 10$

The sum is _10_.

➡ There are 10 marbles in all.

Understand: **Solve word problems by adding three numbers**

■ Some children may be able to use mental math to add all three numbers at once, recognizing 3, 5, and 2 as a combination that makes 10. Make sure these children understand the two-step process that is given so they can apply it in solving more difficult additions later.

■ For children who appear to struggle with the concept, use plain white paper to cover everything on the page except the marbles and numerals representing 3 + 5. Once children have solved that part of the problem, uncover the marbles and numeral for the other addend, 2. Isolating parts of the problem in this way will help children organize their thinking by allowing them to deal with one step at a time.

Support English Language Learners

In previous lessons, children have solved word problems containing the word *some,* used to express an unknown quantity. The introduction of the homophone *sum* in this lesson is likely to confuse English language learners. Display both words and point out that they sound the same but are spelled differently and have different meanings. Tell or read aloud addition word problems that include the use of one of these words. Ask children to listen to the oral problems and point to whether *some* or *sum* makes sense in this context.

Connect: **What you know about adding three numbers to find a missing addend** Use this page to help children understand how to organize given data and count pictured objects to find a missing addend.

■ In this presentation, children analyze a situation and identify what is given, what is missing, and what steps are necessary to find a missing quantity.

■ Some children may recognize the relationship between addition and subtraction and use a known addition or subtraction to solve for the missing number. Children who do not yet demonstrate that level of fluency will have opportunities for connecting addition and subtraction later in this lesson, and in Lesson 5.

■ Some children may need the tactile experience of using counters to model the situation involving two addends, a missing addend, and a sum.

Lesson 3   Problem Solving: Addition of Three Numbers

Guided Instruction

Connect: What you know about adding three numbers to find a missing addend

Derrick has 5 markers. Marsha has 2 markers.
Toby has some markers.
They have 15 markers in all.
How many markers does Toby have?

Step 1

Which addends do you know? __5__ and __2__

What is the sum? __15__

One addend is missing. $5 + 2 + \blacksquare = 15$

Step 2

Use counters to help you find the missing number.

● ● ● ● ● ● ● ● ● ● ● ● ● ● ●

Add the two addends you know. $5 + 2 = $ __7__

$5 + 2 + \blacksquare = 15$

$7 + \blacksquare = 15$

7 plus how many make 15? __8__

$7 + \underline{8} = 15$

$5 + 2 + \underline{8} = 15$

➡ Toby has __8__ markers.

Math-to-Social Studies Connection

Neighborhoods Tell children that they will gather information about their neighborhoods to create addition stories that have three addends. Discuss possible data that children may collect, such as the number of people who live in three houses or apartments, the number of cars in three driveways at a particular time, the number of mailboxes in three rows of a mail receptacle, or the number of street lamps in three blocks. Give children a specific date that they should be prepared to share the information with the class.

The following day or soon after, have children take turns presenting their addition stories about their neighborhoods.

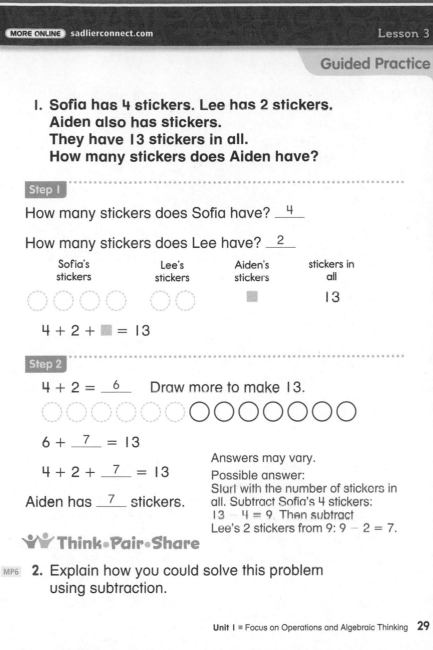

1. Sofia has 4 stickers. Lee has 2 stickers.
   Aiden also has stickers.
   They have 13 stickers in all.
   How many stickers does Aiden have?

Step 1

How many stickers does Sofia have? ___4___

How many stickers does Lee have? ___2___

Sofia's stickers	Lee's stickers	Aiden's stickers	stickers in all

$4 + 2 + \blacksquare = 13$

Step 2

$4 + 2 = \underline{6}$　　Draw more to make 13.

$6 + \underline{7} = 13$

$4 + 2 + \underline{7} = 13$

Aiden has ___7___ stickers.

Answers may vary.
Possible answer:
Start with the number of stickers in all. Subtract Sofia's 4 stickers:
$13 - 4 = 9$. Then subtract Lee's 2 stickers from 9: $9 - 2 = 7$.

✮ Think•Pair•Share

MP6　2. Explain how you could solve this problem using subtraction.

Unit 1 ■ Focus on Operations and Algebraic Thinking　**29**

Observational Assessment

Use page 29 to assess whether children are able to first find the sum of two addends and then use the result to find the other addend by drawing and counting. Observe whether children have difficulty organizing the problem into the appropriate steps.

✮ Think•Pair•Share

Peer Collaboration Break the class into pairs of children. Have partners explain their reasoning to one another. Prompt the discussions with questions such as:

- *What could you draw to help you solve the problem?*

- *If you subtract the number of Sofia's stickers from 13, what will your answer stand for?*

- *If you subtract the number of Sofia's stickers and the number of Lee's stickers from 13, what will your answer stand for?*

Return to the Essential Question

Reread the Lesson 3 Essential Question on page 26: *How do you use addition of three numbers to solve a word problem?*

Tell children to think about what they learned in this lesson to answer this question.
(Possible response: I can use objects or drawings to model groups of objects to add or find a missing addend. I can solve part of the problem first and then solve the next part.)

Have children share any other problem-solving strategies they learned in this lesson.

Mathematical Practices

Mathematical Practice Standards underline the teaching and understanding of all concepts and skills presented. The emphasis of specific practices is noted throughout the guided and independent practice of this lesson.

MP6	**Attend to precision.**

Item 2: Children communicate clearly and precisely the relationship between addition and subtraction.

Independent Practice

Concept Application

Children may work independently on these pages in the classroom or at home. They may refer to the first four pages of the lesson to revisit the instruction or to see a worked-out example.

Common Errors and **Teaching Tips** may help you support learning either in the classroom or as a follow-up for work done at home.

Common Errors

Item 2

When children are not given the two-step solution prompts, they may skip part of the solution or make mental math miscalculations. If children write *5, 10,* or *13* as the sum, ask them to review whether they added all three addends.

Teaching Tips

Items 1–2

Children are likely to complete these problems without too much difficulty because all three addends are given in each situation. Check children's drawings to make sure they correctly transferred the given information to their visual models.

Make sure children understand that reasonable answers will be greater than the greatest addend and greater than the sum of any two addends.

Independent Practice

Draw a picture to help you solve each problem.

1. A box has 2 red crayons, 5 yellow crayons, and 5 blue crayons.
   How many crayons are in the box?

   How many crayons of each color?

   red __2__   yellow __5__   blue __5__

   Add the number of red crayons and the number of yellow crayons.

   $2 + 5 =$ __7__

   Add the number of blue crayons to that sum.

   $7 + 5 =$ __12__

   $2 + 5 + 5 =$ __12__

   There are __12__ crayons in the box.

---

2. Ella has 1 pink button and 4 white buttons.
   Jacob has 9 purple buttons.
   How many buttons do they have in all?

   $1 + 4 + 9 =$ __14__

   They have __14__ buttons in all.

Talking About Math

Compare Pictures and Text Draw three groups of circles on the board to represent 3, 6, and 2. Under the drawing, write 3 + 5 + 2. Ask children to compare the drawings and the numbers. Have children explain if they can be used to show the same addition story. Have children apply what they have learned about problem solving by completing the equation for both the drawing and the underlying equation to determine their sum for comparison. Have children discuss what changes are needed to make them match.

Independent Practice

Draw a picture to help you solve each problem.

3. Three girls are on a bus. One more girl gets on.
   Then some boys get on.
   There are 11 children on the bus now.
   How many boys got on the bus?

   $3 + 1 + \underline{}7\underline{} = 11$

   $\underline{}7\underline{}$ boys got on the bus.

4. Ethan ate 3 raisins. Then he ate 4 grapes.
   Then he ate some strawberries.
   He ate 15 pieces of fruit in all.
   How many strawberries did he eat?

   $3 + 4 + \underline{}8\underline{} = 15$

   Ethan ate $\underline{}8\underline{}$ strawberries.

5. Madison has some pencils.
   Jayden has 8 pencils. Ava has 1 pencil.
   They have 18 pencils in all.
   How many pencils does Madison have?

   $\underline{}9\underline{} + 8 + 1 = 18$

   Madison has $\underline{}9\underline{}$ pencils.

Common Errors

Item 4

Some children may try to solve the problem by adding each given number rather than analyzing the mathematical situation. Have children reread the problem to identify what they are being asked to solve. Also, have children review their answers in the context of the addition story. Prompt logical reasoning by asking children whether the answer will be the sum (greatest number) or an addend.

Teaching Tips

Items 3-5

Children may need hints about possible ways to draw a picture for a missing addend problem. Explain that they can draw the total number given for each problem rather than drawing each addend and a blank. Then they can use their drawing to circle a number of objects that represent each of the two addends that are given. The objects that are not circled represent the missing addend.

Provide extra paper for children who need more space to make their drawings.

Digital Connection

Groups of Counters Use an interactive whiteboard to select counting objects and build three groups of counters that contain up to 5 objects each. Have children add the groups of counters. Then ask volunteers to create other groups of objects to add. Next, create two groups of objects and ask volunteers to make another group that will equal a particular sum. For example, create a group of 3 and a group of 4 counters. Ask a child to build a third group that will make 12 counters in all. Continue the activity to involve several more volunteers.

Independent Practice

Teaching Tips

Items 6-8

This is the first page of the lesson where children write all the numbers in the equation. Help children begin by having them first identify what is to be solved. Although the order of the addends does not matter, children are likely to write them in the order given in the problems. Make sure children understand that the sum is the greatest number and should be placed after the equal sign in these problems.

Items 7-8

Tell children that the word *some* in these problems represents a missing addend. Help children who seem hesitant by suggesting that they read one sentence at a time and record that information in the order that it is given. When they see the word *some,* have them place a counter over that blank in the equation. After they record the *number in all,* have them remove the counter to analyze how the blank relates to the rest of the equation.

Independent Practice

Draw a picture to help you solve each problem.

6. Noah has 6 striped shirts. He has 2 print shirts.
   He also has 5 solid shirts.
   How many shirts does he have in all?

   $\underline{6} + \underline{2} + \underline{5} = \underline{13}$

   Noah has $\underline{13}$ shirts in all.

7. Kate has 7 sailboats. John has 1 rowboat.
   Emma has some motorboats.
   They have 17 boats in all.
   How many motorboats does Emma have?

   $\underline{7} + \underline{1} + \underline{9} = \underline{17}$

   Emma has $\underline{9}$ motorboats.

8. Logan has some red cubes.
   He gets 4 blue cubes and 5 yellow cubes.
   Now he has 16 cubes.
   How many red cubes does Logan have?

   $\underline{7} + \underline{4} + \underline{5} = \underline{16}$

   Logan has $\underline{7}$ red cubes.

Math-to-Math Connection

Algebra and Properties of Operations As children work with three addends, they should understand that they do not need to add the three addends in the order in which they are given. If they find it easier to add numbers in a different order, allow them to do so, but make sure they do not confuse the sum with any of the addends. This also helps them prepare for the introduction of the Commutative Property of Addition, which they will encounter later in this unit and beyond. They will not be using the names of the properties at this grade level, but they should be starting to appreciate how their knowledge of properties such as these can help them become better problem-solvers.

Lesson 3

Independent Practice

MP6 **9.** Talk about different ways you can solve this problem. Then solve.

Matt finds 6 orange leaves.
Lily finds some red leaves.
Nick finds 3 brown leaves.
They find 14 leaves in all.
How many red leaves does Lily find?

Lily finds __5__ red leaves.

MP1 **10.** Make up a problem you can solve adding 3 addends.
Draw a picture to show your problem.
Then solve the problem.

Check children's work.

Teaching Tips

Item 9

Have children attempt to solve the problem independently. Then have them discuss solution strategies. Examine the number equations children used to solve the problem and have them describe how they solved it by naming the operations and the steps they used.

Item 10

Remind children to think through the parts of the problem they will solve. Have them identify the parts of the problem and what is to be solved. Some children may be able to write whole-sentence word problems, but others may write the numbers and some key words to help them share their problems orally. Check children's drawings to make sure they represent the story situation accurately.

Mathematical Practices

MP1	Make sense of problems and persevere in solving them.

Item 10: Children create a problem situation and use pictures to develop and evaluate their solutions.

MP6	Attend to precision.

Item 9: Children use clear definitions and processes to explain possible solution strategies in their own reasoning.

OBJECTIVE
Use the Commutative and Associative Properties of Addition.

ESSENTIAL QUESTION
Read the Essential Question aloud and help children understand its meaning. Explain that *properties* are rules and relate that addition and subtraction are called *operations*. So *properties of operations* are rules for adding and subtracting. In later grades, children will learn that multiplication and division are also operations.

PREREQUISITE SKILLS
Use Foundational Skills Handbook page 251, *Make Names for Numbers,* to review using objects to order numbers in solving problems.

FLUENCY PRACTICE
Fluency practice is available at **sadlierconnect.com**.

Concept Development

Understand: You can add numbers in any order

■ Provide children with connecting cubes of two colors to model the word problem.

■ Be sure children can express the Commutative Property of Addition in their own words. They do not need to know the term *commutative,* but you may have them refer to the concept as the *order property.*

> **Essential Question:** How can the properties of operations help you add?

In this lesson you will learn strategies that will help you add.

Understand: You can add numbers in any order

> Ken has 4 blue balloons and 5 red balloons. How many balloons does he have in all?

You can add numbers in any order and the sum will be the same.

> **Remember!**
> The sum is 9.
> The addends are 4 and 5.

Use cubes to show 4 + 5.

$$4 \quad + \quad 5 \quad = 9$$

Now move your cubes to show 5 + 4.

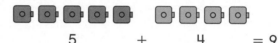

$$5 \quad + \quad 4 \quad = 9$$

The sums are the same.
The order of the addends does not change the sum.

▷ Ken has 9 balloons in all.

Support English Language Learners

Words that have multiple meanings are uncommon in many languages other than English. Have children explore different meanings of the word *order.* Ask them to create ways to act out or describe more than one meaning. Children may mention lining up in a particular order, following directions in order, placing an order at a restaurant, being ordered to do something, or the meaning of *out of order.*

Conclude the activity by asking children to tell what it means to change the order of addends. Make sure children understand that *order* in this context refers to what comes first, second, or third.

MORE ONLINE sadlierconnect.com

Guided Instruction

Understand: You can add three numbers in any order

Add these three numbers.
$3 + 5 + 4 = \blacksquare$

3   5   4

Add the first 2 numbers. $3 + 5 = \underline{8}$

8   +   4

Then add the third number to that sum.

$8 + 4 = \underline{12}$

▶ $3 + 5 + 4 = \underline{12}$

Remember!
You can add in any order.

Here is another way to add.

Add the last two numbers. $5 + 4 = \underline{9}$

3   +   9

Then add the first number to that sum.

$3 + 9 = \underline{12}$

▶ $3 + 5 + 4 = \underline{12}$

Unit 1 ■ Focus on Operations and Algebraic Thinking **35**

Understand: You can add three numbers in any order

■ Explain to children that, just as they added $4 + 5$ in any order in the previous presentation, they can add $3 + 5 + 4$ in any order.

■ The grouping property modeled in this presentation is an informal introduction to the Associative Property of Addition. Children do not need to name the property, but they should be able to describe how the given solutions are different and alike.

■ Provide connecting cubes or other counters for children to act out the problem, if needed.

■ Some children may recognize that other combinations are possible to solve the problem, such as adding $3 + 4$ and then adding 5.

Math-to-Drama Connection

Finger Puppets Provide children with nine animal stickers to place on their fingernails. Have them attach four stickers onto one hand and five onto the other hand. Tell children to use their animal finger puppets to create an addition story about the number of animals on each hand and the number in all.

Now have children cross their hands and explain how their addition story changes. Make sure they understand that the order of the addends changes, but the sum does not change. Have children repeat the activity using different numbers of animal stickers to practice the Commutative (order) Property of Addition.

Connect: You can group addends to help you add. Use this page to help children understand that the addends can be grouped in more than one way.

■ Explain to children that grouping addends in a different way can sometimes make an addition problem easier to solve. Have children discuss why first making a ten helps them solve this problem.

■ In order to understand the making-a-ten method, these Kindergarten concepts should be mastered: knowing the partner number that makes a 10 for any number, knowing how to decompose any number less than 10, and thinking of numbers greater than 10 and less than 20 as $10 + n$.

■ Children may suggest different ways to group the addends. Although the doubles strategy has not yet been taught, some children may recognize that by first adding $2 + 4 = 6$, they can then use the double $6 + 6$ to find the sum, 12.

■ Provide additional math situations containing three addends to help build fluency.

Connect: You can group addends to help you add

Jane has 6 apples, 2 bananas, and 4 oranges. How many fruits does she have in all?

Add to find how many in all.

$6 + 2 + 4 = \blacksquare$

Step 1

Try to make a ten by grouping the addends a different way.

$6 + 2 + 4 = \blacksquare$

$6 + 4 + 2 = \blacksquare$

Step 2

Now you can make a ten.

$6 + 4 + 2 = \blacksquare$

$\underline{10} + 2 = \underline{12}$

$6 + 2 + 4 = \underline{12}$

▷ Jane has $\underline{12}$ fruits in all.

Math-to-Recreation Connection

Carnival Tickets Have children pretend that they are going to a carnival. Tell them that they each have 15 carnival tickets to spend. Display a list of possible carnival activities and the number of tickets that each costs. Have children choose three activities. Then have them add to find the number of tickets needed for all three and tell whether they used all 15 tickets or fewer than 15 tickets. Possible activities may include the following ideas: Face Painting—2 tickets, Thrill Rides—7 tickets, Kiddie Rides—3 tickets, Snacks—5 tickets, Midway Games—6 tickets, and House of Mirrors—4 tickets. Have children write their number equations to show how many tickets they used.

Guided Practice

1. Add these three addends.

5 + 7 + 5 = ■

Step 1

Look at the addends.
Can you make a ten?
5 and 5 make 10.
Circle the 5 and 5 to add.

(5) + 7 + (5) = ■

Add.

5 + 5 = 10

Step 2

Now add the other addend to that sum.

10 + 7 = 17

5 + 7 + 5 = 17

Think•Pair•Share

MP7 **2.** Find each sum.

4 + 0 = 4 0 + 6 = 6 9 + 0 = 9

What happens when you add 0 to any number?

Answers may vary. Possible answer: The sum is the same as the other addend.

Mathematical Practices

Mathematical Practice Standards underline the teaching and understanding of all concepts and skills presented. The emphasis of specific practices is noted throughout the guided and independent practice of this lesson.

MP7	**Look for and make use of structure.**

Item 2: Children look for a pattern when adding 0 to any number.

Observational Assessment

Use page 37 to assess whether children are able to use a strategy, structure, or pattern to solve problems. Observe whether children can readily identify addends that make a ten. Make note of children who continue to need models to add. These children may require additional practice to help them apply strategies to addition.

Think•Pair•Share

Peer Collaboration Break up the class into pairs. Ask children to think about ways to explain what happens when they add zero to a number. Prompt partner discussions with questions such as:

- *How is adding 4 + 0 like adding 9 + 0?*
- *How does adding 0 change the sum in a number problem?*
- *How many sums would you have to find to add three numbers if one of the numbers is 0?*

If time allows, encourage children to discuss how they could show or act out adding zero in a word problem.

Return to the Essential Question

Reread the Lesson 4 Essential Question on page 34: *How can the properties of operations help you add?*

Tell children to think about what they learned in this lesson to answer this question.

(Possible response: I can change the order of the addends to make the addition easier or to check my work. I can group the addends in different ways to use a strategy like making a ten.)

Concept Application

Children may work independently on these pages in the classroom or at home. They may refer to the first four pages of the lesson to revisit the instruction or to see a worked-out example.

Common Errors and **Teaching Tips** may help you support learning either in the classroom or as a follow-up for work done at home.

Common Errors

Item 3

This problem is the only one on the page that places the greater addend first, so some children might interpret the problem as subtraction rather than addition. If children write 4 as the sum, have them reread the problem. Point to the addition symbol and have children review what it means. Also have them reread the directions and define the word *sum*.

Teaching Tips

Items 1–4

Be sure children can clearly identify which numbers represent the addends and which numbers represent the sum in each problem. Remind children that the order of the addends will not change the sum.

Independent Practice

Show that changing the order of the addends does not change the sum.

1. $4 + 8 = \blacksquare$

$\underline{8} + \underline{4} = \underline{12}$

$4 + 8 = \underline{12}$

2. $7 + 9 = \blacksquare$

$\underline{9} + \underline{7} = \underline{16}$

$7 + 9 = \underline{16}$

3. $7 + 3 = \blacksquare$

$\underline{3} + \underline{7} = \underline{10}$

$7 + 3 = \underline{10}$

4. $6 + 8 = \blacksquare$

$\underline{8} + \underline{6} = \underline{14}$

$6 + 8 = \underline{14}$

38 Unit 1 ▪ Focus on Operations and Algebraic Thinking

Talking About Math

Telling Math Stories Have children work in small groups or pairs to create a math story that matches one of the equations on this page. Direct children to include details, such as the names of anyone in the story and the descriptions of the objects to be added. Ask them to identify the parts of the equation as the addends and sum.

Allow time for children to share their stories with the class. Have them include how the stories might change to match a different order of the addends.

Independent Practice

Add. For problems 7–10, addition sentences may vary.
Sample addition sentences are given.

5. $6 + 2 + 3 = $ ■

$6 + 2 = \underline{\ 8\ }$

$8 + 3 = \underline{\ 11\ }$

$6 + 2 + 3 = \underline{\ 11\ }$

6. $1 + 5 + 4 = $ ■

$1 + 5 = \underline{\ 6\ }$

$6 + \underline{\ 4\ } = \underline{\ 10\ }$

$1 + 5 + 4 = \underline{\ 10\ }$

7. $2 + 4 + 5 = $ ■

$2 + \underline{\ 4\ } = \underline{\ 6\ }$

$\underline{\ 6\ } + \underline{\ 5\ } = \underline{\ 11\ }$

$2 + 4 + 5 = \underline{\ 11\ }$

8. $8 + 2 + 7 = $ ■

$\underline{\ 8\ } + \underline{\ 2\ } = \underline{\ 10\ }$

$\underline{\ 10\ } + \underline{\ 7\ } = \underline{\ 17\ }$

$8 + 2 + 7 = \underline{\ 17\ }$

9. $4 + 5 + 6 = $ ■

$4 + \underline{\ 5\ } = \underline{\ 9\ }$

$\underline{\ 9\ } + \underline{\ 6\ } = \underline{\ 15\ }$

$4 + 5 + 6 = \underline{\ 15\ }$

10. $7 + 1 + 8 = $ ■

$7 + \underline{\ 1\ } - \underline{\ 8\ }$

$\underline{\ 8\ } + \underline{\ 8\ } = \underline{\ 16\ }$

$7 + 1 + 8 = \underline{\ 16\ }$

Unit 1 ■ Focus on Operations and Algebraic Thinking   **39**

Common Errors

Items 7-10

For each of these problems, children may begin the second equation with an addend rather than the sum of the first equation. Be sure children understand that the first equation represents the addition of the first two addends and the second equation represents that sum plus the third addend.

Teaching Tips

Items 5-10

Some children may benefit from isolating each problem as they work. Have them use paper to cover the problems on which they are not currently working. Use this technique to help children focus on one problem at a time. This practice will also help children keep their work organized.

Item 8

Only this problem allows children to start the first equation with any addend. Children are most likely to begin with $8 + 2$, but other combinations are equally acceptable. Encourage those children who are struggling with how to start the problem, to use the make-a-ten method. Be sure children understand that the order of the addends chosen will not change the ending sum.

Digital Connection

Addition Software Use addition software or online activities to provide children with practice finding the sums of three 1-digit numbers. To prepare for the activity, review products and make a list of appropriate activities that match the needs of the class. When using the addition software, encourage children to work in pairs to describe the strategies they can use for each activity.

Independent Practice

Teaching Tips

Items 11–14

Be sure children follow directions to use the make-a-ten strategy to solve each problem. This will help to reinforce their understanding of the process for solving equations. They may use other groupings of addends to check their work, but it is important that they practice a specific strategy here as preparation for higher-level addition concepts.

Item 15

Children should use number sentences to show their work, but they may also use drawings if they choose to include them. Allow children the opportunity to use any strategy to solve this problem.

Independent Practice

Make a ten.
Then add the other addend.

11. $6 + 2 + 8 = $ ▮

$2 + 8 = $ __10__

$10 + 6 = $ __16__

12. $5 + 5 + 9 = $ ▮

$5 + 5 = $ __10__

$10 + 9 = $ __19__

13. $3 + 5 + 7 = $ ▮

$3 + 7 = $ __10__

$10 + $ __5__ $ = $ __15__

14. $8 + 9 + 1 = $ ▮

__9__ $ + $ __1__ $ = $ __10__

__10__ $ + $ __8__ $ = $ __18__

Solve the problem. Show your work.

15. Ken had 5 gold fish. He bought 5 more gold fish and 2 angel fish. How many fish does Ken have now?

Ken has __12__ fish now.

Math-to-History Connection

Ancient Number Systems Explain that, even long ago, people used their fingers to count. They also used small clay tokens as numbers. Each token represented one animal. People would string the tokens on a necklace to count the animals. Some necklaces became too long, so they made larger tokens. Each larger one represented ten animals.

Share the information about ancient number systems with children. Then have them use clay to make their own counting tokens. (If clay is not available, have them use small buttons or art paper.) Direct children to poke a hole in the middle of each token before drying the clay. Allow them to place the dried shapes on a string to wear so they can use them to count, add, or compare tokens.

MORE ONLINE sadlierconnect.com   Lesson 4

Independent Practice

MP3 **16.** Mia and Carlos wanted to solve this addition.

$$6 + 9 = \blacksquare$$

Mia added $6 + 9$.
Carlos added $9 + 6$.
Who will get the correct answer? Explain.

Mia and Carlos will both get the same answer, 15, because
changing the order of the addends does not change the sum.

MP1 **17.** Make up a problem for this addition example.
Draw a picture to show your problem.
Then solve your problem.

$$5 + 3 + 5 = \blacksquare$$

Problems may vary. Possible answer: Joe has
5 red marbles, 3 yellow marbles and 5 green marbles.
How many marbles does Joe have in all? $5 + 3 = 8$ and
$8 + 5 = 13$. Joe has 13 marbles in all.

Unit 1 ■ Focus on Operations and Algebraic Thinking **41**

Independent Practice

Teaching Tips

Items 16–17
Have children work in pairs to complete
the problems and discuss their answers.
Make sure they use reliable thought
processes to solve their problems.
Encourage children to make logical
explanations, communicate their
reasoning, and analyze the reasoning
of their partners.

Mathematical Practices

MP1	Make sense of problems and persevere in solving them.

Item 17: Children create a problem situation and use pictures to develop
and evaluate their solutions.

MP3	Construct viable arguments and critique the reasoning of others.

Item 16: Children use previously established conjectures and build a
logical argument to support the conjectures.

OBJECTIVE
Solve and record related addition and subtraction facts to 18.

ESSENTIAL QUESTION
Point out the Essential Question at the top of the page and read it aloud. Explain that, in this lesson, children will learn how to use addition to help them solve subtraction problems and how to use subtraction to solve addition problems.

FLUENCY PRACTICE
Fluency practice is available at sadlierconnect.com.

Concept Application

Understand: Every addition fact has a related subtraction fact

■ Children need to understand that addition and subtraction are inverse, or opposite, operations. This presentation helps children to understand that adding undoes subtracting and vice versa.

■ Children should understand that addition means joining or putting together. Ask children to identify the number of marbles in the first group and the number of marbles being added.

■ Reinforce the idea that subtraction reverses addition by showing that taking away the group that was added leaves only the first group.

■ Have children discuss how the related facts on this page are alike and different. Ask them to make generalizations about how to tell whether an addition fact and a subtraction fact are related.

Lesson 5

Related Addition and Subtraction Facts

Guided Instruction

Essential Question: How can you use an addition fact to help solve a subtraction problem?

Words to Know
related facts

In this lesson you will learn how addition and subtraction are related.

Understand: Every addition fact has a related subtraction fact

> Jo has 4 marbles. Kim gives her 2 more marbles. How many marbles does Jo have now?

Start with 4 marbles. Add 2 marbles.

$$4 + 2 = 6$$

Remember! 4 and 2 are addends. 6 is the sum.

▷ Jo has 6 marbles now.

> Jo has 6 marbles. She gives 2 marbles to Kim. How many marbles does Jo have now?

Start with the 6 marbles. Take away 2 marbles.

$$6 - 2 = 4$$

▷ Jo has 4 marbles now.

Adding to and taking from are opposite operations.

$4 + 2 = 6$ and $6 - 2 = 4$ are related facts.
They use the same numbers.

42 Unit 1 ■ Focus on Operations and Algebraic Thinking

Words to Know

related facts: facts that have the same numbers

Example: $7 + 6 = 13$ $13 - 6 = 7$
 $6 + 7 = 13$ $13 - 7 = 6$
These 4 facts are related facts.

Remind children that, in Lesson 4, they learned that changing the order of the addends in an addition fact does not change the sum (Commutative Property of Addition). While this lesson focuses on the relationship between an addition fact and its related subtraction fact, because of the Commutative Property children can recognize how two addition facts can also be related.

Glossary can be found on pp. 261–272.

MORE ONLINE sadlierconnect.com

Lesson 5

Guided Instruction

Understand: **Use a related subtraction fact to find the missing addend**

> Mary has 9 marbles.
> Four are orange and the rest are blue.
> How many blue marbles does Mary have?

What number added to 4 is equal to 9?

$4 + \blacksquare = 9$

Use a related subtraction fact to find the missing addend.

$9 - 5 = 4$ so $4 + 5 = 9$

Remember!
4 and 5 are addends.
9 is the sum.

➡ Mary has 5 blue marbles.

Understand: **The unknown number is not always in the same position**

> Jon has 8 apples. He gives away some.
> He has 3 apples left. How many apples did he give away?

$8 - \blacksquare = 3$

Write the related addition fact you can use to help you solve the problem.

$\underline{3} + \underline{5} = \underline{8}$ $8 - \underline{5} = 3$

➡ Jon gave $\underline{5}$ apples away.

Unit 1 ■ Focus on Operations and Algebraic Thinking   **43**

Support English Language Learners

Reinforce children's understanding of the terms *fact* and *related fact*. Write *fact* on the board. Read it aloud and then have children read it aloud. Ask children to give several examples of facts: the day of the week, the color of your shoes, or the number of windows in the classroom. Relate the general meaning of *fact* to the mathematical meaning.

Write a basic addition fact on the board, and then write the related addition fact. Say the equations are *related facts*. Have children identify how the equations are alike and different. Explain that related facts use the same numbers, but in a different order. Write the related subtraction fact on the board. Have children explain why the subtraction equation is also related. Ask a volunteer to say or write the other related subtraction equation. Repeat the activity but begin with a subtraction equation.

Understand: Use a related subtraction fact to find the missing addend

■ Point out that sometimes a small box is used in a problem to show that a number is missing. Remind children that addends are numbers that are added together. The box means that one addend is missing.

■ Model the subtraction using the two known quantities. Write the equation on the board to subtract the known addend from the sum to find the missing addend: $9 - 4 = 5$.

■ Discuss how the subtraction equation shown on the page and the subtraction equation written on the board are related.

Understand: The unknown number is not always in the same position

■ Encourage children to use the think-addition strategy for solving basic subtraction facts with sums to ten.

■ Applying the strategy from the previous section, guide children to understand that the problem can be rewritten as a related subtraction problem: $8 - 3 = \blacksquare$.

■ Elicit that the greatest digit in the subtraction fact, 8, is the sum in the related addition fact. Three added to some number equals 8. That number is 5.

■ Some children might benefit from using counters to model the equations.

Connect: What you know about related facts Use this page to help children strengthen their understanding of why certain addition and subtraction facts are said to be *related*.

■ Children should recognize that related subtraction and addition equations begin and end, respectively, with the same number. Provide several related facts to verify this understanding.

■ Remind children that they can use the *count on* strategy to find the missing addend.

■ Encourage children to discuss, predict, and explain whether the answer to a subtraction problem is always greater than or less than the beginning number.

■ Ask children to explain the positions of the numbers in related addition and subtraction problems.

Guided Instruction

Connect: What you know about related facts

Subtract: $13 - 6 = $ ■
Use a related addition fact.

Step 1

Use the two numbers in the subtraction fact to find a related addition fact.

Which number is the sum? $\underline{13}$

Which number is an addend? $\underline{6}$

■ $+ 6 = 13$

Step 2

What is the missing addend in ■ $+ 6 = 13$?

The missing addend is $\underline{7}$.

The related addition fact is $7 + 6 = 13$.
Use the related addition fact to write the subtraction fact.

▷ $13 - 6 = 7$

What related addition fact would you use to subtract?

$14 - 8 = $ ■

$\underline{6} + \underline{8} = \underline{14}$

$14 - 8 = \underline{6}$

Math-to-Math Connection

Arithmetic and Algebra Help children understand that symbols can be used in math to represent unknown numbers. Explain that a box is one kind of *symbol* that can be used to stand for an unknown number. Tell children that in some facts, the box stands for a *missing addend*. In other facts, it stands for the missing sum. Ask children to point out examples in the lesson.

Stress that, even though the box always looks the same, it can stand for different numbers in different facts.

Write several other basic facts on the board. Invite children to come up and replace some numbers in these facts with symbols of their own. Then allow them to call on a classmate to tell what number the symbol stands for.

Lesson 5

Guided Practice

1. **Subtract: 15 − 9 = ▉**
   Use a related addition fact.

Step 1

Use the two numbers in the subtraction fact to find a related addition fact.

Which number should you write as the sum? __15__

Which number should you write as an addend? __9__

▉ + __9__ = __15__

Step 2

Find the missing addend for the related addition fact.

__6__ + 9 = 15

Use the related addition fact to write the subtraction fact.

15 − 9 = __6__

👑 Think•Pair•Share

MP2 **2.** Are these addition and subtraction facts related facts? Tell why or why not.

12 − 7 = 5   5 + 7 = 12   Yes; Answers may vary.
12 − 5 = 7   7 + 5 = 12   Possible answer: These addition and subtraction facts are related because they use the same numbers.

Mathematical Practices

Mathematical Practice Standards underline the teaching and understanding of all concepts and skills presented. The emphasis of specific practices is noted throughout the guided and independent practice of this lesson.

MP2	**Reason abstractly and quantitatively.**

Item 2: Children use properties of operations to identify related facts.

Observational Assessment

Use page 45 to assess whether or not children understand how related addition and subtraction facts can be used to solve problems. Provide counters to children who might benefit from using hands-on models to show related addition and subtraction facts.

👑 Think•Pair•Share

Peer Collaboration Have children work in small groups to answer the question and agree on their reasoning. Listen for groups to address specific aspects of related facts:

- *How are the problems alike and different?*

- *How can the numbers in one problem be rearranged to write a related fact.*

- *What makes some addition and subtraction problems related?*

Return to the Essential Question

Reread the Lesson 5 Essential Question on page 42: *How can you use an addition fact to help solve a subtraction problem?*

Tell children to think about what they have learned in this lesson to answer this question.
(Possible response: I can use the sum of an addition fact as the first number in a subtraction fact. Then when I use one addend to subtract, the answer will be the other addend.)

Ask children to share their responses to the Essential Question and encourage class discussion about each.

Independent Practice

Concept Application

Children may work independently on these pages in the classroom or at home. They may refer to the first four pages of the lesson to revisit the instruction or to see a worked-out example.

Common Errors and **Teaching Tips** may help you support learning either in the classroom or as a follow-up for work done at home.

Teaching Tips

Items 1–3 and 5–6

After children have completed the items, ask them to write the other related subtraction fact and addition fact for each problem.

Remind children that the same three numbers can be used to write a total of two addition facts and two subtraction facts.

Item 4

Ask children to reason why there is only one subtraction fact and one addition fact for this problem. When the addends are the same, changing their order does not change the problem. Provide other examples of doubles facts if children need additional support to explain their reasoning.

Independent Practice

First write a related addition fact that can help you subtract. Then subtract.

1. $7 - 3 = \blacksquare$

   $\underline{4} + 3 = 7$

   $7 - 3 = \underline{4}$

2. $11 - 5 = \blacksquare$

   $\underline{6} + 5 = 11$

   $11 - 5 = \underline{6}$

3. $14 - 6 = \blacksquare$

   $\underline{8} + 6 = 14$

   $14 - 6 = \underline{8}$

4. $16 - 8 = \blacksquare$

   $8 + \underline{8} = 16$

   $16 - 8 = \underline{8}$

5. $10 - 4 = \blacksquare$

   $\underline{6} + 4 = 10$

   $10 - 4 = \underline{6}$

6. $17 - 9 = \blacksquare$

   $\underline{8} + 9 = 17$

   $17 - 9 = \underline{8}$

Talking About Math

Using Models to Explain Have children use connecting cubes to reinforce understanding of how an addition fact and a subtraction fact can be related. Give each pair of children 13 connecting cubes and ask them to work together using the cubes to model an addition fact with a sum of 13. Have children record the addition fact and a related subtraction fact. Ask children to demonstrate their models and explain the related addition and subtraction facts.

After listening to the class' related facts, ask children to consider whether all of the modeled problems are related. Encourage children to discuss how each of the problems could have a sum of 13, yet not be related. Listen for children to explain that related facts use the same numbers to join and separate a group.

Lesson 5

Independent Practice

Write a related addition fact for each subtraction fact.

7. $8 - 6 = 2$

$\underline{2} + \underline{6} = \underline{8}$

8. $12 - 8 = 4$

$\underline{4} + \underline{8} = \underline{12}$

9. $13 - 5 = 8$

$\underline{8} + \underline{5} = \underline{13}$

10. $18 - 9 = 9$

$\underline{9} + \underline{9} = \underline{18}$

Are the facts related addition and subtraction facts? Write yes or no.

11. $18 - 9 = 9$ and $9 + 9 = 18$ ____yes____

12. $13 - 5 = 8$ and $4 + 9 = 13$ ____no____

13. $11 - 6 = 5$ and $5 + 6 = 11$ ____yes____

14. $5 + 7 = 12$ and $12 - 4 = 8$ ____no____

Common Errors

Items 12 and 14

If children fail to notice that the two number sentences in each of these problems are not related, suggest they draw lines connecting like numbers in both equations. Children will see that not every number in the first equation is also found in the second equation; therefore, the equations do not represent related facts.

Teaching Tips

Items 7-9

There are two related addition facts for each subtraction problem. Either order of addends represents a correct related addition fact.

Digital Connection

Internet Resources Provide access to online activities that supply practice with related addition and subtraction facts at the first-grade level.

When searching for grade-appropriate activities, input keywords, such as *related addition and subtraction facts* and *fact families*. You may wish to use the search results to build a list of URL's from which children can choose.

Independent Practice

Common Errors

Items 18–25

Children may not pay close attention to the changing operational signs leading them to write incorrect sums and differences. If so, direct them to circle the operation sign before they solve each problem.

Teaching Tips

Items 15–16

Encourage children to use the related addition fact to find the difference.

Independent Practice

Circle the correct answer.

15. $12 - 7 = $ ■   6   (5)   4

16. $15 - 8 = $ ■   (7)   6   5

17. $6 + 7 = $ ■   11   12   (13)

Add or subtract.

18. $9 - 3 = $ _6_

19. $15 - 6 = $ _9_

20. $8 + 5 = $ _13_

21. $14 - 7 = $ _7_

22. $11 - 4 = $ _7_

23. $6 + 5 = $ _11_

24. $17 - 8 = $ _9_

25. $9 + 7 = $ _16_

Math-to-Language Connection

Reinforce children's understanding of how facts can be related by discussing another meaning of *related*. Draw the analogy between related facts, which have the same numbers, and related people, who have the same family.

Explain that our parents, brothers, sisters, aunts, uncles, cousins, and grandparents are our *relatives*. They are *related to*, or connected to, us because they are in the same family. Ask children to discuss how related people are alike and how related facts are alike. Discuss how one person can be related to different families. Explain that everyone is a member of his or her mother's family and also a member of his or her father's family. Have them consider whether the same number can be related to different fact families.

Lesson 5

Independent Practice

26. Using the numbers 4, 7, and 11 Jeanine wrote
these related addition and subtraction facts.

$$4 + 7 = 11 \qquad 7 + 4 = 11$$

$$11 - 7 = 4 \qquad 11 - 4 = 7$$

What related addition and subtraction facts can
Jeanine write using the numbers 8, 5, and 13?

$$\underline{8} + \underline{5} = \underline{13} \qquad \underline{5} + \underline{8} = \underline{13}$$

$$\underline{13} - \underline{5} = \underline{8} \qquad \underline{13} - \underline{8} = \underline{5}$$

Talk about how you know that the
facts are related.
Answers may vary. Possible answer: They use the same
numbers.

27. Explain why you can only write one addition
fact and one subtraction fact using the numbers
6, 6, and 12. Write the facts.

Answers may vary. Possible answer: The addends are the same
so I can only write one addition fact and one subtraction fact.

$$6 + 6 = 12 \qquad 12 - 6 = 6$$

Unit 1 ■ Focus on Operations and Algebraic Thinking **49**

Teaching Tips

Item 26

Use masking tape to create a number
line from 0 to 20 on the classroom or
hallway floor.

Invite a volunteer to stand on the
13 to represent the total. Ask another
volunteer to choose one of the
remaining numbers, 8 or 5, and stand
on that number. Ask the second child
to count the number of steps along
the number line it takes to get from
his or her starting number to the total.
A child who starts at 8 will take 5 steps
to get to the child standing at 13. On
the board, model how to record the
addition facts as children act them out.

For subtraction, have one volunteer
choose an ending point, 8 or 5. Have
another volunteer start at 13 and walk
backwards, counting the number of
steps it takes to get to the ending
number. Model how to record the
subtraction facts on the board.

Item 27

If children write more than two
equations, ask them to compare all the
facts and cross out any fact that appears
a second time.

Mathematical Practices	
MP4	**Model with mathematics.**
Item 27: Children explain the relationship between quantities.	
MP8	**Look for and express regularity in repeated reasoning.**
Item 26: Children use patterns to relate operations of addition and subtraction.	

OBJECTIVE
Use counting on to add or to subtract.

ESSENTIAL QUESTION
Counting on to add or to subtract is one of the many strategies children will learn and use this year. Explain that this strategy can help them determine the answer when they cannot remember an addition or subtraction fact.

PREREQUISITE SKILLS
Use Foundational Skills Handbook pages 247, *Number Names and Counting,* to review numbers in word form and numerical form.

FLUENCY PRACTICE
Fluency practice is available at **sadlierconnect.com**.

Concept Development

Understand: You can count on to add

■ In this grade, children develop strategies for adding whole numbers based on their prior work with small numbers. Counting on to add allows children to expand their knowledge of counting objects to addition.

■ It is important for children to recognize the connection between counting and addition, for example, counting on 2 and adding 2 produce the same result.

■ To demonstrate counting on tactilely, use counters to show 7 + 3. Have children start with 7. Then have them use the counters and count on 3 to find the sum.

Relate Counting to Addition and Subtraction

Essential Question: How can you use counting on to add or subtract?

Words to Know
count on

Guided Instruction

In this lesson you will learn how to count on to add or subtract.

Understand: You can count on to add

Alex draws 5 red circles and 2 blue circles. How many circles does he draw in all?

$5 + 2 = $ ■

Start with 5. Count on 2.

○○○○○   ○○
$5 \longrightarrow 6 \quad 7$

$5 + 2 = 7$

▷ Alex draws 7 circles in all.

Ida has 8 baseball cards. Jim gives her 4 more cards. How many baseball cards does Ida have in all? Draw a picture. Count on to solve the problem.

▢▢▢▢▢▢▢▢ ▢▢▢▢
$8 \longrightarrow 9 \ 10 \ 11 \ 12$

Start with 8. Count on 4.
$8 + 4 = 12$

Ida has 12 baseball cards in all.

50 Unit 1 ■ Focus on Operations and Algebraic Thinking

Words to Know

count on: start at one number and count in order

Example:

$4 \longrightarrow 5 \quad 6 \quad 7$

$4 + 3 = 7$

Glossary can be found on pp. 261–272.

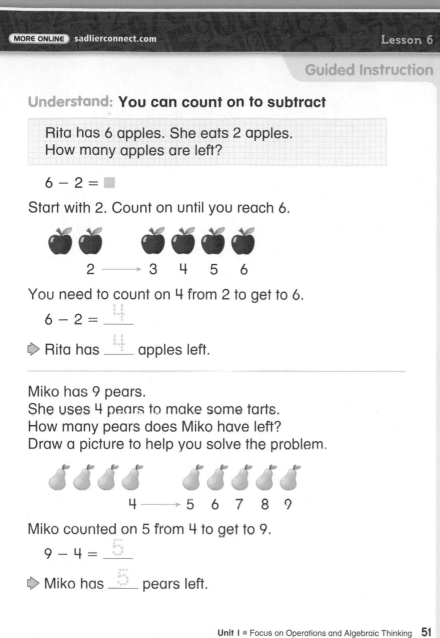

Lesson 6

Guided Instruction

Understand: You can count on to subtract

Rita has 6 apples. She eats 2 apples. How many apples are left?

$6 - 2 = \blacksquare$

Start with 2. Count on until you reach 6.

2 ⟶ 3 4 5 6

You need to count on 4 from 2 to get to 6.

$6 - 2 = \underline{4}$

▷ Rita has __4__ apples left.

Miko has 9 pears.
She uses 4 pears to make some tarts.
How many pears does Miko have left?
Draw a picture to help you solve the problem.

4 ⟶ 5 6 7 8 9

Miko counted on 5 from 4 to get to 9.

$9 - 4 = \underline{5}$

▷ Miko has __5__ pears left.

Unit 1 ▪ Focus on Operations and Algebraic Thinking **51**

Support English Language Learners

Some children might associate *on* as a positional word. For example, a book can be placed *on* a desk. Make a distinction between *on* as a positional word and how *on* is used within the term *counting on.* First, ask children to identify an item on an object within the classroom. Then, demonstrate counting on.

Designate three children as a group. Then select two other children to stand next to the group, ensuring they appear as individual children, not as a group themselves. Tell children that they will count on to reach five. Demonstrate counting on by showing that counting on two shows 5 children in all.

Repeat the activity with different numbers of children and have them verbalize the process.

Understand: You can count on to subtract

■ It is important for children to build their understanding of the relationship between addition and subtraction. Using the count-on strategy to subtract relies on the concept that addition and subtraction are inverse operations.

■ In the previous lesson, children learned how inverse operations are related. In this lesson, counting on to subtract can be thought of as a way to find an unknown addend, which emphasizes the relationship between addition and subtraction.

■ To use the count-on strategy to find the number of pears Miko has left, children must start with 4, the number being subtracted, and then count on until they reach 9. The difference is how many pears they needed to count on to reach 9.

■ Instruct children to identify the number being *taken away*, which is 4. Tell them to start counting on from this number until they reach the total, 9. Encourage children to use their fingers to track the number of times they counted on. Have children hold up 4 fingers to start, and then put up one finger at a time as they count on to reach a total of 9. In this example, it might also be helpful for children to point to or tap each pear as they count on.

■ If children are struggling, encourage them to use the related addition fact to help them find the difference for $9 - 4 = \blacksquare$. You can do this by asking a question such as: *What number plus 4 is equal to 9?*

Guided Instruction

Connect: Counting on and the order of addends

Use the first example to help children strengthen their understanding of the Commutative Property of Addition. The second example provides an opportunity to emphasize that the commutative property does not apply to subtraction.

■ Ask half of the class to find the sum of 3 + 8 by starting at 3 and counting on 8. Ask the other half to find the sum of 8 + 3 by starting at 8 and counting on 3. Once all children have found the sum, ask a volunteer to share their answer.

■ If time permits, have children repeat the process with other addends, such as 9 + 2, 3 + 6, and 4 + 7. Have children discuss which method they prefer, starting the larger or smaller addend.

■ Mathematically proficient children are able to make sense of quantities and their relationships. Being able to identify that it is more efficient to start with the greater addend and count on the lesser addend demonstrates the ability to reason quantitatively.

■ Focus the discussion on determining if there is another way to count on to find 10 − 7 = ■. Watch for children who suggest starting at 10 and counting on 7. If this occurs, guide children so that they use mathematical reasoning to determine there is only one way to count on to subtract. Some discussion points might include:

• the meaning of subtraction,

• which number is being taken away and which number is the total,

• should the answer be greater than or less than the total.

Upon conclusion, be sure children understand that, when adding, the order of the addends does not change the sum, but this is not true for subtraction.

Guided Instruction

Connect: Counting on and the order of addends

> Use counting on to find $3 + 8 = $ ■.

Start with 3. Count on 8.

$$3 \longrightarrow 4 \quad 5 \quad 6 \quad 7 \quad 8 \quad \underline{\ 9\ } \quad \underline{\ 10\ } \quad \underline{\ 11\ }$$

$3 + 8 = \underline{\ 11\ }$

Change the order of the addends so you can count on fewer numbers.

$3 + 8 = 8 + 3$

Start with 8. Count on 3.

$$8 \longrightarrow 9 \quad \underline{\ 10\ } \quad \underline{\ 11\ }$$

Remember!
Changing the order of the addends does not change the sum.

▷ $8 + 3 = 11$

Use counting on to find $10 − 7 = $ ■

Start with 7. Count on until you reach 10.

$$7 \longrightarrow \underline{\ 8\ } \quad \underline{\ 9\ } \quad \underline{\ 10\ }$$

$10 − 7 = \underline{\ 3\ }$

Is there another way to count on to find $10 − 7 = $ ■ ? Explain.

No. Possible explanation: You cannot count on from 10 because 10 is the sum. You cannot change the order of the numbers to subtract.

52 Unit I ■ Focus on Operations and Algebraic Thinking

Math-to-Sports Connection

Basketball Teams Tell children that in a basketball game, each team can have at most 5 players on the court at one time. Provide scenarios, such as: *There are 5 players on the court and 3 more players on the team. How many players in all are on the team?*

Have children model using counters to show the players on the court. Then have them count on with more counters to find the total number of players on the team. Model how to draw a picture to represent the scenario. Have children use your model to count on to find the number of players on the team.

Lesson 6

Guided Practice

I. **Use counting on to find 9 − 3 = ■.**

Step 1

Start with the number you are subtracting.

What number should you start with? __3__

Step 2

Count on until you reach the number you are subtracting from.

What number are you subtracting from? __9__

Start at 3.

Count on.

3 ⟶ __4__ __5__ __6__ __7__ __8__ __9__

You need to count on __6__ from 3 to get to 9.

9 − 3 = __6__

☆ Think·Pair·Share

MP2 2. Talk about how you can use counting on to find 39 + 6. What is the sum?

> Answers may vary. Possible answer: Start at 39 and count on 6 more. 40, 41, 42, 43, 44, 45
> 39 + 6 = 45

Mathematical Practices

Mathematical Practice Standards underline the teaching and understanding of all concepts and skills presented. The emphasis of specific practices is noted throughout the guided and independent practice of this lesson.

MP2   Reason abstractly and quantitatively.

Item 2: Children display quantitative reasoning by applying the count-on strategy to numbers greater than 10.

Observational Assessment

Use page 53 to assess children's understanding of how to use the count-on strategy to subtract. Take note of those children who choose 9, instead of 3, as the number to subtract in the equation. These children may need additional practice determining that the lesser number should be subtracted from the greater number.

☆ Think·Pair·Share

Peer Collaboration Ask pairs to share their work to find 39 + 6. Ask each pair of children questions such as:

- *Which number did you start with? How did you decide on the starting number?*

- *How did you know you found the sum?*

To summarize, point out that whether children start with 39 and count on 6 or start with 6 and count on 39, the sum will be the same; however, in this problem, it will clearly be more efficient to count on the lesser addend. Lead students to understand that it makes sense to apply the count-on strategy to find the sum when at least one of the addends is less than 10.

Return to the Essential Question

Reread the Lesson 6 Essential Question on page 50: *How can you use counting on to add or subtract?*

Tell children to think about what they learned in this lesson to answer this question.
(Possible response: I can add by starting at either number and counting on the other number. I can subtract by starting at the lesser number and counting on until I reach the greater number.)

Independent Practice

Concept Application

Children may work independently on these pages in the classroom or at home. They may refer to the first four pages of the lesson to revisit the instruction or to see a worked-out example.

Common Errors and **Teaching Tips** may help you support learning either in the classroom or as a follow-up for work done at home.

Common Errors

Items 1–4

Children may mistakenly count on one too many because they are looking at how many numbers are between the addend and the sum. For example, in item 2, children may write 11 as the answer because there are three numbers—8, 9, and 10—between 7 and 11. Encourage children to use each picture when counting on.

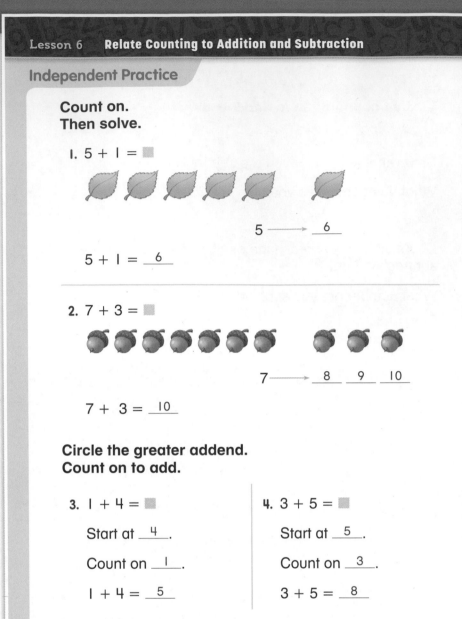

Independent Practice

**Count on.
Then solve.**

1. 5 + 1 = ▨

    5 ⟶ 6

    5 + 1 = 6

2. 7 + 3 = ▨

    7 ⟶ 8   9   10

    7 + 3 = 10

**Circle the greater addend.
Count on to add.**

3. 1 + 4 = ▨

    Start at 4.

    Count on 1.

    1 + 4 = 5

4. 3 + 5 = ▨

    Start at 5.

    Count on 3.

    3 + 5 = 8

Talking About Math

Collaborative Conversations Have children work in pairs and explain to their partner how they solved problem 4. Be sure children name the addend at which they started, how many they counted on, and the sum they arrived at. Then ask some members of a pair to explain their partner's process.

Lesson 6

Independent Practice

Teaching Tips

Items 7–9
Encourage children to draw pictures to help them use counting on to subtract.

Item 10
Have children collect 8 classroom objects of a kind and use them to model 8 – 4. Extend their understanding by asking children to tell a story that uses the subtraction 8 – 4. For example, a child might show 8 crayons in a box and then say, *I have 8 crayons in a box. I let my friend borrow 4 crayons. Now I have 4 crayons left in the box.*

Count on.
Then solve.

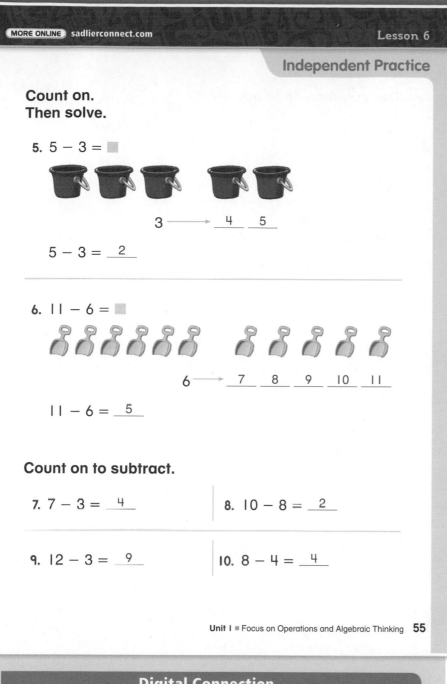

5. $5 - 3 = \blacksquare$

$3 \longrightarrow \underline{4} \quad \underline{5}$

$5 - 3 = \underline{2}$

6. $11 - 6 = \blacksquare$

$6 \longrightarrow \underline{7} \quad \underline{8} \quad \underline{9} \quad \underline{10} \quad \underline{11}$

$11 - 6 = \underline{5}$

Count on to subtract.

7. $7 - 3 = \underline{4}$

8. $10 - 8 = \underline{2}$

9. $12 - 3 = \underline{9}$

10. $8 - 4 = \underline{4}$

Digital Connection

Interactive Whiteboard Using an interactive whiteboard, have children randomly select a number between 1 and 10. Represent their selection as a number of objects on the board. Next, ask children to randomly select another number between 1 and 5. Then represent this number of objects on the board. Ask a volunteer to use counting on to find the total number of objects.

Adapt the above activity, as necessary, to practice counting on to subtract.

Independent Practice

Common Errors

Items 15–18

For each of these subtraction problems, children may start at the greater number and attempt to count on. Remind children that when counting on to subtract, they must start with the lesser number and count on until they reach the greater number.

Teaching Tips

Items 13–14

Since each of these addition problems presents the lesser addend first, children may be struggling to add. If so, suggest that they start with the greater addend and count on to show the lesser addend.

Independent Practice

Use counting on to add.

11. $7 + 3 = \underline{10}$

12. $9 + 5 = \underline{14}$

13. $6 + 9 = \underline{15}$

14. $5 + 7 = \underline{12}$

Use counting on to subtract.

15. $8 - 3 = \underline{5}$

16. $10 - 5 = \underline{5}$

17. $17 - 9 = \underline{8}$

18. $18 - 9 = \underline{9}$

Count on to solve.

19. $2 + 4 = \underline{6}$

20. $7 - 3 = \underline{4}$

21. $12 - 6 = \underline{6}$

22. $8 + 5 = \underline{13}$

23. $7 + 8 = \underline{15}$

24. $16 - 9 = \underline{7}$

Math-to-Literature Connection

Write a Story Have children select one problem from items 19–24. Ask them to tell how the problem could be used as a story in a picture book. If time permits, have children illustrate their story.

Lesson 6

Independent Practice

MP4 **25.** Count on to find 6 + 8.

Draw a picture to show how you counted on to find the answer. Check children's work.

6 + 8 = __14__

MP4 **26.** Count on to find 13 − 6.

Draw a picture to show how you counted on to find the answer. Check children's work.

13 − 6 = __7__

Unit 1 ■ Focus on Operations and Algebraic Thinking **57**

Common Errors

Item 26

Some children may make their drawings with 13 pictures of one kind and 6 of another. Correct this by saying that 13 is the number of objects in all. So their pictures showing how they counted on should end with 13 objects in all.

Teaching Tips

Item 25

Make note of which children started their pictures with the first addend, 6, and which started with the second addend. Ask volunteers who used each way to show and explain their drawings. Use this discussion to reinforce understanding of the Commutative Property of Addition.

Mathematical Practices		
MP4	**Model with mathematics.**	

Item 25: Children interpret their results by drawing a picture to add.

Item 26: Children interpret their results by drawing a picture to subtract.

OBJECTIVE
Use strategies to build fluency in adding and subtracting within 10.

ESSENTIAL QUESTION
After reading the Essential Question aloud, ask children to use their own words to tell what they already know about addition and subtraction strategies. They may describe the order and grouping strategies, making a ten, and counting on. Explain that in this lesson, they will learn to use two more addition strategies. They will also learn how to use addition and subtraction facts together to solve problems.

FLUENCY PRACTICE
Fluency practice is available at **sadlierconnect.com**.

Concept Development

Understand: **You can use doubles and doubles plus 1 to add**

■ In this lesson, children use fluency-level basic facts to develop doubles strategies for adding.

■ Provide children with connecting cubes to use in modeling each problem.

■ Note that the method of adding doubles plus 1 reinforces the skill of adding three addends as introduced in Lesson 3.

Lesson 7 — Addition and Subtraction Facts to 10 (Fluency)

Guided Instruction

Essential Question: What strategies can you use to add and subtract quickly?

Words to Know
doubles
doubles plus 1

In this lesson you will learn strategies to help you add and subtract quickly.

Understand: You can use doubles and doubles plus 1 to add

Add: $4 + 5 = $ ■

Think about doubles. $4 + 4$ is a double.

$4 + 4 = 8$

Now think about doubles plus 1.
$4 + 5$ is 1 more than $4 + 4$.
$4 + 4 = 8$, so $4 + 5$ is 1 more than 8.
$4 + 5$ is $4 + 4 + 1$.

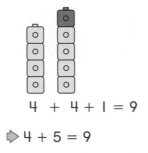

$4 + 4 + 1 = 9$

▷ $4 + 5 = 9$

Words to Know

doubles: adding two numbers that are the same

Example:

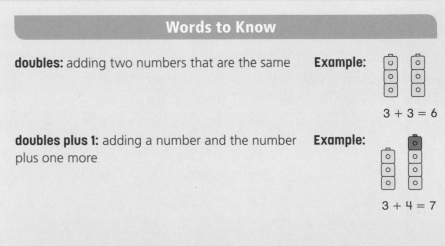

$3 + 3 = 6$

doubles plus 1: adding a number and the number plus one more

Example:

$3 + 4 = 7$

Glossary can be found on pp. 261–272.

MORE ONLINE sadlierconnect.com

Lesson 7

Guided Instruction

Understand: You can use a related addition fact to subtract

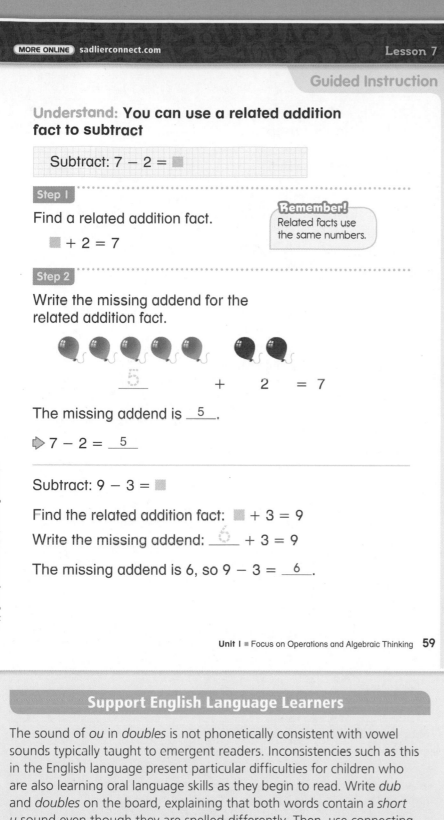

Subtract: 7 − 2 = ▧

Step 1

Find a related addition fact.

▧ + 2 = 7

Remember!
Related facts use the same numbers.

Step 2

Write the missing addend for the related addition fact.

_5_ + 2 = 7

The missing addend is _5_.

▷ 7 − 2 = _5_

Subtract: 9 − 3 = ▧

Find the related addition fact: ▧ + 3 = 9

Write the missing addend: _6_ + 3 = 9

The missing addend is 6, so 9 − 3 = _6_.

Understand: You can use a related addition fact to subtract

■ Most children accomplish fluency with addition facts more quickly than they become fluent with subtraction facts. Understanding subtraction as an unknown-addend addition problem will help children see how addition and subtraction are related.

■ After children complete Step 2, have them point to the blue 5 in the addition fact and the 5 that they wrote on the line for the difference. As they point to each 5, tell them that these facts are related.

■ Children who are already fluent adding and subtracting within 10 may be able to use mental math to complete the last problem on the page. Encourage other children to use what they know about related addition facts to solve.

Support English Language Learners

The sound of *ou* in *doubles* is not phonetically consistent with vowel sounds typically taught to emergent readers. Inconsistencies such as this in the English language present particular difficulties for children who are also learning oral language skills as they begin to read. Write *dub* and *doubles* on the board, explaining that both words contain a *short u* sound even though they are spelled differently. Then, use connecting cubes to display several examples of doubles and non-doubles to help children practice saying and using the term to identify which pairs of cubes show doubles and which pairs do not.

Connect: What you know about addition and subtraction strategies Use this page to help children understand how to relate subtraction facts to addition facts that they already know.

■ Children who are able to analyze and correctly reorder three quantities of related math facts demonstrate the ability to apply reasoning skills.

■ If time permits, provide pairs of children up to 10 connecting cubes to demonstrate their own related addition and subtraction facts.

Connect: What you know about addition and subtraction strategies

> Rose has 10 stamps.
> She gives some stamps to Alex.
> She has 4 stamps left.
> How many stamps does Rose give to Alex?

You can subtract to find how many stamps Rose gives to Alex.

$10 - ■ = 4$

Step 1

Choose a strategy. One strategy is to find a related addition fact.

$4 + ■ = \underline{10}$

Step 2

Write the missing addend for the related addition fact.

$4 + \underline{6} = 10$

The missing addend is $\underline{6}$.

$10 - 6 = \underline{4}$

➡ Rose gives $\underline{6}$ stamps to Alex.

> **Remember!**
> 4 and 6 are the addends.
> 10 is the sum.

Math-to-Games Connection

Number Cubes Ask children to tell about any board game they have played that uses a number cube to determine how many spaces to move. Have children identify the greatest number of spaces they can move in one toss of one number cube. Then have children identify the least number of spaces they can move in one toss of a number cube.

Provide a number cube, two game tokens or counters, and a 12-inch ruler to each pair of children. Have partners take turns tossing the number cube twice and moving a game token along the ruler to show the number of spaces they can move. Tell children to record each addition and write a subtraction fact that uses the same three numbers.

Guided Practice

1. Use a related addition fact to find 9 − 6 = ■.

Step 1

Find a related addition fact.

Which number should you write as the sum? 9

Which number should you write as an addend? 6

■ + 6 = 9

Step 2

What is the missing addend for the addition fact? 3

Write the related addition fact. 3 + 6 = 9

Now write the related subtraction fact.

9 − 6 = 3

Think•Pair•Share

MP3 2. Write a related addition fact you would use to find 10 − 8. Then find the answer.
10 − 8 = ■

2 + 8 = 10

10 − 8 = 2

Could you use the addition fact 8 + 2 = 10 to help you find 10 − 8 = 2? Explain.

See Additional Answers.

Mathematical Practices

Mathematical Practice Standards underline the teaching and understanding of all concepts and skills presented. The emphasis of specific practices is noted throughout the guided and independent practice of this lesson.

MP3	**Construct viable arguments and critique the reasoning of others.**

Item 2: Children justify their conclusions, communicate them to others, and respond to the arguments of others.

Observational Assessment

Use page 61 to assess whether children are able to use a problem-solving process to solve related addition and subtraction facts. Observe those children who have difficulty transposing the numbers into the addition and subtraction facts. These children may need additional practice using models to demonstrate related facts.

Think•Pair•Share

Peer Collaboration Have pairs of children share their mathematical conjectures and arguments with one another. Prompt the discussions with questions such as:

- *How did you decide on your answer to the last question?*
- *What materials can you use to show how you found the answer?*
- *Can the answer to this question be both yes and no? Why or why not?*

Point out that children do not have to use the same ways of solving to agree on their conclusions. Have children explain how their arguments are the same or different.

Return to the Essential Question

Reread the Lesson 7 Essential Question on page 58: *What strategies can you use to add and subtract quickly?*

Tell children to think about what they learned in this lesson to answer this question.
(Possible response: I can use doubles or doubles plus 1 to add basic facts. I can use related addition and subtraction facts to find a sum, a difference, or a missing addend.)

Additional Answers

Item 2: Yes; Answers may vary. Possible answer: Changing the order of the addends does not change the sum so 8 + 2 has the same sum as 2 + 8.

Independent Practice

Concept Application

Children may work independently on these pages in the classroom or at home. They may refer to the first four pages of the lesson to revisit the instruction or to see a worked-out example.

Common Errors and **Teaching Tips** may help you support learning either in the classroom or as a follow-up for work done at home.

Common Errors

Items 1–6

If children incorrectly answer a doubles-plus-1 addition, have them recheck the doubles sum to make sure it is correct. Allow them to use counters to verify answers, if needed.

Teaching Tips

Items 1–6

Children can quickly check their own work if they recognize a pattern in each pair of answers. Each item asks children to solve the doubles addition first and then the doubles-plus-1 addition. A quick review of all answers will indicate that the second sum is always 1 more than the first sum.

Independent Practice

Use doubles and doubles plus 1 to add.

1. $1 + 2 = \blacksquare$

   $1 + 1 = \underline{2}$

   $1 + 2 = \underline{3}$

2. $3 + 4 = \blacksquare$

   $3 + 3 = \underline{6}$

   $3 + 4 = \underline{7}$

3. $2 + 3 = \blacksquare$

   $2 + 2 = \underline{4}$

   $2 + 3 = \underline{5}$

4. $4 + 5 = \blacksquare$

   $4 + 4 = \underline{8}$

   $4 + 5 = \underline{9}$

5. $2 + 1 = \blacksquare$

   $1 + 1 = \underline{2}$

   $2 + 1 = \underline{3}$

6. $4 + 3 = \blacksquare$

   $3 + 3 = \underline{6}$

   $4 + 3 = \underline{7}$

Talking About Math

Describe the Connection Display the following additions on the board: $3 + 3 = 6$, $3 + 4 = 7$, $3 + 1 + 3 = 7$, $3 + 3 + 1 = 7$. Ask children to name the doubles fact $(3 + 3)$ and the doubles-plus-1 fact $(3 + 4)$ that are shown. Then have children analyze the other additions and describe how they also show doubles plus 1. Guide children to understand that the grouping property can be used to apply the doubles and doubles-plus-1 strategies.

Have each child write another doubles-plus-1 fact using two addends and then three addends. In the second addition, have them circle the numbers that they grouped first. Allow time for children to share their additions and describe the strategies that they used.

Lesson 7

Independent Practice

First write a related addition fact that can help you subtract. Then subtract.

7. $8 - 6 = \blacksquare$

$\underline{2} + 6 = 8$

$8 - 6 = \underline{2}$

8. $7 - 4 = \blacksquare$

$\underline{3} + 4 = 7$

$7 - 4 = \underline{3}$

9. $9 - 5 = \blacksquare$

$\underline{4} + 5 = 9$

$9 - 5 = \underline{4}$

10. $10 - 6 = \blacksquare$

$\underline{4} + 6 = 10$

$10 - 6 = \underline{4}$

11. $6 - 2 = \blacksquare$

$\underline{4} + 2 = 6$

$6 - 2 = \underline{4}$

12. $10 - 7 = \blacksquare$

$\underline{3} + 7 = 10$

$10 - 7 = \underline{3}$

Common Errors

Items 7–12

Since the words *addition* and *subtract* both appear in the directions, children who are not familiar with addition and subtraction symbols may attempt to add each item. Review the directions with children. Provide a hint that no answer on this page will be the greatest number in a problem, because each answer will stand for either an unknown addend or the result of subtraction.

Teaching Tips

Items 7–12

Have children focus on the second equation in each problem to recognize that addition with an unknown addend can be used to solve the subtractions. For children who are struggling, provide paper so they can draw a picture to model each problem.

Items 10 and 12

Tell children that they can use the make-a-ten strategy to solve.

Digital Connection

How-To Videos Use a search engine or educational resources library to locate videos that teach children how to use related addition and subtraction facts. Key words for the search might include *basic facts, addition, subtraction, math fluency,* and *grade 1 math.* Preview available resources and make a list of suggestions for children to use.

Teaching Tips

Items 13-20

The symbols for addition (+) and subtraction (–) have not been implicitly taught in grade 1, but most children will remember them from kindergarten math. The symbols have been used in previous lessons, but this page is the first time children are asked to use the symbols to determine whether addition or subtraction is indicated. Check children's answers to items 13 and 15 to make sure they have correctly completed at least one subtraction and one addition. Provide a review of the symbols if needed.

Items 21-24

The format of these items provides introductory skills needed for taking standardized tests. Children may benefit from masking all answer choices, solving the item, and then removing the mask to select the number that matches their solution.

Lesson 7   **Addition and Subtraction Facts to 10 (Fluency)**

Independent Practice

Add or subtract.

13. $7 - 1 = \underline{6}$

14. $10 - 5 = \underline{5}$

15. $3 + 4 = \underline{7}$

16. $8 - 4 = \underline{4}$

17. $9 - 2 = \underline{7}$

18. $5 + 5 = \underline{10}$

19. $7 + 3 = \underline{10}$

20. $6 - 3 = \underline{3}$

Circle the correct answer.

21. $10 - 7 = \blacksquare$ ③   4   5

22. $8 - 1 = \blacksquare$ 9   8   ⑦

23. $2 + 8 = \blacksquare$ 8   9   ⑩

24. $6 + 2 = \blacksquare$ 7   ⑧   9

Math-to-Physical Education Connection

Jumping Rope Arrange children in pairs to complete a jump-rope challenge. Have each child jump rope and count the number of times he or she can skip without missing. Limit each turn to 5 skips, although many children can continue far beyond that number without a miss. After each member of a pair completes the challenge, have children record their scores and add them. The greatest possible score for a pair will be $5 + 5 = 10$. Then ask children to try jumping 10 skips without a miss. After this part of the activity, have partners use subtraction to compare their scores. This time, a perfect score will result in $10 - 10 = 0$.

Lesson 7

Independent Practice

Teaching Tips

Item 25

Children may interpret the direction to show their work in more than one way. They may employ methods such as making drawings, using manipulatives, acting out a process, and writing additions. Make sure children understand the expectations before they begin to solve. Point out that they should label any drawings with numbers and symbols. Provide connecting cubes for children who want to model their work before they make drawings.

MP4 25. Show how you can use doubles and doubles plus 1 to solve this problem. Then solve.

Answers may vary.
Possible answer: I can use blocks to see that $3 + 3 = 6$ and $3 + 4 = 7$.

$4 + 3 = $ ▨

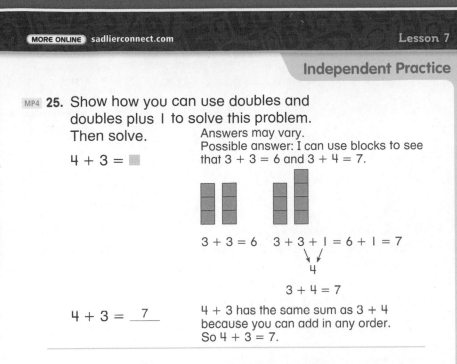

$3 + 3 = 6$ $3 + 3 + 1 = 6 + 1 = 7$
$\downarrow \downarrow$
4

$3 + 4 = 7$

$4 + 3 = \underline{7}$

$4 + 3$ has the same sum as $3 + 4$ because you can add in any order. So $4 + 3 = 7$.

Item 26

Children may argue that it is easier to count on from the greater number, 6, instead of from 2. Be sure children understand that Juan *wanted* to complete the problem in a specific way, Larry insisted that he would *have to* start at 6, but that starting at either number would be correct for solving the problem.

MP3 26. Juan wanted to use counting on to find $2 + 6$. He said that he could start at 2 and count on 6 more numbers to find the sum. Larry said that Juan would have to start at 6 and count on 2 to find the sum. Who is correct? Try both ways and talk about your answers.

Juan is correct. Answers may vary. Possible answer:

$2 \rightarrow \underbrace{3, 4, 5, 6, 7, 8}$
$\quad 2 + 6 = 8$

$6 \rightarrow \underbrace{7, 8}$
$\quad 6 + 2 = 8$

Juan is correct. The order of addends does not change the sum, so you can start at either number and count on. If Juan starts at 6, then he would be able to count on fewer numbers to find the answer. But, even if he starts at 2 and counts on 6, he will get the same answer, 8.

Mathematical Practices	
MP3	**Construct viable arguments and critique the reasoning of others.**
Item 26: Children understand and use stated assumptions and build a logical argument to support or refute the assumptions.	
MP4	**Model with mathematics.**
Item 25: Children use models to demonstrate how doubles and properties help them add.	

OBJECTIVE
Use making 10 and other strategies to add and subtract within 20.

ESSENTIAL QUESTION
Read the Essential Question aloud. Focus children on how the addition and subtraction strategies they have used so far might help them add greater numbers.

PREREQUISITE SKILLS
Use Foundational Skills Handbook page 252, *Make a Ten,* to review using a 10-frame to show sums of 10.

FLUENCY PRACTICE
Fluency practice is available at **sadlierconnect.com**.

Concept Development

Understand: Making 10 to Add

■ Make sure children understand that a 10-frame shows 10 spaces whether it is filled with counters or not.

■ Remind children that if a number of counters fills a 10-frame and part of another frame, that number is greater than 10 and less than 20.

■ Two-color counters work well to model each addend and their sum, but counters of any two colors can be used if they fit in a 10-frame.

Lesson 8 | **Addition and Subtraction Facts to 20**

Essential Question: What different strategies can help you learn addition and subtraction facts to 20?

Guided Instruction

In this lesson you will learn more strategies to help you add and subtract.

Understand: Making 10 to add

Dan has 7 toy cars.
Marta has 5 toy cars.
How many toy cars do they have in all?
$7 + 5 = \blacksquare$

Use a 10-frame and counters. Show 7 and 5.

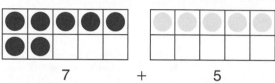

7   +   5

Move some counters over to make 10.

$7 + 5$ and $10 + 2$ are both names for the same number.

$10 + 2 = 12$, so $7 + 5 = 12$.

▷ Dan and Marta have 12 toy cars in all.

Support English Language Learners

Previous lessons have named specific counting objects for adding and subtracting, such as apples, balloons, and connecting cubes. In this lesson, however, children will refer to the counting objects as *counters*. This word has more than one meaning, and it is also sometimes referred to as a generic way to name different types of counting objects. This may confuse children who are not familiar with ways in which the term is used in math. Demonstrate for children that a two-color counter is a circular disc that is one color on one side and another color on the other side. Explain that they are called *counters* because they are used for counting objects or groups of objects.

Lesson 8

Guided Instruction

Understand: **Making 10 to subtract**

There are 14 fish in a pond.
Then 5 swim away.
How many fish are left?

$14 - 5 = $ ■

Show 14 counters.

Take away some counters to make 10.

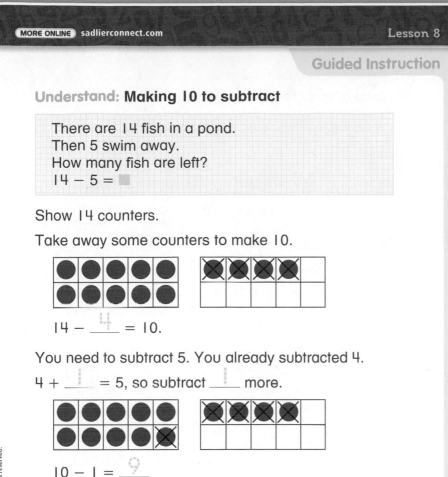

$14 - \underline{} = 10.$

You need to subtract 5. You already subtracted 4.

$4 + \underline{} = 5$, so subtract _____ more.

$10 - 1 = \underline{}$

$14 - 5$ and $10 - 1$ are both names
for the same number.

$10 - 1 = \underline{9}$, so $14 - 5 = \underline{9}$.

▷ There are __9__ fish left in the pond.

Understand: **Making 10 to subtract**

■ Children use increasingly sophisticated strategies to fluently add and subtract. Using 10-frames helps children visualize how to first take away enough objects to get to 10 and then figure out how many more to subtract.

■ Some children may have difficulty understanding why $14 - 5$ and $10 - 1$ are both names for 9. Have children look at the second model on the page and name the total number of counters shown, the number crossed out, and the number not crossed out.

Math-to-Consumer Connection

Boxed Sets Help children make connections between the use of 10-frames and consumer goods that are packed in boxes of ten. For example, a set of pencils, chalk, or crayons may be sold in a box that holds exactly ten. Explain to children that sometimes these boxes are filled by machines. A machine may fill many boxes each day, with the same number in each box. If there are fewer than ten objects left over, these are saved for another day. In a similar way, when children use a 10-frame to add numbers, they can fill the frame to show ten and then save the others for use in another frame.

Guided Instruction

Connect: Use different subtraction strategies

Use this page to help children understand that they may choose different strategies to subtract.

■ Make-a-ten and using a related fact are two subtraction strategies modeled on this page. Be sure children understand how counting on is another strategy that could be used for subtraction.

■ The goal of teaching several strategies is so children can use whichever is easiest for them. As children become increasingly proficient in using basic facts, they are likely to choose different strategies for different types of problems and to use mental math for facts they have memorized.

Connect: Use different subtraction strategies

Use different strategies to subtract: $12 - 8 = $ ▪

Step 1

Think about some different subtraction strategies.

   count on   use a related addition fact   make 10

Step 2

Choose a strategy.

The problem gives the numbers 12 and 8. You can use those numbers to find a related addition fact.

   __4__ + 8 = 12, so 12 − 8 = __4__.

▷ 12 − 8 = __4__

> **Remember!**
> Related facts use the same numbers.

Step 3

Choose another strategy.

You can also make 10 to find 12 − 8.

   12 − __2__ = 10

You need to subtract 8. You already subtracted 2.

   2 + __6__ = 8, so subtract __6__ more.

10 − 6 = __4__

▷ 12 − 8 = __4__

68   Unit 1 ■ Focus on Operations and Algebraic Thinking

Math-to-Career Connection

Office Numbers Many children have visited the places where their parents or other family members work. Some of those places may be office buildings. Explain that inside office buildings are rows of rooms called offices, similar to classrooms in a school. Point out that each office may have a number. Draw a row of 18 squares on the board to represent offices along a wall of an office building. Ask children to write or tell a story about reasons for numbering the offices and ways in which the offices might be numbered.

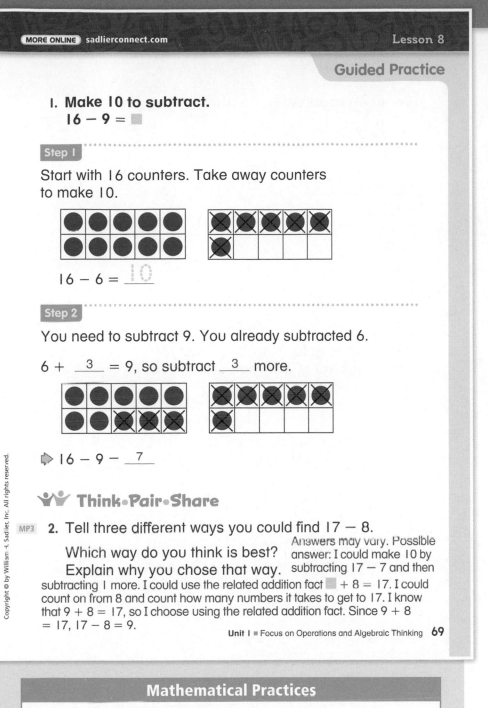

MORE ONLINE sadlierconnect.com

Lesson 8

I. Make 10 to subtract.

16 − 9 = ▣

Step 1

Start with 16 counters. Take away counters to make 10.

16 − 6 = _10_

Step 2

You need to subtract 9. You already subtracted 6.

6 + _3_ = 9, so subtract _3_ more.

➡ 16 − 9 − _7_

👑👑 Think•Pair•Share

MP3 **2.** Tell three different ways you could find 17 − 8.

Which way do you think is best? Explain why you chose that way.

Answers may vary. Possible answer: I could make 10 by subtracting 17 − 7 and then subtracting 1 more. I could use the related addition fact ▣ + 8 = 17. I could count on from 8 and count how many numbers it takes to get to 17. I know that 9 + 8 = 17, so I choose using the related addition fact. Since 9 + 8 = 17, 17 − 8 = 9.

Unit 1 ■ Focus on Operations and Algebraic Thinking **69**

Mathematical Practices

Mathematical Practice Standards underline the teaching and understanding of all concepts and skills presented. The emphasis of specific practices is noted throughout the guided and independent practice of this lesson.

MP3	**Construct viable arguments and critique the reasoning of others.**

Item 2: Children describe multiple approaches to a problem situation and defend the strategy they select as the best.

Observational Assessment

Use page 69 to assess whether children are able to use the make-a-ten strategy or to select another strategy. Observe whether children struggle to see how subtracting 6 helps them subtract 9 in the first problem. Make note of children who need further practice with the make-a-ten strategy.

👑👑 Think•Pair•Share

Peer Collaboration Have pairs of children work together to explain possible solution strategies. Point out that they do not have to agree on which strategy is the best to use, but children should be able to explain what they think. Ask each pair questions such as:

- *How can you use counting on to solve the problem?*

- *Do you know an addition fact that can help you subtract 17 − 8?*

- *How can you show the subtraction using 10-frames?*

- *Which strategy do you think works best here? Is it the same choice for both of you? Explain.*

Encourage children to listen carefully to arguments made for different choices and to consider whether those arguments alter their opinions.

Return to the Essential Question

Reread the Lesson 8 Essential Question on page 66: *What different strategies can help you learn addition and subtraction facts to 20?*

Tell children to think about what they learned in this lesson to answer this question.

(Possible response: I can use the strategy that makes the most sense to me for different problems. If I add or subtract 1, 2, or 3, I might count on. If I know an addition fact, I can use it to solve a related subtraction fact. If I need to model the problem, I might make a 10. I can use more than one strategy to check my work.)

Concept Application

Children may work independently on these pages in the classroom or at home. They may refer to the first four pages of the lesson to revisit the instruction or to see a worked-out example.

Common Errors and **Teaching Tips** may help you support learning either in the classroom or as a follow-up for work done at home.

Common Errors

Items 9–12

Some children may assume that each fact representing a problem must begin with the same number. Remind them that related facts use the same numbers in different orders.

Teaching Tips

Items 1–8

Children will not necessarily demonstrate that they are counting on to solve each item. It is more important to observe how children approach a problem that they seem to find difficult. If they are counting on their fingers, it is likely that they are using the counting-on strategy. Children can count on to find the sum in an addition or count on to find an unknown addend in a subtraction.

Lesson 8 **Addition and Subtraction Facts to 20**

Independent Practice

Count on to solve.

1. $9 + 3 = \underline{12}$ | 2. $11 - 9 = \underline{2}$

3. $10 - 8 = \underline{2}$ | 4. $8 + 3 = \underline{11}$

5. $8 - 5 = \underline{3}$ | 6. $7 + 6 = \underline{13}$

7. $4 + 7 = \underline{11}$ | 8. $9 - 2 = \underline{7}$

Write a related fact that can help you add or subtract. Then add or subtract.

9. $9 - 6 = \blacksquare$
$\underline{3} + 6 = 9$
$9 - 6 = \underline{3}$

10. $6 + 8 = \blacksquare$
$\underline{14} - 8 = 6$
$6 + 8 = \underline{14}$

11. $7 + 9 = \blacksquare$
$\underline{16} - 9 = 7$
$7 + 9 = \underline{16}$

12. $14 - 5 = \blacksquare$
$\underline{9} + 5 = 14$
$14 - 5 = \underline{9}$

Talking About Math

Provide Reasons to Support an Answer Have children select one item on the page for which they would choose a different addition or subtraction strategy to solve. Arrange children in pairs or small groups to discuss their choices and provide reasons for them. If time is available, ask volunteers to share their choices and reasons for choosing them with the class.

Independent Practice

Teaching Tips

Item 13

Provide two-color counters and a drawing of a 10-frame for children who appear to need help in approaching the item. As children enter the first addend, complete the first frame, and then fill part of the next frame, make sure they understand how each of these steps relates to the additions in the problem.

Items 14–15

Encourage children who are struggling with these items to use counters or draw a picture to demonstrate the use of the make-a-ten strategy.

Make 10 to solve.

13. $9 + 4 = \blacksquare$

 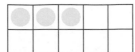

$9 + 1 = 10$

You need to add 4. You already added 1.
How many more do you need to add?

$1 + \underline{3} = 4$, so you need to add $\underline{3}$ more.

$10 + 3 = \underline{13}$, so $9 + 4 = \underline{13}$.

14. $8 + 5 = \blacksquare$

$8 + 2 = 10$

You need to add 5.
You already added 2.

$2 + \underline{3} = 5$

You need to add
3 more.

$10 + 3 = \underline{13}$

$8 + 5 = \underline{13}$

15. $7 + 8 = \blacksquare$

$8 + 2 = 10$

You need to add 7.
You already added 2.

$2 + \underline{5} = 7$

You need to add
5 more.

$10 + 5 = \underline{15}$

$7 + 8 = \underline{15}$

Unit 1 ■ Focus on Operations and Algebraic Thinking **71**

Digital Connection

Math Videos Use an Internet search engine to look for addition and subtraction videos that teach how to use 10-frames. Review available choices and make a list of those videos or electronically bookmark them for children to access easily. Allow children to work in pairs to view the videos and practice the examples that are given.

Independent Practice

Common Errors

Items 16-27

Children who answer only one or two items incorrectly may have made simple calculation errors and should be encouraged to check their work. Making excessive errors on the page may indicate that children are not paying attention to the symbols or that they need additional help mastering the basic addition and subtraction facts.

Teaching Tips

Items 16-23

Children may use any strategy to solve each item independently. Provide drawing paper or counters for children who need them.

Items 24-27

Children's answers are limited due to the test format of these items and the given choices. Some children may informally use a guess-and-check strategy for selecting one of the possible answers. If children claim that the correct answer is not among the given choices, make sure that they read the operation symbols correctly and then add or subtract appropriately.

Independent Practice

Add or subtract.

16. $18 - 9 =$ ___9___

17. $11 - 2 =$ ___9___

18. $5 + 6 =$ ___11___

19. $8 - 5 =$ ___3___

20. $15 - 9 =$ ___6___

21. $9 + 8 =$ ___17___

22. $7 + 9 =$ ___16___

23. $12 - 3 =$ ___9___

Circle the correct answer.

24. $8 + 3 = \blacksquare$ (11)   12   13

25. $10 - 7 = \blacksquare$ (3)   4   5

26. $8 + 6 = \blacksquare$ 12   13   (14)

27. $13 - 7 = \blacksquare$ 5   (6)   7

Math-to-Shopping Connection

Keeping Up with Dollars Tell children that they will each pretend to have 15 one-dollar bills with which to go shopping. Provide 15 strips of paper to each child to represent the dollars. Have them create their own purchasing scenarios and act them out with a partner. Make sure they record each transaction as a subtraction. Children might also benefit from drawing pictures to represent each transaction.

MORE ONLINE sadlierconnect.com

MP2 **28.** Explain how making 10 can help you solve $6 + 9 = $ ■. Draw counters to help.

Check children's work.

Answers may vary. Possible answer: I can draw 6 counters in the first frame and 9 counters in the second frame. When I move 4 counters over to fill the first frame, I will have 10 counters in the first frame and 5 counters in the second frame. So $6 + 9$ and $10 + 5$ are different names for the same number. $10 + 5 = 15$, so $6 + 9 = 15$.

$6 + 9 = \underline{15}$

MP2 **29.** Explain how making 10 can help you solve $15 - 8 = $ ■. Draw counters to help.

Check children's work. Answers may vary. Possible answer: I can draw 10 counters in the first frame and 5 counters in the second frame to start with 15 counters. To make 10, I put an X on the 5 counters in the second frame. There are 10 counters left. I need to subtract 8, and I already subtracted 5. Since $5 + 3 = 8$, I need to subtract 3 more counters. After I put an X on the last 3 counters in the first frame, I see that there are 7 counters left. So $10 - 3$ and $15 - 8$ are different names for the same number. $10 - 3 = 7$, so $15 - 8 = 7$.

$15 - 8 = \underline{7}$

Common Errors

Item 28

Some children may place 6 counters in the first frame and 9 counters in the second frame. Have these children use counters to show what they have done so far. Then have them move counters from the second frame to the first frame until the first frame is full.

Items 28-29

Children may record a correct answer on the line but fail to complete the drawing or write an explanation to show their work. Point out that the directions tell them to use a specific strategy and that the item is not complete unless they do all the parts.

Teaching Tips

Items 28-29

Provide counters and 10-frames to children who need concrete support.

Mathematical Practices	
MP2	**Reason abstractly and quantitatively.**

Items 28 and 29: Children consider an equation and explain how to represent it symbolically on a 10-frame.

OBJECTIVE
Use models and equation symbols to tell whether an equation is true or false.

ESSENTIAL QUESTION
Read the Essential Question aloud and have children share any ideas they might have about proving whether an equation is true or false.

FLUENCY PRACTICE
Fluency practice is available at **sadlierconnect.com**.

Concept Development

Understand: Meaning of the equal sign in an addition equation

■ In kindergarten, children were introduced to equations, but were not required to write them. In first grade, children learn to use the equal sign and to write equations to represent an addition or subtraction situation.

■ Provide children with counters to help them find or justify their answers.

■ Make sure children are able to understand and explain how the models show two addends in each 10-frame.

Lesson 9 — Addition and Subtraction Equations

In this lesson you will learn to tell if an equation is true or false.

Understand: Meaning of the equal sign in an addition equation

> Is the addition equation true?
> $4 + 6 = 3 + 7$
> Tell how you know.

A number sentence with an equal sign is called an equation.

You need to find out if $4 + 6 = 3 + 7$ is a true equation.

An equation is true if both sides of the equal sign represent the same amount.

Compare the models. Are the amounts the same?

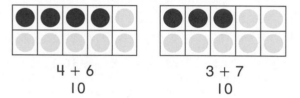

| $4 + 6$ | $3 + 7$ |
| 10 | 10 |

Since $10 = 10$, both sides of the equation represent the same amounts.

▷ So $4 + 6 = 3 + 7$ is a true equation.

Words to Know

equal sign (=): is equal to

Example:

$$1 + 1 = 2$$

is equal to

equation: a number sentence with an equal sign

Example: $5 + 6 = 11$ $8 - 6 = 2$

Glossary can be found on pp. 261–272.

Lesson 9

Guided Instruction

Understand: Meaning of the equal sign in a subtraction equation

Is the subtraction equation true or false?
$3 = 5 - 2$
Tell how you know.

Model the amount on each side of the equal sign.

△ △ △   △ △ △ ⤫ ⤫
  3   = $5 - 2$

Compare. Are the amounts on both sides the same?

  3   =   3

▷ Since $3 = 3$, the equation $3 = 5 - 2$ is __true__.

Is the subtraction equation true or false?

$8 - 4 = 9 - 6$

Tell how you know.

$8 - 4 = 9 - 6$

Is 4 the same amount as 3? __no__

4 is not equal to 3, so the equation is __false__.

Understand: Meaning of the equal sign in a subtraction equation

■ Make sure children are able to comprehend and explain how the models match the equation.

■ Before starting with the presentation, ask children if the equation is set up correctly. This is a rare instance in which children will see a single number to the left of the equal sign.

■ Help children understand the use of the terms *true* and *false* pertaining to the equations. Children likely have experience using these terms in non-mathematical situations, determining whether a person is telling the truth or telling a lie. Point out that in equations, the terms simply tell whether the amounts shown are equal or not.

Support English Language Learners

Help children recognize connections between the terms *equal* and *equation*. Point out that the beginning of the word *equation, equa-,* is the same as the beginning of the word *equal* and that the meanings of these words are similar. Children are likely familiar with the concept of equality in the context of fairness or fair shares. Explain that equality in an equation has a similar meaning. Learning to recognize the meaning of *equa-* will also help children understand higher-level math skills that use forms of equivalency.

Connect: What you know about addition and subtraction equations Use this page to help children analyze each equation and explain their thinking about whether each is true or false.

■ The goal of this presentation is not simply that children can correctly identify the comparisons as true or false; rather, the goal is that they can understand and justify their conclusions.

■ Encourage children to explain their answers in their own words or to use pictures to make the comparisons.

Lesson 9   Addition and Subtraction Equations

Guided Instruction

Connect: What you know about addition and subtraction equations

Is the equation $12 - 7 = 8 + 5$ true or false? Tell how you know.

Step 1

Find the equal sign.

$$12 - 7 = 8 + 5$$

> **Remember!**
> An equation is true if both sides of the equal sign represent the same amount.

Step 2

Look at each side of the equation.
Add or subtract as the signs tells you to do.
Compare the amounts.

$$12 - 7 = \underline{5} \qquad 8 + 5 = \underline{13}$$

➤ Since 5 <u>is not</u> equal to 13, the equation is <u>false</u>.

Is the equation $14 - 7 = 2 + 5$ true or false?
Find the equal sign. Look at each side of the equation.
Add or subtract as shown.

$$14 - 7 = \underline{7} \qquad 2 + 5 = \underline{7} \qquad 7 = 7$$

Are the amounts on each side of the equation the same? <u>yes</u>

The equation is <u>true</u>.

76 Unit I ■ Focus on Operations and Algebraic Thinking

Math-to-Trades Connection

Constructing Buildings Have children imagine that they are building an office building. One wall of the building is made up entirely of large cement blocks. The opposite wall of the building is made up of cement blocks and windows. Each window is the same height as one cement block.

Have children work in pairs or small groups to write an equation that compares the heights of the two sides of the building. Make sure children understand that the number of cement blocks on one side must match the number of cement blocks and windows on the opposite side. Allow children to draw the two walls of their buildings or use connecting cubes to verify that the walls are the same height.

Guided Practice

I. **Is the equation 7 + 2 = 11 − 2 true or false?**
Tell how you know.

Step 1

Look at each side of the equation. Add or subtract as shown. Find the amount on each side of the equal sign. You can use cubes to help.

One side of the equation is 7 + 2.   7 + 2 = __9__

The other side is 11 − 2.   11 − 2 = __9__

Step 2

Compare the two answers.
Are the amounts on both sides of the equal sign

the same? __yes__

9 __=__ 9, so the equation is __true__.

☆ Think•Pair•Share

MP7 2. Write a true equation that has both
a plus sign and a minus sign.
Tell how you know the equation is true.

____ + ____ = ____ − ____   See Additional Answers.

Mathematical Practices

Mathematical Practice Standards underline the teaching and understanding of all concepts and skills presented. The emphasis of specific practices is noted throughout the guided and independent practice of this lesson.

MP7 **Look for and make use of structure.**

Item 2: Children look closely to discern a pattern or structure to assure that the values on both sides of an equation are equal.

Guided Practice

Observational Assessment

Use page 77 to assess whether children are able to determine if the values on both sides of an equation are equal. Observe whether children have difficulty moving from using models to completing equations. Provide connecting cubes for children to use if they need additional support.

☆ Think•Pair•Share

Peer Collaboration Arrange children in pairs. Have them each write their own true equation, and then share their equations with their partners. Then, have pairs explain and prove their equations to the class. As children present their equations, prompt discussions with questions such as:

• *What is the first step you used?*

• *Did you solve one side of the equation before or after you wrote the second side of the equation?*

• *How can you prove that your equation is true?*

Watch for children who use a guess-and-check method. Encourage them to draw pictures, counters, or use connecting cubes if they need help in writing true equations.

Return to the Essential Question

Reread the Lesson 9 Essential Question on page 77: *How do you know if an equation is true or false?*

Tell children to think about what they learned in this lesson to answer this question.
(Possible response: I can use objects or drawings to model the value of each side of an equation. I can solve each side of the equation and compare the values to find out if they show the same amount.)

Have children describe any difficulty they experienced while comparing the sides of the equations and the strategies they used to get beyond the difficulty.

Concept Application

Children may work independently on these pages in the classroom or at home. They may refer to the first four pages of the lesson to revisit the instruction or to see a worked-out example.

Common Errors and **Teaching Tips** may help you support learning either in the classroom or as a follow-up for work done at home.

Common Errors

Items 5–8

Children are more likely to make computational errors on these problems than on previous problems on this page. Allow children to use drawings or connecting cubes to check their work, if needed.

Teaching Tips

Items 1–2

Children informally use the reflexive property of equality to complete these problems, which states that any number is equal to itself. Explain that because a number is equal to itself, it is not also equal to any other number.

Item 3

Children may use the Commutative Property of Addition, or order property, to complete this item. If called upon to justify their answer, children may describe the solution for each side of the equation or simply state that the order of the addends does not change the sum.

Item 4

Children use a basic addition fact or the doubles-plus-1 strategy to solve this item.

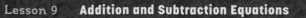

Independent Practice

Draw counters to model each equation. Write *true* or *false* for each equation.

1. $5 = 5$

   true

2. $7 = 17$

   false

3. $5 + 3 = 3 + 5$

   true

4. $11 = 5 + 6$

   true

5. $10 - 1 = 9 - 2$

   false

6. $8 - 0 = 10 - 2$

   true

7. $15 - 6 = 5 + 5$

   false

8. $11 - 2 = 6 + 3$

   true

Talking About Math

Use Illustrations and Details Have pairs of children work together to explain the strategies they used to answer each item on this page. Encourage them to use drawings or connecting cubes to verify their conclusions. Tell children to pay close attention to items that they answered incorrectly. Have them analyze their response, identify errors, and make necessary corrections.

Lesson 9

Circle the amount that makes the equation true.

9. $4 + 3 = $ ■   (10 − 3)   10 − 4   5 + 3

10. $9 + 6 = $ ■   18 − 9   (8 + 7)   7 + 7

11. ■ $= 10 − 3$ 11 − 2   5 + 3   (1 + 6)

12. ■ $= 13 − 8$ 3 + 3   (9 − 4)   8 − 1

Write *true* or *false* for each equation.

13. $5 + 9 = 9 + 5$ _true_

14. $16 − 7 = 17 − 9$ _false_

15. $14 − 8 = 5 + 1$ _true_

16. $3 + 8 = 10 − 2$ _false_

Unit 1 ■ Focus on Operations and Algebraic Thinking   **79**

Teaching Tips

Items 9–12

Children may benefit from writing answers to the given side of each equation before they attempt to select a matching value for each problem. This initial step may keep them from forgetting the value that they are looking for in the given answer choices.

Suggest to children that they do not necessarily need to find the value of every answer choice. In some cases, children may be able to use mental math to quickly recognize a match. When the choices are more difficult, they might try evaluating each choice only until they find a match, understanding that each problem has only one answer choice that is correct.

Digital Connection

Interactive Whiteboard On an interactive whiteboard, have a child write an addition name for a number less than 20 followed by an equal sign. Then have another child write either an addition or a subtraction name on the right side of the equal sign. The rest of the children can decide if the result is a true equation. If time allows, repeat the activity until all the children have had an opportunity to write an expression on the whiteboard.

Independent Practice

Teaching Tips

Items 17–20

Children who recognize that all these matches follow a pattern demonstrate proficiency in using the Commutative (order) Property of Addition.

Independent Practice

Match to make true equations.

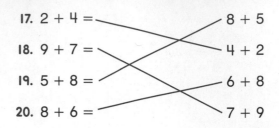

17. 2 + 4 =   8 + 5

18. 9 + 7 =   4 + 2

19. 5 + 8 =   6 + 8

20. 8 + 6 =   7 + 9

Write true or false for each equation.

21. 20 = 20 <u> true </u>	**22.** 7 + 4 = 11 <u> true </u>
23. 5 + 3 = 5 − 3 <u> false </u>	**24.** 12 = 9 + 3 <u> true </u>
25. 13 − 5 = 12 − 6 <u> false </u>	**26.** 8 + 4 = 9 + 5 <u> false </u>
27. 12 − 5 = 3 + 4 <u> true </u>	**28.** 2 + 5 = 11 − 3 <u> false </u>

Math-to-Family Connection

Comparing Ages Have children write an equation to add their age to the age of a brother or sister. (If children have no siblings, allow them to use the age of a friend for the second addend.) Then, tell children to change the order of the addends and write another equation. Discuss with children whether the sum changed. Next, ask children to write just one equation that shows their addends on both sides of the equation but in different order, such as 6 + 8 = 8 + 6.

Lesson 9

Independent Practice

Teaching Tips

Item 30

Children are likely to understand that the value of an addition expression may be equal to the value of a subtraction expression, but they may struggle to explain why this is true. If so, they might need a prompt for getting started. Remind these children that the equal sign simply means that the amounts on both sides have the same value.

MP7 **29.** Explain how you can make the equation true without adding.

$9 + 7 = 7 + \blacksquare$

Write another true equation of the same kind.

Answers may vary. Possible answer: If the amounts on both sides of the equal sign are the same, the equation will be true. There is already a 7 on both sides and a 9 on one side. So, if I write a 9 on the other side, the numbers will be the same and the equation will be true.

$5 + 7 = 7 + 5$ is the same kind of true equation.

MP4 **30.** Explain how an equation can be true if it has a plus sign on one side of the equal sign and a minus sign on the other side. Write an example.

$\underline{\quad 6 \quad} + \underline{\quad 3 \quad} = \underline{\quad 11 \quad} - \underline{\quad 2 \quad}$

Answers may vary. Possible answer: As long as the amounts on both sides of the equal sign are the same, the equation will be true. $6 + 3 = 11 - 2$ has a plus on one side and a minus on the other and the amounts on both sides are equal to 9.

Unit 1 ■ Focus on Operations and Algebraic Thinking   **81**

Mathematical Practices	
MP4	**Model with mathematics.**
Item 30: Children analyze a mathematical relationship and create a mathematical model to illustrate it.	
MP7	**Look for and make use of structure.**
Item 29: Children look closely to discern a pattern or structure to ensure that the values of both sides of an equation are equal.	

OBJECTIVE

Use counting on or the relationship between addition and subtraction to find the missing number in an equation.

ESSENTIAL QUESTION

Focus children on the Essential Question by reading it aloud. Have children tell what they already know about finding a missing number in an equation.

FLUENCY PRACTICE

Fluency practice is available at **sadlierconnect.com**.

Concept Development

Understand: You can count on to find a missing addend or sum

■ Be sure children begin counting on with the next number rather than the given number. Children should be able to identify the missing number as the number of numbers they counted on rather than the number where they ended.

Understand: Use a related fact to find a missing addend or sum

■ Children should understand that the greatest number in a subtraction fact is the number from which one of the other numbers is being subtracted. It is the sum in the related addition sentence.

■ Children should be fluent with basic addition and subtraction facts within 10. They can also work with other addition and subtraction facts within 20 by using strategies they have learned, including counting on, making a ten, and the relationship between addition and subtraction.

Lesson 10 — Find Missing Numbers in Equations

Essential Question: How can you find the missing number in an addition or subtraction equation?

In this lesson you will learn how to find the missing number in an addition or subtraction equation.

Understand: You can count on to find a missing addend or sum

Find the missing addend: $6 + \blacksquare = 11$

Start with 6. Count on to 11.

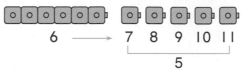

$$6 \longrightarrow 7 \quad 8 \quad 9 \quad 10 \quad 11$$
$$5$$

Count on 5 numbers to 11.
The missing addend is 5.

▷ $6 + 5 = 11$

Understand: Use a related fact to find a missing addend or sum

Find the missing addend: $\blacksquare + 5 = 11$

Use a subtraction fact you know that has the numbers 5 and 11.

$$11 - 5 = 6$$

▷ $6 + 5 = 11$

Remember!
Related facts use the same numbers.

Support English Language Learners

Point out that the word *missing* in a sentence such as "The girl is *missing* her friend." does not mean the same thing as when it is used in math. Have children discuss the meaning of *missing* in the context of missing parts of an equation. Mention some terms that might be used to address the same general concept, such as *blank space, unknown addend, unknown sum,* or *hidden number.*

Present models using the term missing in a sentence frame: e.g., *The _____ is missing.* Start with hiding objects and have children suggest what to write in the blank space. Then move on to writing equations with missing numbers.

Ask children to write or state a sentence that uses *missing* in the same way as it is used in math, such as, *My pencil is missing.*

Lesson 10

Understand: You can find the missing number in a subtraction equation by counting on

Find the missing number: $12 - \blacksquare = 9$

Use counters or a drawing. Start with 12.
Group 9 together. Count on from 9 to get to 12.

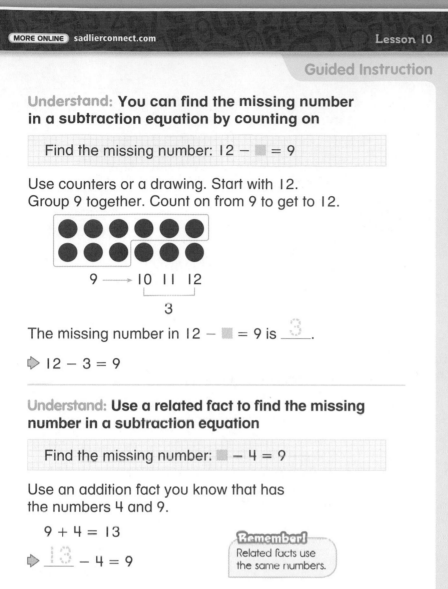

$$9 \longrightarrow 10 \quad 11 \quad 12$$
$$3$$

The missing number in $12 - \blacksquare = 9$ is ____.

▷ $12 - 3 = 9$

Understand: Use a related fact to find the missing number in a subtraction equation

Find the missing number: $\blacksquare - 4 = 9$

Use an addition fact you know that has the numbers 4 and 9.

$9 + 4 = 13$

▷ $\underline{13} - 4 = 9$

Remember!
Related facts use the same numbers.

Concept Development

Understand: You can find the missing number in a subtraction equation by counting on

■ Children should understand that if the missing number in a subtraction fact comes after the subtraction sign, it will be less than the number that comes before the subtraction sign. The number after the subtraction sign is the number being subtracted. The number being subtracted is always being subtracted from a greater number. When counting on, start with a lesser number and count on to a greater number. In the problem shown, since 9 is less than 12, start at 9 and count on to 12.

Understand: Use a related fact to find the missing number in a subtraction equation

■ In the problem shown, the missing number comes before the subtraction sign. It is the number from which another number is being subtracted. So the missing number is the greatest number in the subtraction fact. It is the sum in the related addition fact.

Math-to-Socialization Connection

Setting the Table Provide each pair of children with a paper rectangle, a paper circle, and 11 to 16 counters. Tell children that they are setting two tables for a party and that the counters represent plates. Allow children to choose how many *plates* they will set at each table in order to use all of the counters. After children place the counters on the circle and rectangle paper tables, have them write an addition sentence and a subtraction sentence that includes the number of plates in all and a missing part. Then have pairs of children share their equations and solutions with the class.

Connect: What you know about finding missing numbers. Use this page to help children understand how to analyze word problems to write equations.

■ In an addition sentence, the numbers being added are the addends. The other number is the sum. In the given problem, the two addends are the missing number and 8, so 17 is the sum. The sum in an addition fact is the number from which another number is being subtracted. Be sure children understand that knowing these relationships will help them recognize the related subtraction fact, $17 - 8 = 9$.

■ Children combine what they know about word problems and equations to record their work.

■ Children demonstrate fluency applying strategies to solving problems.

■ Have children reread the question to make sure they have answered the problem.

Connect: What you know about finding missing numbers

Hyun has some strawberries and 8 blueberries. She has 17 berries in all. How many of the berries are strawberries?

Step 1

Write an equation.

Use ■ for the number of strawberries.

$$■ + 8 = 17$$

some strawberries   blueberries   berries in all

Step 2

Think of a related fact with the numbers 8 and 17.

Find the number that makes the equation true.

$17 - 8 = \underline{\ 9\ }$

$17 - 8 = 9$ is a related fact that uses the numbers 8 and 17.

The missing number in ■ $+ 8 = 17$ is $\underline{\ 9\ }$.

$9 + 8 = 17$

▷ Hyun has $\underline{\ 9\ }$ strawberries.

Math-to-Transportation Connection

How to Arrange Riders Tell children that they will use cubes or their chairs to show how 15 people can take a trip in two vans. Allow children to decide how many people each van will hold and to show how many people will ride in each van. Have volunteers write the resulting equations on the board, including addition and subtraction and a missing number in each equation. Discuss with the class how to find the value for each missing number.

Guided Practice

1. Find the missing number in this equation.

■ − 5 = 7

Step 1

Write the two numbers given in the problem.

_5_ and _7_

Step 2

Write the related addition fact that has the same numbers.

_7_ + _5_ = _12_

Is the missing number an addend or the sum? _sum_

7 + 5 = _12_

The missing number in ■ − 5 = 7 is _12_.

_12_ − 5 = 7

♕ Think•Pair•Share

MP3

2. Write two addition facts and two subtraction facts using the numbers 9, 6, and 15. Talk about how these facts are related. See Additional Answers.

___ + ___ = ___   ___ + ___ = ___

___ − ___ = ___   ___ − ___ = ___

Mathematical Practices

Mathematical Practice Standards underline the teaching and understanding of all concepts and skills presented. The emphasis of specific practices is noted throughout the guided and independent practice of this lesson.

MP3	**Construct viable arguments and critique the reasoning of others.**

Item 2: Children use previously established results in constructing arguments and justifying their answers.

Observational Assessment

Use page 85 to assess whether children are able to construct addition and subtraction facts containing a missing number to solve an equation. Observe whether children can readily recall and write related addition and subtraction facts. Help children who are having difficulty by supplying manipulatives or drawing paper.

♕ Think•Pair•Share

Peer Collaboration Have children think about ways they might explain the concept of related facts. Prompt peer discussions with questions such as:

- *How is adding 9 + 6 similar to adding 6 + 9?*

- *Which of the three given numbers must you start with to write a subtraction problem? Why?*

- *What is an example of a fact that is not related to those in problem 2? How do you know?*

Ask volunteers to write their facts on the board. Ask the class to discuss whether any of them listed a different fact and resolve the error.

Return to the Essential Question

Reread the Lesson 10 Essential Question on page 82: *How can you find the missing number in an addition or subtraction equation?*

Tell children to think about what they learned in this lesson to answer this question.
(Possible responses: I can count on to find the missing number in an addition or subtraction equation. I can also use related addition and subtraction equations to find a missing number.)

Additional Answers

Item 2: Answers may vary. Possible answer: 9 + 6 = 15, 6 + 9 = 15, 15 − 6 = 9, 15 − 9 = 6; The facts are related because they use the same numbers.

Concept Application

Children may work independently on these pages in the classroom or at home. They may refer to the first four pages of the lesson to revisit the instruction or to see a worked-out example.

Common Errors and **Teaching Tips** may help you support learning either in the classroom or as a follow-up for work done at home.

Teaching Tips

Items 1–4

Encourage children to use addition and subtraction strategies rather than objects to complete each equation.

Items 3–4

Suggest to children who seem hesitant that they might think about facts that are doubles or near doubles to help them.

Count on to find the number that makes the equation true.

1. $9 + \blacksquare = 13$

   $9 \longrightarrow 10, 11, 12, 13$

   How many numbers did you count on? __4__

   $9 + \underline{\ 4\ } = 13$

2. $14 = \blacksquare + 8$

   $8 \longrightarrow 9, 10, 11, 12, 13, 14$

   How many numbers did you count on? __6__

   $14 = \underline{\ 6\ } + 8$

Use a related fact to find the number that makes the equation true.

3. $4 + \blacksquare = 10$

   $10 - 4 = \underline{\ 6\ }$

   $4 + \underline{\ 6\ } = 10$

4. $\blacksquare - 9 = 9$

   $9 + 9 = \underline{\ 18\ }$

   $\underline{\ 18\ } - 9 = 9$

Talking About Math

Ask and Answer Questions Have children work in small groups to create and answer questions they can ask one another about the strategies they used. Tell them to ask for details about why a particular strategy does or does not work in certain situations, based on opinions. Encourage them to discuss their favorite strategies and listen carefully to others, even if there are differing opinions.

Lesson 10

Independent Practice

Find the number that makes the equation true. Use counters, pictures, or numbers to check your work.

5. $8 + 7 = \underline{15}$

6. $\underline{12} - 6 = 6$

7. $16 = 9 + \underline{7}$

8. $14 - \underline{8} = 6$

Unit 1 ■ Focus on Operations and Algebraic Thinking **87**

Teaching Tips

Items 5–8
Emphasize that children should try to complete each equation first using the strategies shown in the lesson. They should use counters, pictures, or numbers only to check their answers.

Help children who are struggling to recall or find the related fact by having them use a known fact that is close. For example, if they have trouble with $8 + 3 = 11$, remind them to recall $8 + 2 = 10$ and then think about what they need to do to make 11 instead of 10.

Item 7
If children struggle with this problem, ask them to try $16 = 10 + \underline{\hspace{1cm}}$ and then compare it to the given problem.

Item 8
Children may use a variety of strategies to solve the problem. Those who are proficient using basic facts may recognize that the solution will be close to $14 - 7 = 7$.

Digital Connection

Addition Software Use addition and subtraction software or online activities that provide practice in basic facts. Review available products and make a list of particularly helpful programs for children to choose. Encourage children to work in pairs to describe the strategies they can use for each activity.

Independent Practice

Teaching Tips

Items 9–12

Children informally practice a standardized test format by analyzing the given answer choices. After the page has been completed, ask children whether they found it easier to first solve the equation and then look for their answer among the choices or to test each choice in the given equation.

Items 13–20

Tell children to carefully read each problem, evaluate whether they will use addition or subtraction, and make note of the position of the missing number in the equation. Taking the time to analyze each problem in this way will help them avoid careless errors.

Independent Practice

Circle the number that makes the equation true.

9. $\blacksquare = 8 + 6$ 16   15   (14)

10. $\blacksquare + 2 = 8$ 7   (6)   5

11. $12 - 9 = \blacksquare$ (3)   4   5

12. $\blacksquare - 8 = 9$ 16   (17)   18

Find the number to make the equation true.

13. $8 = 4 + \underline{4}$

14. $5 + \underline{7} = 12$

15. $13 - 6 = \underline{7}$

16. $\underline{11} - 5 = 6$

17. $16 = \underline{9} + 7$

18. $\underline{7} + 7 = 14$

19. $15 - \underline{8} = 7$

20. $\underline{12} - 7 = 5$

Math-to-Everyday Connection

Missing Pieces A box of crayons, a carton of eggs, or various other everyday items come in a set of a particular number. If part of the set is missing, the box or carton is not full. Have children write a math story about a time they have noticed a set of items that was not full. Tell them to explain how they found out the number of items that had been used or were missing. For example, when children put away their crayons, how do they know whether they included all of the crayons? How do they know the number of crayons that are missing?

Lesson 10

Independent Practice

MP2 **21.** Pedro has 14 stickers.
He gives some to Ella.
Now he has 8 stickers.
How many stickers does he give to Ella?

Write an equation and use it to
solve the problem.

Answers may vary. Possible answers: $14 - 6 = 8$, $8 + 6 = 14$
Check children's work.

MP3 **22.** Beth wants to find the missing number
that will make this equation true.

$9 = \blacksquare - 3$

She says that the number must be less than 9
because the related addition sentence is $3 + \blacksquare = 9$
and the sum must be greater than either addend.
Is Beth correct? Tell why or why not.

Answers may vary. Possible answer: Beth is not correct.
To make the equation true, both sides of the equation
must be equal. So 3 subtracted from the missing number is 9.
To find the missing number, 3 must be added to 9. The related
addition sentence is $9 + 3 = \blacksquare$. The missing
number is 12.

Unit 1 ■ Focus on Operations and Algebraic Thinking **89**

Teaching Tips

Item 21
Make sure children understand that
there can be more than one correct
equation to represent the problem and
that they only need to write one of
them. Also remind children to indicate
the answer to the problem, the number
of stickers that Pedro gives to Ella.

Item 22
If children struggle to answer the
problem, ask questions to determine
whether they are having trouble reading
the problem, understanding Beth's
argument, or solving the given equation.
This will help determine the source of
confusion and allow for a resolution that
fits the child's need.

Return to the

Progress Check

Remind children to return to the
Progress Check self-assessment, page 7,
to check off additional items they have
mastered during the unit.

Mathematical Practices		
MP2	**Reason abstractly and quantitatively.**	
Item 21: Children make sense of quantities and their relationships in a problem situation.		
MP3	**Construct viable arguments and critique the reasoning of others.**	
Item 22: Children analyze the reasoning that is presented, distinguish reasoning that is flawed, and make a plausible argument to support correct reasoning.		

The Unit 1 Review covers all the standards presented in the unit. Use it to assess your students' mastery of the unit's concepts and skills.

Depth of Knowledge

The depth of knowledge is a ranking of the content complexity of assessment items based on Webb's Depth of Knowledge (DOK) levels. The levels increase in complexity as shown below.

Level 1: Recall and Reproduction
Level 2: Basic Skills and Concepts
Level 3: Strategic Reasoning and Thinking
Level 4: Extended Thinking

Item	DOK
1	2
2	2
3	1
4	1
5	1
6	1
7	1
8	1
9	2
10	3
11	3
12	1
13	1
14	1
15	1
16	2
17	2
18	2
19	4
20	4

Unit **Review**

**Make a ten.
Then add the other addend.**

1. $7 + 1 + 9 =$ ▮

   $1 + 9 = \underline{\ 10\ }$

   $10 + 7 = \underline{\ 17\ }$

2. $6 + 3 + 4 =$ ▮

   $6 + 4 = \underline{\ 10\ }$

   $10 + 3 = \underline{\ 13\ }$

Count on to solve.

3. $1 + 7 = \underline{\ 8\ }$

4. $9 + 2 = \underline{\ 11\ }$

5. $9 - 7 = \underline{\ 2\ }$

6. $12 - 9 = \underline{\ 3\ }$

7. $8 + 5 = \underline{\ 13\ }$

8. $11 - 8 = \underline{\ 3\ }$

Write a related addition fact that can help you subtract. Then subtract.

9. $13 - 7 =$ ▮

   $\underline{\ 6\ } + 7 = 13$

   $13 - 7 = \underline{\ 6\ }$

Solve each problem.
Draw a picture to help you solve the problem.

10. Matt has 4 more blocks than Jordan.
Matt has 12 blocks.
How many blocks does Jordan have?

_12_ − _4_ = _8_

Jordan has _8_ blocks.

11. Abby has 5 toys. Will has some toys.
Jake has 8 toys. They have 15 toys in all.
How many toys does Will have?

5 + _2_ + 8 = 15

Will has _2_ toys.

Add or subtract.

12. 8 + 6 = _14_

13. 13 − 5 = _8_

14. 11 − 7 = _4_

15. 9 + 9 = _18_

This chart correlates the Unit 1 Review items with the lessons in which the concepts and skills are presented.

Item	Lesson
1	4
2	4
3	6, 7
4	6
5	6, 7
6	6
7	6
8	6
9	5
10	2
11	1, 3
12	8
13	8
14	8
15	8
16	7, 9
17	9
18	10
19	5
20	5

Talking About Math

Direct students to respond to the Unit 1 Essential Question. (This can also be found on page 9.)

> **Essential Question:**
> How are addition and subtraction related?

Possible responses:
- Addition is the opposite of subtraction.
- Subtraction is the opposite of addition.
- You can use addition to check the answer to a subtraction problem.

Unit Assessment

- Unit 1 Review, *pp. 90–92*
- Unit 1 Performance Task ONLINE

Additional Assessment Options

Optional Purchase:
- iProgress Monitor ONLINE
- Progress Monitor Student Benchmark Assessment Booklet

Circle the amount that makes the equation true.

16. $5 + 5 = \blacksquare$ $9 + 2$ (9 + 1) $10 - 3$

17. $17 = \blacksquare$ (9 + 8) $9 + 9$ $7 + 9$

18. $\blacksquare - 6 = 8$ 13 (14) 15

MP4 19. This model shows these addition and subtraction facts:

$3 + 2 = 5, 2 + 3 = 5, 5 - 2 = 3$, and $5 - 3 = 2$.

Write all the addition and subtraction facts that this model shows.

$6 + 7 = 13; 7 + 6 = 13; 13 - 7 = 6; 13 - 6 = 7$

MP2 20. How many addition and subtraction facts is it possible to write using only the three numbers 8, 8, and 16? Write these facts. How do you know you have found all the possible facts?

There is only one possible addition fact: $8 + 8 = 16$. There is only one possible subtraction fact: $16 - 8 = 8$. Answers may vary. Possible answer: When I add, the biggest number is the sum. The sum has to be 16. When I subtract, I subtract a smaller number from a bigger number. I can only subtract 8 from 16. So I know that I have found all the possible addition and subtraction facts.

Mathematical Practices
MP2   **Reason abstractly and quantitatively.**
Item 20: Children make sense of quantities to determine all possible addition and subtraction facts.
MP4   **Model with mathematics.**
Item 19: Children write addition and subtraction equations to describe the models.

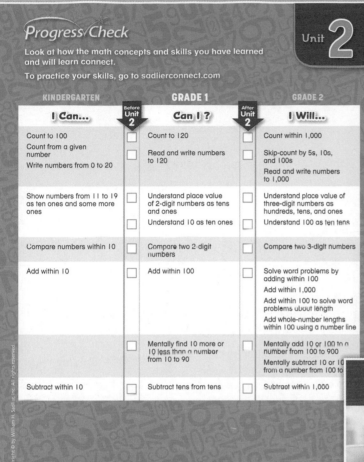

I Can... (KINDERGARTEN)	Before Unit 2	Can I ? (GRADE 1)	After Unit 2	I Will... (GRADE 2)
Count to 100	☐	Count to 120	☐	Count within 1,000
Count from a given number	☐	Read and write numbers to 120	☐	Skip-count by 5s, 10s, and 100s
Write numbers from 0 to 20				Read and write numbers to 1,000
Show numbers from 11 to 19 as ten ones and some more ones	☐	Understand place value of 2-digit numbers as tens and ones	☐	Understand place value of three-digit numbers as hundreds, tens, and ones
	☐	Understand 10 as ten ones	☐	Understand 100 as ten tens
Compare numbers within 10	☐	Compare two 2-digit numbers	☐	Compare two 3-digit numbers
Add within 10	☐	Add within 100	☐	Solve word problems by adding within 100
				Add within 1,000
				Add within 100 to solve word problems about length
				Add whole-number lengths within 100 using a number line
	☐	Mentally find 10 more or 10 less than a number from 10 to 90	☐	Mentally add 10 or 100 to a number from 100 to 900
				Mentally subtract 10 or 100 from a number from 100 to 900
Subtract within 10	☐	Subtract tens from tens	☐	Subtract within 1,000

Unit 2 ■ Focus on Number and Operations in Base Ten

Student Page 93

Progress Check

Progress Check is a self-assessment tool that children can use to gauge their own progress. Research shows that when children take accountability for their learning, motivation increases.

Before children begin work in Unit 2, have them check any items they know they can do well. Explain that it is fine if they don't check any of the boxes; they will have the opportunity to learn and practice all the standards through the course of the unit.

Let children know that at the end of the unit they will review their checklists to check their progress. After children have completed the last lesson of the unit, before they begin the Unit 2 Review, you will be prompted to have children revisit this page. Remind them to keep this page in a safe place where they can find it later.

HOME ◆ CONNECT...

The Home Connect feature is a way to keep parents or other adult family members apprised of what their children are learning. The key learning objectives are listed, and some ideas for related activities and discussions are included.

Explain to children that they can share the Home Connect page at home with their families. Let children know there is an activity connected to their classroom learning that they can do with their families.

Encourage children and their parents to share their experiences using the suggestions on the Home Connect. You may wish to invite children to share this work with the class.

HOME ◆ CONNECT...

In this unit your child will:

- Count to 120.
- Understand tens and ones in place value.
- Compare numbers.
- Add two-digit numbers.
- Find 10 more than and 10 less than a number.
- Subtract multiples of 10.

In first grade, your child will learn about the value of digits in a number, called place value. Your child will learn that 10 ones is equal to 1 ten. Your child will write numbers in a place-value chart to show how many tens and ones.

tens	ones
1	2

The 1 in 12 is in the tens place. It has a value of 1 ten or 10. The 2 in 12 is in the ones place. It has a value of 2 ones or 2. 12 has 1 ten and 2 ones.

Place value is a very important concept in first grade math and in all the math that will follow.

Ways to Help Your Child

Provide your child with opportunities to count. For example, a calendar is a great tool for counting. Choose a holiday or special event, and count the number of days since or until that day on the calendar with your child.

Activity: A hundred chart is a tool that will help your first grader with many concepts through the year. Make a hundred chart poster to hang in your home. Use tens and ones patterns on the hundred chart to find 10 more or 10 less than a number. For example, if you point to 29 on the chart, the number directly below it, 39, is 10 more than the number 29. The number directly above it, 19, is 10 less than the number 29.

ONLINE
For more Home Connect activities, continue online at sadlierconnect.com

94 Unit 2 ■ Focus on Number and Operations in Base Ten

Student Page 94

UNIT PLANNER

Lesson	Objective
11 Count to 120	Use patterns in a counting sequence or in a number chart to count from any number to 120.
12 Read and Write Numbers	Use numerals and number words to read, count, and write how many.
13 Understand Place Value: Tens and Ones	Use drawings and place-value charts to identify two-digit numbers by a number of tens and ones.
14 Compare Numbers	Use concrete objects, drawings, symbols, and place value to compare numbers and record the comparisons.
15 Add Two-Digit Numbers	Use place value to add a two-digit number and a one-digit number or a multiple of 10.
16 Find 10 More or 10 Less	Use place-value models, tens and ones charts, number charts, and mental math to find 10 more and 10 less than a number.
17 Subtraction with Tens	Use models, place-value charts, and number charts to subtract a multiple of 10 from a multiple of 10.

Essential Question	Words to Know
How can you use patterns to count on from any number to 120?	rows columns digits
How can you use both numbers and words to count and to tell how many?	number names
How can you use tens and ones to help you understand numbers?	tens ones place-value chart
How can you compare numbers?	greater than (>) less than (<) equal to (=)
How can you use tens and ones to add two-digit numbers?	
How can you find 10 more or 10 less than a number?	
How can you subtract tens from tens?	

Unit Assessment

- Unit 2 Review, *pp. 152–154*
- Unit 2 Performance Task (ONLINE)

Additional Assessment Options

- Performance Task 1, *pp. 155–158*
  (ALSO ONLINE)

Optional Purchase:

- iProgress Monitor (ONLINE)
- Progress Monitor Student Benchmark Assessment Booklet

(ONLINE) Digital Resources

- Home Connect Activities
- Unit Performance Tasks
- Additional Practice
- Fluency Practice
- Teacher Resources
- iProgress Monitor (optional purchase)

Go to SadlierConnect.com to access your Digital Resources.

For more detailed instructions see page T3.

LEARNING PROGRESSIONS

This page provides more in-depth detail on the development of math concepts and skills across the grade levels. See also the unit Progress Check page in the Student Edition for a roadmap of the Learning Progressions.

Grade K

- Students count to 100 by ones and tens. They count forward beginning from a given number without having to start over at 1.
- Students write numbers from 0 to 20 and use them to represent a number of objects.
- Students compare two numbers within 10 presented as written numerals.
- Work with the numbers 11 to 19 provides foundation for place value. Students compose and decompose these numbers into ten ones and some more ones.
- Students add and subtract within 10 to solve word problems.

Grade 1

- Students count to 120 from any number less than 120, and read and write numerals from 0 to 120.
- Students understand place value of two-digit numbers as tens and ones.
- Students compare two two-digit numbers using >, =, and < symbols.
- Students add within 100 using models and strategies based on place value, properties of operations, and/or the relationship between addition and subtraction.
- Students mentally find 10 more or 10 less than a given two-digit number.
- Students subtract multiples of 10 from multiples of 90 in the range 10 to 90.

Grade 2

- Students add and subtract within 100 to solve word problems.
- Students extend their understanding of place value to hundreds, viewing a hundred as a new unit composed of 10 tens.
- Students count within 1,000 and skip count by 5s, 10s, and 100s.
- Students read and write numbers to 1,000 using numerals, number names, and expanded form (hundreds + tens + ones).
- Students compare two 3-digit numbers using >, =, and < symbols.
- Students add and subtract with 1,000 using place value strategies.
- Students mentally add or subtract 10 or 100.
- Students add and subtract within 100 to solve word problems involving length.
- Students represent addition and subtraction on a number line.

Focus on Number and Operations in Base Ten

Unit 2

Essential Question:
How does understanding place value help you add and subtract?

As children become involved with the Essential Question they will use place value strategies to compare numbers to 120, add tens and ones, subtract tens from tens, find 10 more or 10 less, and add two-digit numbers.

Conversation Starters

Have children discuss the photograph. Ask question such as: *Have you ever seen a counting tool that looks like this? Do you know what it is called? If there are ten beads on each row and ten rows, how is this like a hundred chart? How is it different?*

Tell children that the picture shows an abacus that has ten rows of ten beads each, but that all of the rows and beads are not shown.

Ask children to discuss their observations about the abacus in the picture. *If the abacus has ten rows of beads, how many rows are not shown? How can you tell?* (You can subtract 10 rows minus 9 rows to find that 1 row is not shown.) *How could you use an abacus to show that 10 + 10 + 10 equals 30?* (You can count the number of beads in three full rows.)

Tell children that an abacus is one of the oldest tools used for counting, adding, and subtracting. Demonstrate a classroom abacus or ask children whether anyone has an abacus that they can bring to school. If children have seen a different kind of abacus, have them describe what it looks like.

Activity

Materials: various colors of connecting cubes
Give pairs of children 10 connecting cubes of one color and 10 connecting cubes of a second color. If possible, give different colors to each pair of children. Tell children to work together to make single-color rows of ten. Ask them to record the total number of cubes that they have. Then combine pairs of children to make small groups of 4 or 6 members and ask children to record the number of cubes in all.

Lead a class discussion to have children explain how they found each total and to discuss how ten cubes are similar to a row of ten beads on an abacus. If time allows, have children take away one row of ten cubes and discuss how to find the difference.

OBJECTIVE

Use patterns in a counting sequence or in a number chart to count from any number to 120.

ESSENTIAL QUESTION

Focus children on the Essential Question by reading it aloud and asking children what they already know about counting. Tell children that in this lesson they will look for specific number patterns to help them count accurately.

FLUENCY PRACTICE

Fluency practice is available at **sadlierconnect.com**.

Concept Development

Understand: You can count all the objects in a group

■ Children can use counting strategies to help keep them organized as they count. When they count to find the number of objects in a group, they start with 1 and count on.

■ Be sure children understand that an accurate count of the number of objects in a group means starting at 1 and counting on in order, with only one number being associated with each object and no two objects having the same number.

Understand: You can count from any number

■ Make sure children understand the visual model that begins with a number greater than 1. It may help them to think of the box as a number of baseballs that have already been counted and the other baseballs as additional baseballs that will be placed in the box as they are counted.

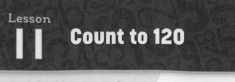

Lesson 11 Count to 120

In this lesson you will learn how to count to 120 starting from any number.

Essential Question:
How can you use patterns to count on from any number to 120?

Words to Know
rows
columns
digits

Understand: You can count all the objects in a group

How many flowers are there?

Count the flowers. Mark each one as you count.

▷ There are 12 flowers.

Understand: You can count on from any number

There are 24 baseballs in a box and some baseballs outside the box.
How many baseballs are there in all?

Start at 24. Count on in order.

| 24 | 25 | 26 | 27 | 28 | 29 | 30 | 31 | 32 |

▷ There are 32 baseballs in all.

Words to Know

rows: the lines of a table or chart that go across from left to right

columns: the lines of a table or chart that go down from top to bottom

Glossary can be found on pp. 261–272.

Lesson 11

Guided Instruction

Understand: Patterns in a number chart can help you count

What patterns do you see in the number chart?

1	2	3	4	5	6	7	8	9	10
11	12	13	14	15	16	17	18	19	20
21	22	23	24	25	26	27	28	29	30
31	32	33	34	35	36	37	38	39	40
41	42	43	44	45	46	47	48	49	50

Rows go across. Columns go up and down.
Use digits 1, 2, 3, 4, 5, 6, 7, 8, 9, 0 to write numbers.

Look at the red digits in the top 3 rows.
What pattern do you see?

1, 2, 3, 4, 5, _6_, _7_, _8_, _9_, _0_

Look at the first column.

What is each red digit in that column? _1_

What pattern do you see in the blue digits in the first column?

The blue digits are in counting order from _1_ to _4_.

▷ In each row, the last digits are 1, 2, 3, 4, 5, 6, 7, 8, 9, 0. In each column, starting with row 2, the first digits of each number are in counting order. The last digit of each number is the same as the red digit at the top of the column.

Unit 2 ■ Focus on Number and Operations in Base Ten **97**

Understand: Patterns in a number chart can help you count

■ Examining the number chart can help children recognize patterns in the base-ten number system and begin to understand its structure.

■ Children who are already fluent in counting to 100 may be able to describe additional patterns that they see in the number chart, such as alternating columns of even and odd numbers.

■ To help children see each number pattern that is described in the last paragraph, you may wish to mask off a single row and ask children to describe the relationships of the digits. Then mask off a single column and ask similar questions.

Words to Know

digits: 1, 2, 3, 4, 5, 6, 7, 8, 9, 0 are used to write numbers

Example: 2 4

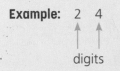
digits

Glossary can be found on pp. 261–272.

Connect: What you know about patterns on a number chart Use this page to help children count on from any number up to 100.

■ Many children may find it easy to start at the first of a row and fill in the missing number as they count orally. Allow children to follow the row of numbers with a finger or other pointer if it helps them remember how far they have counted.

■ Children may have more difficulty identifying 82 than 66 because of its position in the row. Have them look across the entire row and name the digits. Then have them look down the column and name the digits. Encourage children to explain how these steps can help them identify any number that is missing in a number chart.

Lesson 11   Count to 120

Guided Instruction

Connect: What you know about patterns on a number chart

What numbers do the shapes stand for?

51	52	53	54	55	56	57	58	59	60
61	62	63	64	65	●	67	68	69	70
71	72	73	74	75	76	77	78	79	80
81	♥	83	84	85	86	87	88	89	90
91	92	93	94	95	96	97	98	99	100

Step 1

To find the number that the ● stands for, start at 61 and count on.

Write the number. _66_

Step 2

To find the number that the ♥ stands for, start at 81 and count on.

Write the number. _82_

▷ The ● stands for _66_.

  The ♥ stands for _82_.

Support English Language Learners

English language learners often struggle with words that have multiple meanings, such as *rows, columns,* and *digits.* Children are likely to understand the meanings of rows and columns in a table such as a number chart. If they have trouble remembering the difference between columns and rows, you might point out that columns on buildings go up and down like the columns in a number chart. *Digits* may be a term that needs further attention because it is not as commonly used. Just as a hand is made up of fingers, numbers in the base-ten number system are represented by digits 1, 2, 3, 4, 5, 6, 7, 8, 9, 0. A number may be represented by just one digit, such as the number 9, or by more than one digit, such as the number 92.

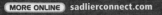

Lesson 11

Guided Practice

1. What number does each shape stand for?

101	102	103	☆	105	106	107	108	109	110
▲	112	113	114	115	116	117	118	119	■

Step 1

Start at 101 and count forward to ☆.

Write the number that the ☆ stands for. _104_

Step 2

Start at 105 and count forward to ▲.

Write the number that the ▲ stands for. _111_

Step 3

Start at 112 and count forward to ■.

Write the number that the ■ stands for. _120_

The missing numbers are ☆ _104_, ▲ _111_, and ■ _120_.

👑 Think·Pair·Share

MP7 **2.** Start at 98. Write the next 5 numbers.

Talk about how you know what number is next.

98, _99_, _100_, _101_, _102_, _103_
See Additional Answers.

Mathematical Practices

Mathematical Practice Standards underline the teaching and understanding of all concepts and skills presented. The emphasis of specific practices is noted throughout the guided and independent practice of this lesson.

MP7 **Look for and make use of structure.**

Item 2: Children look closely at the number charts they have seen so far to analyze structure in number patterns.

Observational Assessment

Use page 99 to assess whether children are able to apply what they have learned about counting to 100 and then up to 120. Observe whether children demonstrate oral or written counting fluency, analyze and apply number patterns, or have difficulty using the patterns to identify missing numbers.

👑 Think·Pair·Share

Peer Collaboration Have pairs of children share their work and counting strategies with one another. Prompt the discussions with questions such as:

- *How did you find the number that comes after 99?*
- *How is counting from 101 and beyond similar to counting from 1?*
- *Why is the 0 important in number 101?*

Return to the Essential Question

Reread the Lesson 11 Essential Question on page 96: *How can you use patterns to count on from any number to 120?*

Tell children to think about what they learned in this lesson to answer this question.
(Possible responses: I can use the patterns in a number chart. I can count from 1 to 20 and then use the same pattern to count from 101 to 120.)

Additional Answers

Item 2: Possible response: I use the pattern 1, 2, 3, 4, 5, 6, 7, 8, 9, 0. The number after 98 is 99, because 9 comes after 8 in the pattern. The number after 99 is 100 because 0 comes after 9 in the pattern. The number just after 100 is 101 because the pattern starts over again with 1. The last two numbers are 102 and 103, because the pattern continues.

Concept Application

Children may work independently on these pages in the classroom or at home. They may refer to the first four pages of the lesson to revisit the instruction or to see a worked-out example.

Common Errors and **Teaching Tips** may help you support learning either in the classroom or as a follow-up for work done at home.

Common Errors

Items 1-3

Some children may start counting with 1, disregarding the number on the box. Point out that they need to begin counting with the next number that comes after the number on each box.

Item 3

If children write 71 to solve this problem, they likely named the first bug 61, as on the box, rather than starting with the next number after 61.

Teaching Tips

Item 1

Focus children's thinking by telling them that the next number after 35 has the same first digit but its second digit changes. If another hint is needed, cover the 3 in 35 and have children count on from 5 to 14. Then help them make the connection between counting 5 to 14 and 35 to 44.

Items 1-3

Make sure children understand that the first number in each row represents the number of objects that have already been counted. Use counters for children who need a more concrete approach to move from the given number to the next objects.

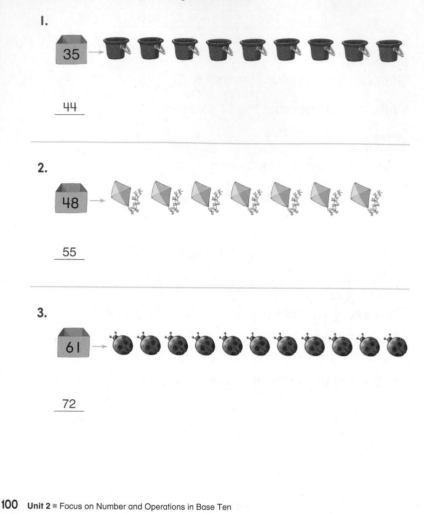

Lesson 11   Count to 120

Independent Practice

Count on to find how many. Write the number. Mark each object as you count it.

1.
44

2.
55

3.
72

100   Unit 2 ■ Focus on Number and Operations in Base Ten

Copyright © by William H. Sadlier, Inc. All rights reserved.

Math-to-Housing Connection

Apartment Numbers Ask volunteers to discuss what they know about how apartments are numbered. Children who do not have prior knowledge of apartment dwellings may instead think of how hotel rooms or some classrooms are usually numbered. Explain that the first digit in most apartment numbers or room numbers is the floor on which the unit is located. The next number usually follows an organized sequence that counts the units in a row from 1 or 01. This means that the first apartment on the first floor might be numbered 11 or 101. Have children discuss how following a pattern might help them find a particular apartment when they go to visit someone.

100   Unit 2 ■ Focus on Number and Operations in Base Ten

Independent Practice

Start at the number shown.
Write the next 5 numbers.

4. 23, _24_, _25_, _26_, _27_, _28_

5. 15, _16_, _17_, _18_, _19_, _20_

6. 47, _48_, _49_, _50_, _51_, _52_

7. 88, _89_, _90_, _91_, _92_, _93_

Circle the missing number.

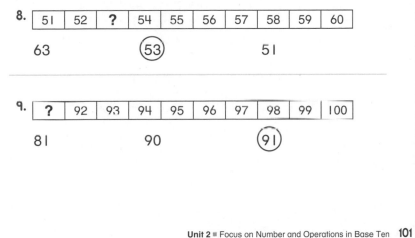

8.

| 51 | 52 | ? | 54 | 55 | 56 | 57 | 58 | 59 | 60 |

63   (53)   51

9.

| ? | 92 | 93 | 94 | 95 | 96 | 97 | 98 | 99 | 100 |

81   90   (91)

Unit 2 ■ Focus on Number and Operations in Base Ten **101**

Common Errors

Items 4-7
Some children may write the given number in the first blank and then count forward. Be sure to point out that they should begin with the next number in the sequence, or one more than the given number.

Item 8
If children select 63, have them use the number chart on page 98 to explain the pattern of the first digits in the row that begins with 51. If children select 51, point out that each number across the row is 1 more rather than 1 less and that a number chart does not show the same number twice.

Item 9
An answer of 81 or 90 indicates an error in the sequence of digits. Children who begin the row with 90 may need to look back at previous number charts to see the last digit of the number at the beginning of each row.

Talking About Math

Identify Basic Similarities Ask children to describe how counting from 5 to 15 is similar to counting from 25 to 35. Have children work with a partner to explain how they can know the number that comes after 9 and 29. Provide counting objects for pairs of children who need them.

Independent Practice

Common Errors

Items 10–13

Children may make common counting errors by writing the same number twice or skipping a number. Help them evaluate their own errors by explaining how they determined the next number in the sequence.

Teaching Tips

Items 10–13

Have children try to complete each table without looking back to previous number charts in the book or other displays of number charts. If children struggle to get started, provide them with a ruler that has numbers above 10 masked off, therefore showing only a counting sequence from 1 to 10. Tell them to notice how the numbers on the ruler are similar to each row of numbers in the charts.

Independent Practice

Fill in the missing numbers.

10.

1	2	3	4	5	6	7	8	9	10
11	12	13	14	15	16	17	18	19	20

11.

61	62	63	64	65	66	67	68	69	70
71	72	73	74	75	76	77	78	79	80

12.

21	22	23	24	25	26	27	28	29	30
31	32	33	34	35	36	37	38	39	40
41	42	43	44	45	46	47	48	49	50

13.

91	92	93	94	95	96	97	98	99	100
101	102	103	104	105	106	107	108	109	110
111	112	113	114	115	116	117	118	119	120

Digital Connection

Random Number Generator Use a search engine to find a random number generator Web site. Assign parameters for the random number generator to select a number between 16 and 95. Pair children together and assign each group a randomly selected number. Have each pair write their number and draw five objects beside it. Tell children to count on from the given number and write the number that is represented by their work. If time permits, continue with other randomly selected starting numbers.

Lesson 11

Independent Practice

MP8 **14.** Fill in the missing numbers on this number chart. Explain how you found the missing numbers.

1	2	3	4	5	6	7	8	9	10
11	12	13	14	15	16	17	18	19	20
21	22	23	24	25	26	27	28	29	30
31	32	33	34	35	36	37	38	39	40
41	42	43	44	45	46	47	48	49	50
51	52	53	54	55	56	57	58	59	60
61	62	63	64	65	66	67	68	69	70
71	72	73	74	75	76	77	78	79	80
81	82	83	84	85	86	87	88	89	90
91	92	93	94	95	96	97	98	99	100
101	102	103	104	105	106	107	108	109	110
111	112	113	114	115	116	117	118	119	120

Answers may vary. Possible answer: I looked for patterns that used the digits in the order 1, 2, 3, 4, 5, 6, 7, 8, 9, 0.

MP7 **15.** Yoki's ticket to the school show is the number that comes just before 110. What is Yoki's ticket number? Tell how you know.

Yoki's ticket number is 109; Answers may vary. Possible answer: The last digit of the number 110 is 0 and the first digits are 11. In the number chart, the numbers that end with 0 are in the last column. The first digits of the numbers in the last column are in the order 1, 2, 3, 4, 5, 6, 7, 8, 9, 10, 11, 12. So I can look in the last column and find where I wrote 110 in the chart. The number that comes just before 110 is 109.

Unit 2 ■ Focus on Number and Operations in Base Ten **103**

Common Errors

Item 15

Some children may reason that 100 is the number just before 110 because 10 is the number just before 11. Help children understand that they must look at the last two digits. Have children write 110 on a piece of paper. Mask the first digit and ask children to identify the number that comes just before 10. After children write 9 under the 0 in 10, remove the mask and have children write 1 just under the first digit in 110. Make sure children understand where to write the 0 to make the number show 109 rather than 19.

Teaching Tips

Item 14

Encourage children to check their work by analyzing the patterns in each row and then in each column.

Mathematical Practices

MP7	**Look for and make use of structure.**

Item 15: Children look closely to discern a pattern or structure of a number chart and describe the significance of the pattern.

MP8	**Look for and express regularity in repeated reasoning.**

Item 14: Children use repeated patterns to look for general methods and for shortcuts. They continually evaluate the reasonableness of their intermediate results.

OBJECTIVE
Use numerals and number words to read, count, and write how many.

ESSENTIAL QUESTION
Read aloud the Essential Question. Have children tell what they know about ways to name a number. Tell them that in this lesson they will learn to match numbers and number words.

FLUENCY PRACTICE
Fluency practice is available at **sadlierconnect.com**.

Concept Development

Understand: There are different ways to show numbers

■ Some children may understand that numerals 11 through 19 indicate 10 plus a number 1 through 9, but these number words may require additional practice. Have children compare how eleven through nineteen is similar and different from twenty-one through twenty-nine.

■ Help children identify number words that you say aloud. Make sure children can point to the correct turtle that you name. Ask a volunteer to write the number and number word on the board. Repeat until each child has had a turn or until children demonstrate fluency with the task.

Lesson 12 Read and Write Numbers

Essential Question: How can you use both numbers and words to count and to tell how many?

Words to Know number names

Guided Instruction

In this lesson you will learn how to read and write numbers and number names.

Understand: There are different ways to show numbers

> Becky sees some turtles at the zoo. How many turtles does she see?

Say and write numbers as you count.

Number names are the words you say when you count and tell how many.

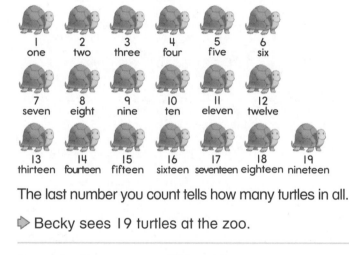

The last number you count tells how many turtles in all.

▷ Becky sees 19 turtles at the zoo.

Say: nineteen   Write: 19

Words to Know

number names: the word name for a number

Example: 26
                     twenty-six ◀— number name

Glossary can be found on pp. 261–272.

Connect: What you know about reading and writing numbers

> What are the number names for numbers from 20 to 30?

The chart shows number names for numbers that end with zero.

Use these number names and the pattern 1, 2, 3, 4, 5, 6, 7, 8, 9, 0 to read and write numbers and number names.

➯ Numbers and number names for numbers from 20 to 30 are shown below.

Number	Number Name
10	ten
20	twenty
30	thirty
40	forty
50	fifty
60	sixty
70	seventy
80	eighty
90	ninety
100	one hundred

20 twenty   21 twenty-one

22 twenty-two   23 twenty-three

24 twenty-four   25 twenty-five

26 twenty-six   27 twenty-seven

28 twenty-eight   29 twenty-nine

30 thirty

Connect: What you know about reading and writing numbers

Use this page to help children strengthen their understanding of writing the number names for numbers from 20 to 30.

■ In kindergarten, children are expected to read and identify quantities to 20. In Grade 1, they think of greater numbers as a number of digits in order to build higher-level number sense.

■ Help children find the patterns involved in writing the name for each ten from twenty to ninety, a hyphen, and the word that names the second digit.

Support English Language Learners

Many number words to ten have homophones that may present comprehension problems for children. Display the words *one, two, four, eight,* and *ten* on an erasable board or on a chart. Ask volunteers to read each word and describe its meaning. Then write the homophones under each word: *won, to* and *too, for,* and *ate.* Explain that these words sound the same as the number words but do not have the same meanings. Discuss what each of the homophones mean. Finally, say one of the words aloud and state whether you are referring to the number word or not. Have children point to the correct spelling of the word. Continue until children demonstrate fluency in recognizing the words that refer to numbers.

Observational Assessment

Use pages 106-107 to assess whether children have an understanding of how to read and write numbers to represent quantities. As the amount of scaffolding drops off, note those children who struggle with writing the number names for quantities greater than twenty.

Guided Practice

1. **Use numbers and number names to tell how many marbles there are.**

Step 1

Count the marbles. Mark each one as you count.

Step 2

Write the number. 39

Write the number name. thirty-nine

➡ There are 39 marbles.

There are thirty-nine marbles.

---

2. Write the missing numbers and number names for numbers from 30 to 39.

30	thirty	31	thirty-one
32	thirty-two	33	thirty-three
34	thirty-four	35	thirty-five
36	thirty-six	37	thirty-seven
38	thirty-eight	39	thirty-nine

Math-to-Social Studies Connection

Addresses The most common way to write a street address is to use numbers, but sometimes number words are used for numbers less than 100 or simply because a person chooses to write an address that way. Have children use number words to write their addresses. If the number is longer than two digits, allow children to use only the last two digits. For children who do not recall their addresses, have them use the school's address.

Lesson 12

Guided Practice

3. Write the number for fifty-seven.

Step 1

Write the number for the
first part of the number name.   **fifty**-seven   50

Step 2

Write the number for the
second part of the number name.   fifty-**seven**   7

Step 3

Count on 7 from 50.

Write the number. 57

ꙮ Think•Pair•Share

MP6 **4.** Sam sees 41 animals at the zoo.
Nan sees 3 more animals than Sam.
What is the number name for the number
of animals that Nan sees? Tell how you know.

_____forty-four_____

Answers may vary. Possible answer: I know that Sam sees 41.
The 3 numbers after 41 are 42, 43, and 44. So Nan sees 44.
The number name for 40 is forty. The number name for 4 is
four. So the number name for 44 is forty-four.

ꙮ Think•Pair•Share

Peer Collaboration Have pairs of
children explain their calculations and
number words to one another. Prompt
the discussions with questions such as:

- *How did you find the number that is
  3 more than 41?*

- *What number does the first part of
  that number name stand for?*

- *What number does the second part
  of that number name stand for?*

Some children may solve the problem
accurately but struggle to explain or
justify their work. Encourage them
to share the steps they used or the
shortcuts they were able to take by
using a strategy such as mental math.

Return to the Essential Question

Reread the Lesson 12 Essential Question
on page 104: *How can you use both
numbers and words to count and to tell
how many?*

Tell children to think about what
they learned in this lesson to answer
this question.
(Possible responses: When I count aloud,
I say the number words but think of the
numbers. I can count a group of objects
and show the amount using a number or
a number word.)

Mathematical Practices

Mathematical Practice Standards underline the teaching and
understanding of all concepts and skills presented. The emphasis of
specific practices is noted throughout the guided and independent practice
of this lesson.

MP6	**Attend to precision.**

Item 4: Children calculate accurately and efficiently, expressing number
word answers with a degree of precision and attention to details.

Independent Practice

Concept Application

Children may work independently on these pages in the classroom or at home. They may refer to the first four pages of the lesson to revisit the instruction or to see a worked-out example.

Common Errors and **Teaching Tips** may help you support learning either in the classroom or as a follow-up for work done at home.

Teaching Tips

Items 1-3

If children struggle to count the objects, suggest that they mark each number as they count. If they continue to have difficulty, ask them to say aloud the numbers as they count so that you can listen for skipped or repeated numbers.

Independent Practice

Count. Write how many.

1.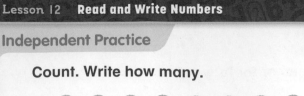

   __17__ fish

2.

   __28__ apples

3.

   __33__ marbles

Talking About Math

Compare Pictures and Text Ask children to describe how the pictures of objects match the numbers that they counted. Some children might notice that the first digit in each number matches the number of rows with 10 objects, and the second digit matches the number of objects in the row that has less than 10 objects. Encourage them to talk about patterns they used to identify the numbers of digits. Ask children to describe how they might have tracked their counting if the objects had been arranged randomly rather than in rows of ten.

Independent Practice

Fill in the blanks to write the number for the number name.

4. thirty-two

The first part of thirty-two is __30__.

Count on __2__ from __30__. Thirty-two is __32__.

5. eighty-six

The first part of eighty-six is __80__.

Count on __6__ from __80__. Eighty-six is __86__.

**Read the number name.
Circle that number.**

6. forty-five	55	54	(45)
7. seventy-six	(76)	70	67
8. ninety	99	(90)	9

Common Errors

Items 6–8

If children selected 54 or 67, they likely transposed the digits. Point out to them that the digits should be in the same order as the number words. Children who circled 9 in problem 8 may have made a similar error transposing digits or simply misread *ninety*.

Teaching Tips

Items 4–5

If children do not understand the format of problems 4 and 5, use page 107 as a guide to help them break apart the steps to fill in the blanks. For children who continue to demonstrate confusion, check their work on problem 4, guide them in necessary revisions, and then allow them to complete problem 5 independently.

Digital Connection

Matching Use an interactive whiteboard to select or enter a column of number words for several two-digit numbers. Then have children drag and drop digits 0 to 9 to build the numbers that represent the given number words. Repeat the activity with other number words if time allows.

Independent Practice

Teaching Tips

Items 9–12
Children must carefully evaluate the value of the digit 3 in each number. The matching problems are somewhat self-correcting because each of the choices have a match.

Item 13
Have children look for a pattern in the order of the number and number name pairs. Some children may choose to write all of the numerals in the left column and then write all of the number words in the right column. Tell children to check their own work by making sure each part of the list is in the correct order and that each number and number word match.

Independent Practice

Draw lines to match the numbers to the number names.

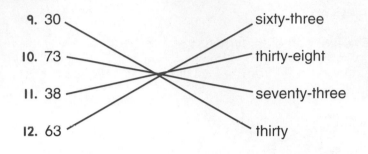

9. 30 — thirty
10. 73 — seventy-three
11. 38 — thirty-eight
12. 63 — sixty-three

13. Write the missing numbers and number names.

97   ninety-seven

_98_   ninety-eight

99   _ninety-nine_

100   one hundred

101   one hundred one

_102_   _one hundred two_

_103_   _one hundred three_

_104_   _one hundred four_

105   _one hundred five_

Math-to-Literature Connection

Number Words in Book Titles Children may be familiar with various storybooks that contain numbers or number names from 1 to 120 in their titles. Select several books from the school or other local library that contain numbered titles and display them for children. Have pairs of children select one of the books and write the number or number name and its match. Encourage them to look for other numbers and number names used in the story.

MORE ONLINE sadlierconnect.com

Lesson 12

Independent Practice

MP1 **14.** I am a number with 2 digits.
The first digit is two more than three.
The second digit is one less than five.
What number am I?

Write the number and the number name.
Explain how you found the number.

number **54**

number name **fifty-four**

Explanations may vary. Possible explanation: I know that
$3 + 2 = 5$. So the first digit is 5. $5 - 1 = 4$. So the second
digit is 4. The number is 54. The number name for 54 is
fifty-four.

MP3 **15.** Julia wants to write some number names
in counting order. She writes this list of
number names:

seventy-eight, seventy-nine, eighty-one,
eighty-two, eighty-three, eighty-four

Is Julia's list correct? Explain why or why not.

No; Explanations may vary. Possible explanation: Julia went
from seventy-nine to eighty-one. The number eighty comes just
after seventy-nine and just before eighty-one.

Teaching Tips

Item 14
Explanations should include children's
thinking processes used to identify
each digit.

Item 15
Encourage children to use strategies to
check each of the given number names,
such as looking for a pattern in the
number of digits or using a count on
strategy. Writing numerals from 78 to
84 may also help them identify whether
they have the same number of number
names as the numbers that they wrote.

Mathematical Practices

MP1	Make sense of problems and persevere in solving them.

Item 14: Children process given clues, constraints, and relationships to
identify and explain a number and its number name.

MP3	Construct viable arguments and critique the reasoning of others.

Item 15: Children analyze a list of number names to recognize whether
the sequence is accurate, identify the error, and justify their solution.

OBJECTIVE
Use drawings and place-value charts to identify two-digit numbers by a number of tens and ones.

ESSENTIAL QUESTION
Focus children on the Essential Question by reading it aloud. Explain that the lesson will help them understand what each digit of a two-digit number represents.

FLUENCY PRACTICE
Fluency practice is available at **sadlierconnect.com**.

Concept Development

Understand: You look at the place of a digit in a number to find its value

■ Build upon children's understanding that 10 ones make 1 ten by using illustrations and concrete objects.

■ Provide additional examples if needed to help children understand how to model tens and ones and record the tens and ones in a place-value chart.

Lesson
13 Understand Place Value: Tens and Ones

Essential Question: How can you use tens and ones to help you understand numbers?

Words to Know
tens
ones
place-value chart

Guided Instruction

In this lesson you will learn about the value of digits in a number.

Understand: You look at the place of a digit in a number to find its value

How many tens and ones are in 15?

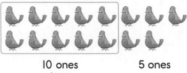

15 ones

Circle a group of 10 ones. 10 ones make 1 ten.

10 ones   5 ones
1 ten

To show how many tens and ones, you can write the number in a place-value chart.

This place-value chart shows 15.

tens	ones
1	5

The 1 in 15 is in the tens place. Its value is 1 ten, or 10.
The 5 in 15 is in the ones place. Its value is 5 ones, or 5.

▷ 15 has 1 ten and 5 ones.

112   Unit 2 ■ Focus on Number and Operations in Base Ten

Words to Know

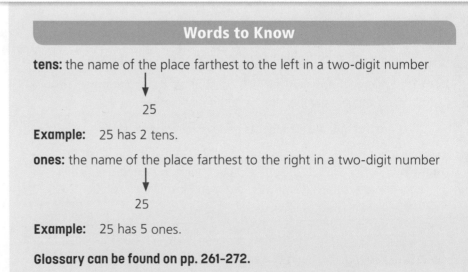

tens: the name of the place farthest to the left in a two-digit number

↓

25

Example: 25 has 2 tens.

ones: the name of the place farthest to the right in a two-digit number

↓

25

Example: 25 has 5 ones.

Glossary can be found on pp. 261–272.

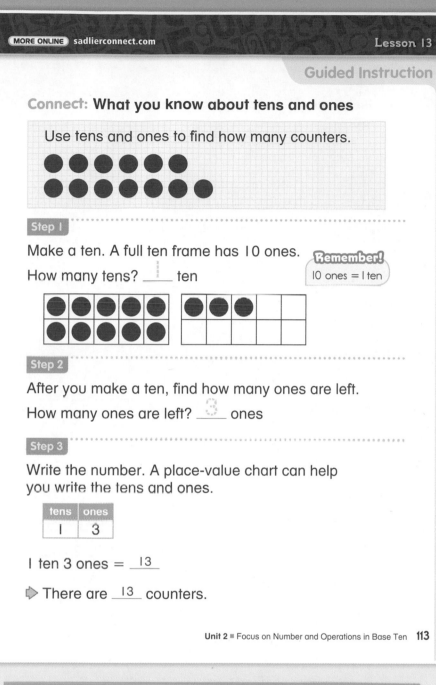

MORE ONLINE sadlierconnect.com

Guided Instruction

Connect: **What you know about tens and ones**

Use tens and ones to find how many counters.

Step 1

Make a ten. A full ten frame has 10 ones.

How many tens? ____ ten

Remember!
10 ones = 1 ten

Step 2

After you make a ten, find how many ones are left.

How many ones are left? ____ ones

Step 3

Write the number. A place-value chart can help you write the tens and ones.

tens	ones
1	3

1 ten 3 ones = ___13___

▷ There are ___13___ counters.

Connect: **What you know about tens and ones** Use this page to help children strengthen their understanding of place value, specifically tens and ones.

■ Children may be able to count and identify that there are 13 counters in the first illustration; however, that skill does not necessarily translate to a functional understanding of the place-value system. Using ten frames provides visual support for the place-value chart.

■ If children do not see the correlation between the group of counters and the counters in the ten frames, have them circle pairs of counters in the first group, matching each pair with a column in the ten frame. Children will see that there are three counters left over, and that these counters can be matched with the three counters in the second ten frame.

■ Have children answer the problem in Step 2, and then record the number in the place-value chart in Step 3. Take a few moments to discuss the similarities and differences between the two models.

Words to Know

place-value chart: a chart that shows the value of each digit of a number

Example:

tens	ones
6	4

64 is 6 tens and 4 ones.

Glossary can be found on pp. 261–272.

Observational Assessment

Use pages 114–115 to assess whether children are able to match models to the numbers that they represent. Observe whether children have difficulty writing the values of ones, tens, and the resulting two-digit number.

Lesson 13   **Understand Place Value: Tens and Ones**

Guided Practice

1. Use place value to tell how many cubes in all.

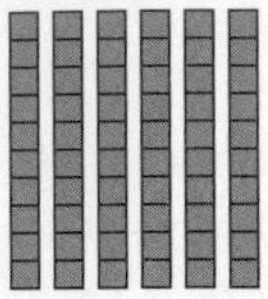

There are 10 cubes in each stack.

Step 1

A stack of cubes can stand for 1 ten.

Count the tens.

There are ___6___ tens.

Count by tens. 10, 20, __30__, __40__, __50__, __60__

6 tens = __60__

Step 2

Count the ones that are left.

There are __0__ ones left.

Step 3

Write the number.

tens	ones
6	0

6 tens 0 ones = __60__

There are __60__ cubes in all.

Support English Language Learners

Make sure children understand the meaning of *place* in *place-value chart*. The word *place* is often used as a noun or as a verb, a language usage that is uncommon in languages other than English. Clarify the difference in usage by pointing out that a place-value chart shows the place, or position, of each digit in a number. To place an object somewhere is to move the object into a specific position.

Lesson 13

Guided Practice

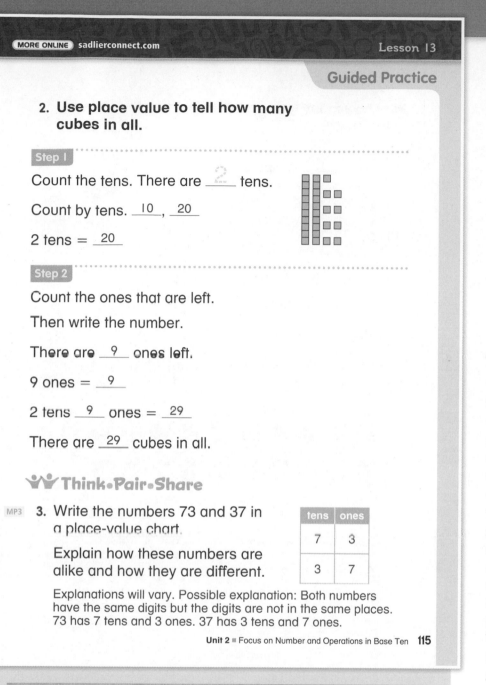

2. **Use place value to tell how many cubes in all.**

Step 1

Count the tens. There are __2__ tens.

Count by tens. __10__ , __20__

2 tens = __20__

Step 2

Count the ones that are left.

Then write the number.

There are __9__ ones left.

9 ones = __9__

2 tens __9__ ones = __29__

There are __29__ cubes in all.

☻ Think•Pair•Share

MP3 3. Write the numbers 73 and 37 in a place-value chart.

Explain how these numbers are alike and how they are different.

tens	ones
7	3
3	7

Explanations will vary. Possible explanation: Both numbers have the same digits but the digits are not in the same places. 73 has 7 tens and 3 ones. 37 has 3 tens and 7 ones.

Unit 2 ■ Focus on Number and Operations in Base Ten **115**

☻ Think•Pair•Share

Peer Collaboration Have pairs of children explain their reasoning processes to each other. Prompt the discussions with questions such as:

- *How did you list the numbers in the place-value chart?*

- *Which number has more tens? Explain how the chart supports your answer.*

- *How do the ones digits compare?*

- *How are the numbers alike?*

Some children may use drawings or physical models to support their reasoning.

Return to the Essential Question

Reread the Lesson 13 Essential Question on page 112: *How can you use tens and ones to help you understand numbers?*

Tell children to think about what they learned in this lesson to answer this question.

(Possible responses: I can use models to show that 10 cubes will make 1 column called a ten. I can count columns to count by tens and use single cubes to count by ones. I can use models or place-value charts to show a number of tens and ones.)

Have children discuss counting strategies and other number concepts that they learned in this lesson.

Mathematical Practices

Mathematical Practice Standards underline the teaching and understanding of all concepts and skills presented. The emphasis of specific practices is noted throughout the guided and independent practice of this lesson.

| MP3 | **Construct viable arguments and critique the reasoning of others.** |

Item 3: Children make conjectures about numbers and build a logical progression of statements to explain the truth of their conjectures.

Concept Application

Children may work independently on these pages in the classroom or at home. They may refer to the first four pages of the lesson to revisit the instruction or to see a worked-out example.

Common Errors and **Teaching Tips** may help you support learning either in the classroom or as a follow-up for work done at home.

Common Errors

Items 1-2

If children answer problems 1 and 2 as 20 and 19, the error was most likely making an incorrect assumption that each whole row shows ten objects. Have children recheck their work, counting each row one object at a time.

Teaching Tips

Item 1

The easiest way to visually organize the art is to circle the first five baseballs in each row. However, children who circle the first row plus one more baseball are also correct. It may be helpful to have children first count to see whether a row contains as many as ten baseballs so they can evaluate how they prefer to circle a group of ten.

Item 2

The rows of bugs contain at least ten objects, so children may find it easiest to circle rows of ten, leaving the last bug in the first row outside of the first circle. As in item 1, circling the bugs in a different way will work as long as children demonstrate that there are 2 tens and 1 one.

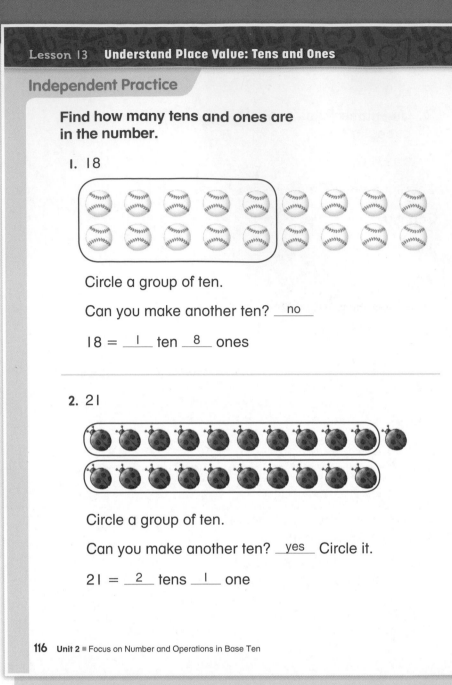

Find how many tens and ones are in the number.

1. 18

Circle a group of ten.

Can you make another ten? __no__

18 = __1__ ten __8__ ones

2. 21

Circle a group of ten.

Can you make another ten? __yes__ Circle it.

21 = __2__ tens __1__ one

Math-to-Drama Connection

Act Out Tens and Ones Tell children that they will act out the last model on the page by standing to represent each ten that a number represents and sitting to represent each one that a number represents. The number of children standing represents the number of tens in a number. The number of children sitting represents the number of ones in a number. Begin by asking children to name the number of children who need to stand. Choose 2 volunteers to stand at the front of the classroom. Then ask how many children need to sit on the floor. Have 1 volunteer sit on the floor. Have children identify the standing and sitting numbers as 2 tens 1 ones, or 21. Continue having children act out other two-digit numbers as time allows.

Find how many counters.

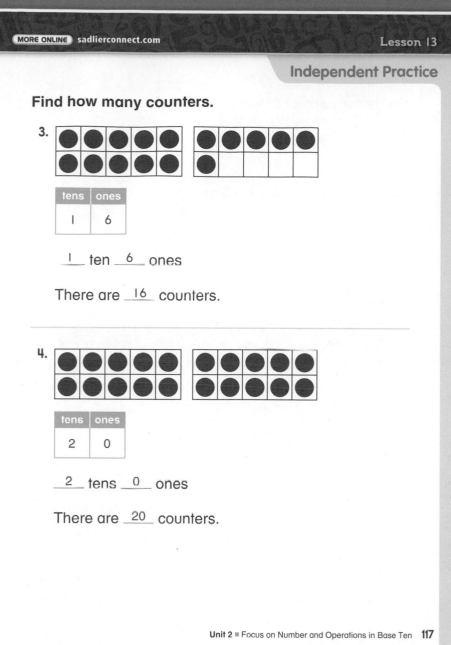

3.

tens	ones
1	6

__1__ ten __6__ ones

There are __16__ counters.

4.

tens	ones
2	0

__2__ tens __0__ ones

There are __20__ counters.

Teaching Tips

Items 3-4

Observe whether children demonstrate an understanding of the relationships between the 10-frames, the place-value charts, the number of tens and ones, and the number of counters in all. For children who struggle with the problems, provide counters and 10-frames for further practice.

Talking About Math

Use Illustrations to Describe a Situation Have children draw two rows of objects that are between 6 and 12 objects in length, not including rows of 10. Then ask children to tell a partner about the objects, count them, and discuss a logical way to draw a circle to make one ten and another circle if they can make another ten. Have children tell the number of objects in all by describing how they made groups of ten, how they counted the ones, and the resulting number of objects.

Independent Practice

Teaching Tips

Items 5-6

Point out that each choice contains the digit 9 but that children must look carefully to identify the value of that digit based on its position in the number. Make sure children can fluently identify the tens place and the ones place in a two-digit number.

Items 7-8

Children are likely to understand the format of these problems after the similar presentations of models in the lesson. If children hesitate to initiate an approach to the problems, offer to let them use connecting cubes to get started.

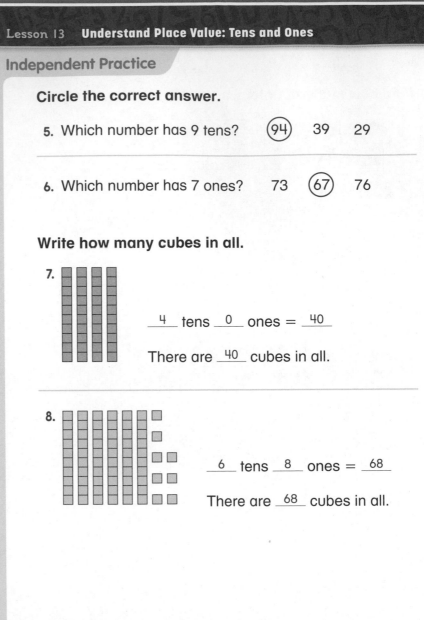

Lesson 13   **Understand Place Value: Tens and Ones**

Independent Practice

Circle the correct answer.

5. Which number has 9 tens?   ⟨94⟩   39   29

6. Which number has 7 ones?   73   ⟨67⟩   76

Write how many cubes in all.

7.

   4 tens 0 ones = 40

There are 40 cubes in all.

8.

   6 tens 8 ones = 68

There are 68 cubes in all.

Digital Connection

Tens Frames Use an interactive whiteboard to select two 10-frames. Have children write a number between 10 and 20 on the board and then drag and drop counters to fill the first frame and keep placing counters in the second frame until it shows the selected number. Have children work together in pairs to explain their work and discuss the number of tens and ones represented.

Lesson 13

Independent Practice

MP1 **9.** I am a 2-digit number with 6 ones.
I have 2 more tens than ones.
What number am I?
Draw a picture and explain how you know.

__86__

Drawings and explanations will vary. Sample explanation:
6 + 2 = 8, so there are 8 tens and 6 ones.
Check children's drawings.

MP1 **10.** I am a 2-digit number.
My tens and ones digits have a sum of 9.
My tens digit is 1 less than my ones digit.
What number am I?
Write the number in the place-value chart.
Explain how you found the number.

__45__

tens	ones
4	5

Explanations will vary. Sample explanation: I found all the sums
of 9. Then I used 4 + 5 = 9 because 4 is 1 less than 5. So there
are 4 tens and 5 ones.

Unit 2 ■ Focus on Number and Operations in Base Ten **119**

Common Errors

Items 9-10

Make sure children did not use the digit 2 in *2-digit number* as part of their calculations. Also check whether children transposed the digits in either answer.

Teaching Tips

Items 9-10

Check children's explanations to make sure they evaluated each clue correctly rather than used a guessing method to solve the problems.

Mathematical Practices	
MP1	**Make sense of problems and persevere in solving them.**

Items 9-10: Children process given clues, constraints, and relationships to identify a number, make a drawing or place-value chart to represent it, and explain their answers.

OBJECTIVE

Use concrete objects, drawings, symbols, and place value to compare numbers and record the comparisons.

ESSENTIAL QUESTION

Read aloud the Essential Question and ask children to tell what they know about comparing numbers. Explain that this lesson will help them understand the symbols they can use to show comparisons.

PREREQUISITE SKILLS

Use Foundational Skills Handbook page 248, *Comparing Numbers,* to help children review how to compare two one-digit numbers.

FLUENCY PRACTICE

Fluency practice is available at **sadlierconnect.com**.

Concept Development

Understand: A number can be greater than, less than, or equal to another number

■ Some children may understand a commonly used analogy for remembering the difference between the greater than and less than symbols—the alligator's mouth looks for the bigger meal. Explain that the smaller side of the symbol points to the smaller (lesser) number and the larger (wider, open) side of the symbol is toward the larger (greater) number.

■ Make sure children understand that equal models show the same number of tens and the same number of ones.

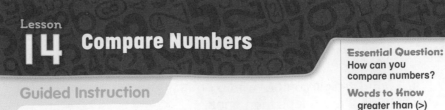

Lesson 14 — Compare Numbers

Essential Question: How can you compare numbers?

Words to Know
greater than (>)
less than (<)
equal to (=)

Guided Instruction

In this lesson you will learn how to compare numbers.

Understand: A number can be greater than, less than, or equal to another number

Compare 30 and 10.

30   10

Look at the number for each group of cubes.

▷ **>** means **greater than.**
30 is greater than 10.
30 > 10

Compare 20 and 40.

20   40

▷ **<** means **less than.**
20 is less than 40.
20 < 40

Compare 12 and 12.

12   12

▷ **=** means **equal to.**
12 is equal to 12.
12 = 12

Words to Know

greater than (>): greater than

Example: 13 is greater than 12

13   >   12

less than (<): less than

Example: 13 is less than 22

13   <   22

Glossary can be found on pp. 261–272.

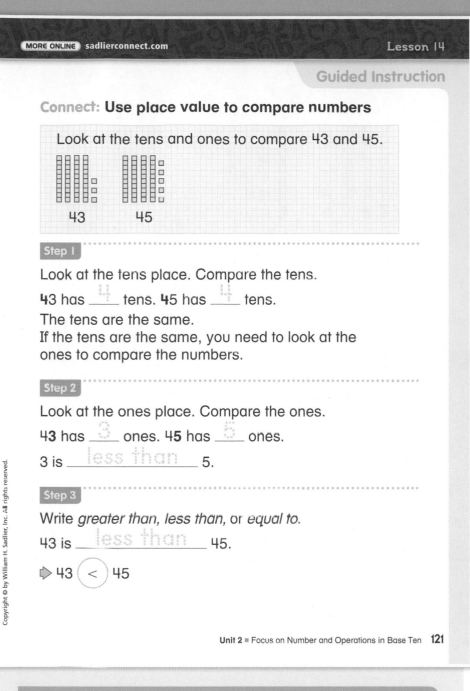

sadlierconnect.com

Lesson 14

Connect: Use place value to compare numbers

Look at the tens and ones to compare 43 and 45.

43   45

Step 1

Look at the tens place. Compare the tens.

43 has ___ tens. 45 has ___ tens.

The tens are the same.

If the tens are the same, you need to look at the ones to compare the numbers.

Step 2

Look at the ones place. Compare the ones.

43 has _3_ ones. 45 has _5_ ones.

3 is ___less than___ 5.

Step 3

Write *greater than*, *less than*, or *equal to*.

43 is ___less than___ 45.

➡ 43 (<) 45

Unit 2 ▪ Focus on Number and Operations in Base Ten **121**

Connect: Use place value to compare numbers Use this page to help children strengthen their understanding of comparing two two-digit numbers.

■ Point out to children that the steps show the comparison of tens before the comparison of ones. In the example shown, this distinction is not important, but it matters when the number of tens is not the same.

■ If needed for clarification, allow children to use connecting cubes or place-value manipulatives to model the numbers and line them up vertically. They can use one-to-one correspondence to match the tens and ones, noting that the tens are the same and that the column of ones in 43 stops before the column of ones in 45

Words to Know

equal to (=): two quantities that have the same value

Example: 1 + 1 = 2

↑

is equal to

Glossary can be found on pp. 261-272.

Guided Practice

Observational Assessment

Use pages 122–123 to assess whether children are able to compare two 2-digit numbers. Observe whether children are able to complete the problems without using a drawing or counting manipulatives. Make note of children who need additional practice with tens and ones models before moving to Independent Practice.

Guided Practice

1. Use place value to compare 32 and 17.

32   17

Step 1

Look at the tens place. How many tens are shown?

32 has ___3___ tens.

17 has ___1___ ten.

Step 2

Compare the tens.

3 is ___greater than___ 1.

Step 3

Compare the numbers 32 and 17.
Write *greater than, less than,* or *equal to.*

32 is ___greater than___ 17.
Write >, <, or = to compare 32 and 17.

32 (>) 17

122 Unit 2 ▪ Focus on Number and Operations in Base Ten

Support English Language Learners

Allow children to have fun with the term *greater* by exploring its homophone. Without any introduction, clues, or hints, display a household cheese grater and ask children to raise their hands if they think they know the name of the object. If available, use a plastic cheese grater rather than a metal one for safety. Call on one of the children to name the object. Write *grater* and *greater* on the board and point out which one means to shave cheese and which one means to compare numbers.

Lesson 14

Guided Practice

2. Use place value to compare 26 and 29.

Step 1

Look at the tens place. Compare the tens.

26 has __2__ tens. 29 has __2__ tens.
The tens are the same.

2 is _____equal to_____ 2.

If the tens are the same, you need to look at the ones to compare the numbers.

Step 2

Look at the ones place. Compare the ones.

26 has __6__ ones. 29 has __9__ ones.

6 is _____less than_____ 9.

Step 3

Write >, <, or = to compare 26 and 29.

26 (<) 29

♛ Think•Pair•Share

MP1

3. I am a number greater than 70.
I am less than 75.
What number could I be? _____
Answers may vary. Possible answers: 71, 72, 73, or 74.

Unit 2 ■ Focus on Number and Operations in Base Ten **123**

♛ Think•Pair•Share

Peer Collaboration As pairs of children discuss their answers and solution methods, prompt the discussions with questions such as:

- *What numbers did you eliminate after you read the first clue?*

- *How does the second clue limit the numbers again?*

- *If you and your partner do not have the same number, can you both be right? Explain why.*

Some children may list all the possible solutions. Point out that the question asks for a possible answer rather than a solitary correct response.

Return to the Essential Question

Reread the Lesson 14 Essential Question on page 120: *How can you compare numbers?*

Tell children to think about what they learned in this lesson to answer this question.
(Possible responses: I can use objects or drawings to model and compare the numbers. I compare the tens first, then the ones.)

Have children share other problem-solving strategies they learned in this lesson.

Mathematical Practices

Mathematical Practice Standards underline the teaching and understanding of all concepts and skills presented. The emphasis of specific practices is noted throughout the guided and independent practice of this lesson.

| MP1 | **Make sense of problems and persevere in solving them.** |

Item 3: Children explain the meaning of the problem and plan how to approach the solution.

Concept Application

Children may work independently on these pages in the classroom or at home. They may refer to the first four pages of the lesson to revisit the instruction or to see a worked-out example.

Common Errors and **Teaching Tips** may help you support learning either in the classroom or as a follow-up for work done at home.

Teaching Tips

Item 1

Most children will see that these numbers and models are equal. Check for deeper understanding by asking whether the models would still show equal amounts if they were rearranged or if some of the tens columns were broken apart.

Items 2–3

Help children think logically about comparing numbers by thinking about a counting sequence. If they count from 1 to 100, the first of the two numbers that they reach is the lesser number.

Children are not expected to use symbols on this page. Have them read their answer sentences aloud and explain how they can verify their answers.

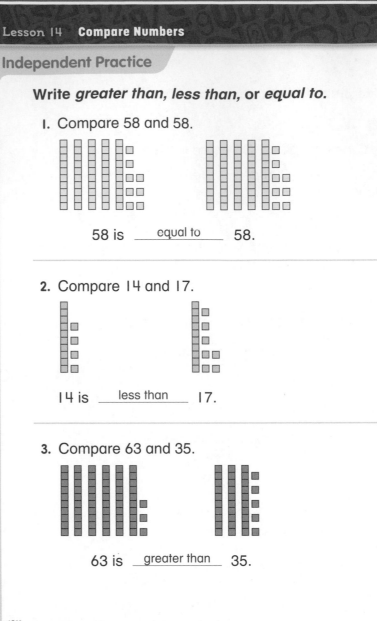

Lesson 14   **Compare Numbers**

Independent Practice

Write *greater than, less than,* or *equal to.*

1. Compare 58 and 58.

   58 is ___equal to___ 58.

2. Compare 14 and 17.

   14 is ___less than___ 17.

3. Compare 63 and 35.

   63 is ___greater than___ 35.

124 Unit 2 ■ Focus on Number and Operations in Base Ten

Math-to-Shopping Connection

Saving for Something Special Have children imagine that they want to buy something special for themselves or for a gift. Have each child write a two-digit number representing the number of dollars they think the item might cost. Then randomly place children in pairs, regardless of the numbers they wrote. Have one child in each pair be the seller and display his or her number as the real price of the desired object. Then have the second child reveal her or his number as if that is the amount of money saved. Tell children to determine whether the buyer has enough money and to write the comparison between the cost and the amount saved.

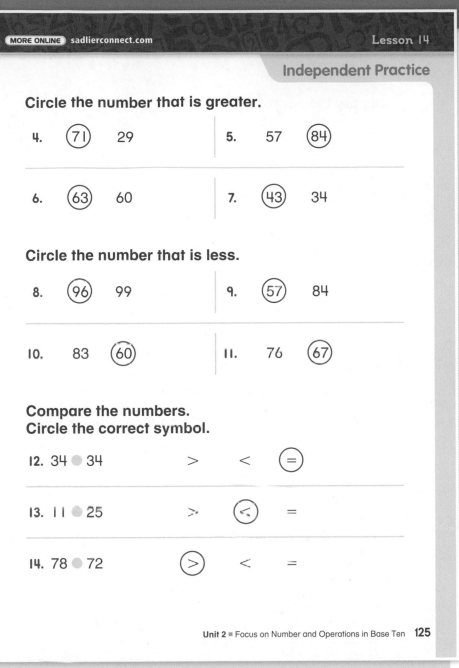

Independent Practice

Circle the number that is greater.

4. (71) 29

5. 57 (84)

6. (63) 60

7. (43) 34

Circle the number that is less.

8. (96) 99

9. (57) 84

10. 83 (60)

11. 76 (67)

**Compare the numbers.
Circle the correct symbol.**

12. 34 ● 34   >   <   (=)

13. 11 ● 25   >   (<)   =

14. 78 ● 72   (>)   <   =

Unit 2 ■ Focus on Number and Operations in Base Ten **125**

Common Errors

Items 13-14

Children may correctly identify the greater or lesser numbers but transpose the meanings of the symbols. Help them find an easy way to readily identify which symbol has which meaning, using their own language. Examples may include the alligator analogy *(an open mouth goes for a bigger bite),* an arrow analogy *(small side points to small number)* or any ideas of their own that they find helpful.

Teaching Tips

Items 4-11

Provide a blank piece of paper for children who need to draw a picture for one or more of these problems. Suggest that the numbers can be quickly illustrated using a straight line for each ten and a dot for each one.

Talking About Math

Describe Another Way Have children work in pairs or small groups to describe ways to compare numbers other than using connecting cubes. Tell each group to draw a picture or write a list to describe their ideas. If children struggle to get started, tell them to think about any counting methods or place-value methods they have used so far. Listen to the discussions for ideas such as using a place-value chart, a number chart, or place-value tens and ones models.

Independent Practice

Common Errors

Items 23–24

If children compare only the first and last digits of each three-digit number, their answers will be incorrect. Have children cover the 1 in the hundreds place of each number and compare the digits that remain. Then make sure children answer all parts of the questions, including a brief explanation in the blank after *because*.

Teaching Tips

Items 15–22

As children write their own comparison symbols, express to them the importance of drawing each symbol clearly. Check a few answers to make sure the answers can be easily identified.

Items 23–24

These independent practice problems extend the comparisons to three-digit numbers. Children may need extra support to know the way to approach the problems, such as telling them that comparisons always begin by looking at digits having the greatest place value.

Independent Practice

Compare the numbers. Write >, <, or =.

15. 72 (=) 72   16. 53 (<) 81

17. 89 (>) 39   18. 30 (<) 40

19. 90 (<) 95   20. 80 (>) 65

21. 41 (>) 38   22. 27 (=) 27

23. Amber has 117 stamps in her album.
Cindy has 109 stamps in her album.
Whose album has the greater number of stamps?

_____Amber_____'s album has the greater number

of stamps because ___117 is greater than 109___.

24. Juan's book has 102 pages.
Kareem's book has 111 pages.
Whose book has the greater number of pages?

_____Kareem_____'s book has the greater number

of pages because ___111 is greater than 102___.

Digital Connection

Compare Random Numbers Set up a random number generator to select two two-digit numbers. Have children use these numbers to compare them, using illustrations, hands-on manipulatives, or a chart or other display. If children work in small groups to make the comparisons, assign each group member a task such as preparing an oral explanation, drawing a picture, writing the comparison using *greater than* or *less than*, or writing the comparison using <, >, or = symbols. If time allows, have children take turns in each role.

Lesson 14

Independent Practice

MP7 **25.** Use each of these digits only once.

Write two 2-digit numbers.

3   5   4   8

____   ____

Answers may vary. Possible answers: 54 and 83.

Compare. Use your numbers to complete.

__ > __

____ < ____

Answers may vary. Possible answers: 83 > 54; 54 < 83.

MP3 **26.** Name three numbers that are less than 40 but greater than 25.

____   ____   ____

Answers may vary. Possible answers: 37   26   30

Write >, <, or = to compare two of your numbers.

____ ◯ ____

Answers may vary. Possible answer: 30 > 26

Unit 2 ■ Focus on Number and Operations in Base Ten **127**

Teaching Tips

Item 25

Make sure children understand that there are many two-digit numbers that can be created from the given digits. Check to be sure that children used each digit only once and that the comparison sentences are true.

Item 26

Children may select any three numbers in the range 26–39. No further parameters to make the problem more difficult are necessary. Even consecutive numbers such as 31, 32, and 33 can be used to write the comparison. The problem does not explicitly state that the same number can be used twice, but it will most likely be assumed. If children write a comparison using an equal sign, the response can be possible only if two of the three numbers are the same.

Mathematical Practices

MP3	Construct viable arguments and critique the reasoning of others.

Item 26: Children analyze clues to identify examples and counterexamples and justify their answers.

MP7	Look for and make use of structure.

Item 25: Children use what they know about the structure of base-ten numerals to identify appropriate numbers and use them to make a comparison.

OBJECTIVE
Use place value to add a two-digit number and a one-digit number or a multiple of 10.

ESSENTIAL QUESTION
After reading aloud the Essential Question, ask children to discuss what they already know about adding, place value, and how they might combine these skills to add two-digit numbers.

FLUENCY PRACTICE
Fluency practice is available at **sadlierconnect.com**.

Concept Development

Understand: You can use models to help you add

■ Be sure children understand that, when adding 2-digit numbers, the ones digits are added first. Note that a place-value chart helps ensure that ones will be added to ones and tens will be added to tens.

Lesson 15 Add Two-Digit Numbers

Essential Question: How can you use tens and ones to add two-digit numbers?

Guided Instruction

In this lesson you will learn how to add two-digit numbers.

Understand: You can use models to help you add

> There are 23 children on the bus. Then 5 more children get on the bus. Now how many children are on the bus?

Add to find how many. $23 + 5 =$ ■

Show 23 and 5 with models.

23   5

2 tens 3 ones   0 tens 5 ones

Show 23 and 5 in a place-value chart.
Add the ones. Then add the tens.

tens	ones
2	3
+	5
2	8

3 ones + 5 ones = 8 ones
2 tens + 0 tens = 2 tens

$23 + 5 = 28$

▷ There are 28 children on the bus.

Support English Language Learners

Children often struggle with the spellings and meanings of *two*, *too*, and *to*, even when their primary language is English. The term *two-digit* numbers may be further complicated by a common emergent-reader error of writing or reading *two* and *toe* the same way. This error may leave children questioning whether the term refers to digits as numbers or digits as toes. Lead children in a brief discussion of what is meant by *two-digit numbers* and allow volunteers to write examples on the board.

Lesson 15

Guided Instruction

Understand: **You can make a ten when you add**

Natalie reads 36 pages. She has 7 more pages to read in the book. How many pages are in Natalie's book?

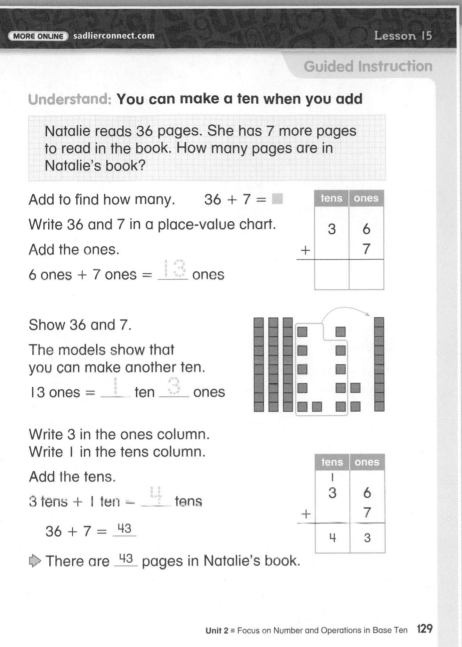

Add to find how many.   36 + 7 = ▨

Write 36 and 7 in a place-value chart.

Add the ones.

6 ones + 7 ones = __13__ ones

tens	ones
3	6
+	7

Show 36 and 7.

The models show that you can make another ten.

13 ones = __1__ ten __3__ ones

Write 3 in the ones column.
Write 1 in the tens column.

Add the tens.

3 tens + 1 ten = __4__ tens

36 + 7 = __43__

tens	ones
1	
3	6
+	7
4	3

▷ There are __43__ pages in Natalie's book.

Unit 2 ■ Focus on Number and Operations in Base Ten **129**

Understand: You can make a ten when you add

■ Use this page to build a concrete understanding of the math algorithm involved when making a ten from 10 ones.

■ Provide 43 connecting cubes to each pair of children. Have children use the cubes to replicate the model shown on this page. Then discuss with children how making a ten created a total of 4 tens and some ones left over.

■ As children work through the final algorithm in the place-value chart, make sure they understand why there is a 1 above the 3 in 36.

■ You may wish to have children count on to find the number that is 7 more than 36 to verify that the result is the same when they use the algorithm.

Math-to-Farming Connection

Farmer's Market Sometimes farmers sell their fruits and vegetables at a farmer's market rather than selling to big stores. Tell children that they will pretend to be farmers who are getting ready for a farmer's market. Provide paper bags and paper cutouts of apples for small groups of children. Have children in each group work together to make as many bags of 10 apples as they can from the materials that you supplied. After each group has completed the task, have children share the number of completed bags, the number of apples that make less than 10 that are left, and the total number of apples counted. Then have each group add 8 more apples to their total. Have them use a place-value chart to record the addends and then write an addition sentence to show the result.

Connect: You can add two-digit numbers Use this page to help children understand how to add a two-digit number and a multiple of 10.

■ Although there is no regrouping involved in the given problem, children should get in the habit of adding the ones first, then adding the tens.

■ If children do not remember how to add zero to a number, remind them that any number plus zero is that number.

Connect: You can add two-digit numbers

Add: 54 + 30 =

You can use models to help you add.

Step 1

Write the numbers in a place-value chart. Add the ones.

4 ones + 0 ones = ____ ones
Write 4 in the ones column.

tens	ones
5	4
+ 3	0
	4

Step 2

Add the tens.

5 tens + 3 tens = ____ tens
Write 8 in the tens column.

54 + 30 = ____

▷ 54 + 30 = 84

tens	ones
5	4
+ 3	0
8	4

Math-to-Sports Connection

Final Scores Provide newspaper sports pages or clippings and ask children to find the final score of a football game. Have children imagine that each team scored 20 more points than their actual final score. Children should use the addition algorithm to find the "new" final score for each team. Provide connecting cubes for children to use if they need to make a ten or want to demonstrate how they found the sum.

Guided Practice

1. $42 + 9 = $ ■

Step 1

Write the numbers in a place-value chart.
Add the ones.

2 ones + 9 ones = __1__ ones

Use models to help you make another ten.

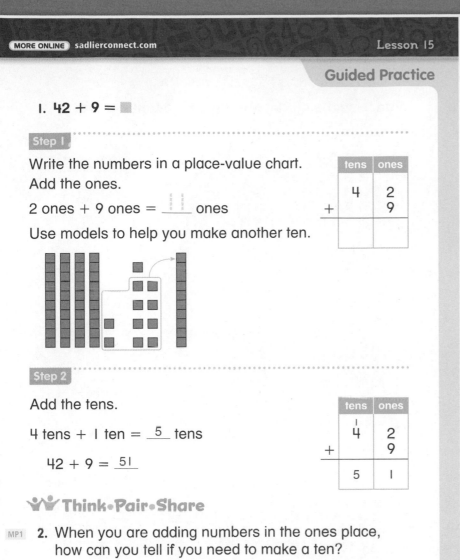

tens	ones
4	2
+	9

Step 2

Add the tens.

4 tens + 1 ten = __5__ tens

$42 + 9 = $ __51__

tens	ones
1 4	2
+	9
5	1

👑 Think•Pair•Share

MP1
2. When you are adding numbers in the ones place, how can you tell if you need to make a ten?

> Answers may vary. Possible answer: You need to make a ten whenever the sum of the ones is greater than 9.

Mathematical Practices

Mathematical Practice Standards underline the teaching and understanding of all concepts and skills presented. The emphasis of specific practices is noted throughout the guided and independent practice of this lesson.

MP1	**Make sense of problems and persevere in solving them.**

Item 2: Children use reasoning to explain a general math conjecture about adding numbers that involve regrouping.

Observational Assessment

Use page 131 to assess whether children are able to add a two-digit number and a one-digit number. Observe whether children show an understanding of the need to list the tens and ones in separate columns and to make a ten when there are more than 9 ones.

👑 Think•Pair•Share

Peer Collaboration Have children think about how they can know when they must make a ten. Prompt peer discussions with questions such as.

- *If you add 3 ones and 6 ones, is it necessary to make a ten? Why not?*

- *What happens when you add 3 ones and 9 ones?*

To summarize, point out that it is important always to add the ones first. When the sum of the ones is a two-digit number, write the ones at the bottom of the ones column and the new ten at the top of the tens column.

Return to the Essential Question

Reread the Lesson 15 Essential Question on page 128: *How can you use tens and ones to add two-digit numbers?*

Tell children to think about what they learned in this lesson to answer this question.

(Possible responses: I need to add the ones first. I can make a ten if I have more than 9 ones. Then I can add the tens.)

Concept Application

Children may work independently on these pages in the classroom or at home. They may refer to the first four pages of the lesson to revisit the instruction or to see a worked-out example.

Common Errors and **Teaching Tips** may help you support learning either in the classroom or as a follow-up for work done at home.

Common Errors

Item 3

Children who identified the sum as 26 either did not regroup the 10 ones, or they forgot to add the regrouped ones to the tens. Help children compare their answer with the addends and use logic to explain why 29 + 7 cannot possibly be 26.

Teaching Tips

Items 1–2

Ask children to explain why they will not make a ten when adding the ones in problems 1 and 2. Make sure they understand why it is not correct to write a small 1 at the top of the tens column of the place-value chart.

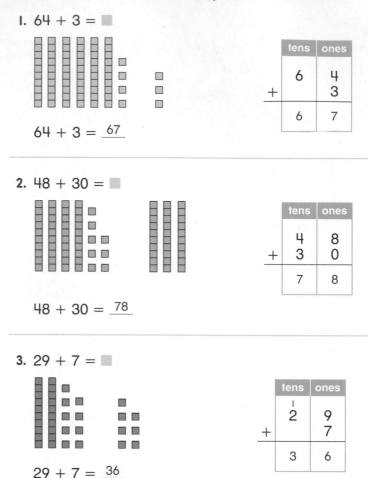

Lesson 15 **Add Two-Digit Numbers**

Independent Practice

Add. Use the model and the place-value chart.

1. 64 + 3 = ▓

64 + 3 = __67__

2. 48 + 30 = ▓

48 + 30 = __78__

3. 29 + 7 = ▓

29 + 7 = __36__

132 Unit 2 ■ Focus on Number and Operations in Base Ten

Copyright © by William H. Sadlier, Inc. All rights reserved.

Talking About Math

Describe Similarities in Different Representations Have children work in small groups or pairs. Ask each group to choose one of the problems on the page to discuss. Have children describe how the addition sentence, the models, and the place-value chart show the same information.

Allow time, if available, for each group of children to share their explanations with the class. Encourage a class discussion about which way of showing the problem children like best or think is most useful.

132 Unit 2 ■ Focus on Number and Operations in Base Ten

Lesson 15

Independent Practice

Add. Use the model and the place-value chart.

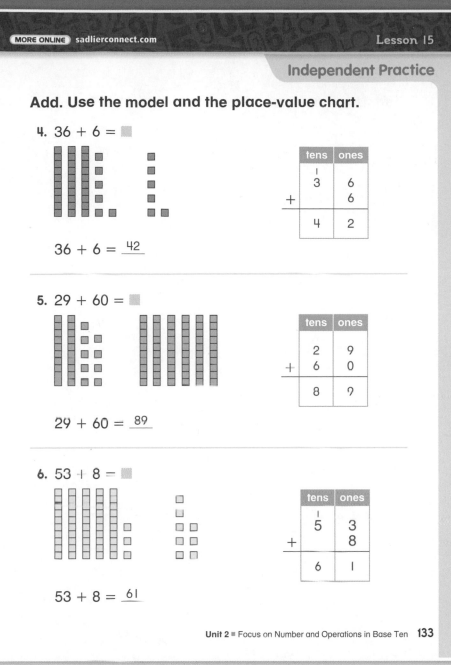

4. 36 + 6 = ■

	tens	ones
	1 3	6
+		6
	4	2

36 + 6 = __42__

5. 29 + 60 = ■

	tens	ones
	2	9
+	6	0
	8	9

29 + 60 = __89__

6. 53 + 8 = ■

	tens	ones
	1 5	3
+		8
	6	1

53 + 8 = __61__

Common Errors

Items 4–5

The second addends in problems 4 and 5 are 6 and 60. If children place the 6 in the wrong column of either place-value chart, their answers might be 96 and 35. Ask questions to help children recognize their errors and then have children make corrections in their charts.

Teaching Tips

Items 4 and 6

Have children circle the new ten in the models. Be sure that they also write an additional ten in the place-value charts.

Items 4–6

Encourage children to use connecting cubes if needed to model each problem.

Digital Connection

Place-Value Blocks Use a whiteboard to build the models shown in problem 4. Have children move the parts of the models to show how to combine the ones to make a ten. Ask children to identify the addition problem and the sum. Then have children model problems 5 and 6 similarly.

Common Errors

Items 8, 9, 12, 15, and 17

Children whose answers for these problems are ten less than the correct answers most likely failed to write the new ten at the top of the tens column in their worked out problems.

Items 8, 9, 12, 13, 15, and 17

Watch for children who mistakenly place the second addend in the tens column, rather than the ones column. Have them use the count-on strategy to check the reasonableness of their answers.

Teaching Tips

Items 7–18

Practice problems on this page include adding a multiple of ten as well as adding a two-digit number and a one-digit number, with and without making a ten to add. Help children recognize that they must read and evaluate each problem carefully to think about what is needed. Encourage children to check their work by using drawings, models, or a count-on strategy.

Items 9–18

Provide extra paper for children to use to write the problems vertically. Tell children to make sure they align the tens with tens and the ones with ones.

Items 7, 10, 11, 14, 16, and 18

Mathematically proficient children may recognize that, when adding a two-digit number to a two-digit multiple of ten, making a ten will never be involved.

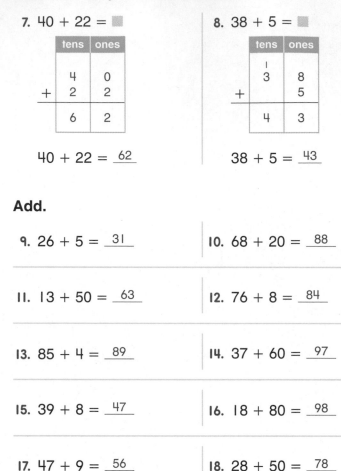

Lesson 15 Add Two-Digit Numbers

Independent Practice

Add. Use the place-value chart.

7. 40 + 22 = ▓

tens	ones
4	0
+ 2	2
6	2

40 + 22 = __62__

8. 38 + 5 = ▓

tens	ones
1 3	8
+	5
4	3

38 + 5 = __43__

Add.

9. 26 + 5 = __31__

10. 68 + 20 = __88__

11. 13 + 50 = __63__

12. 76 + 8 = __84__

13. 85 + 4 = __89__

14. 37 + 60 = __97__

15. 39 + 8 = __47__

16. 18 + 80 = __98__

17. 47 + 9 = __56__

18. 28 + 50 = __78__

Math-to-Career Connection

Firefighting Gear Firefighters train for their jobs by practicing while wearing their gear. This way they learn to move around quickly while wearing heavy uniforms and equipment. A firefighter's coat usually weighs about 15 pounds, and the boots and trousers can weigh as much as 30 pounds. All of the firefighting uniform can weigh between 60 and 70 pounds. This weight does not include what the firefighter might need to carry, such as emergency first aid packs, air masks, and fire hoses. Share facts about firefighters such as these with children and have them add the weight of a coat plus the boots and trousers set, 15 + 30 pounds.

Lesson 15

Independent Practice

MP2 **19.** Write a number between 10 and 50.
Add 9 to your number. Find the sum.
Use models or drawings to help.
Talk about how you added the numbers.

_____ + _____ = _____

Answers will vary. Check children's work.

MP3 **20.** A friend does not understand how to
add two-digit numbers.
Help your friend understand how to
find the sum of 27 + 40.
Use words, drawings, or models to help you.

27 + 40 = _67_

Answers will vary. Check children's work.

Unit 2 ■ Focus on Number and Operations in Base Ten **135**

Teaching Tips

Items 19–20

Have children work in pairs to complete
the problems and discuss their answers.
Make sure they can make logical
explanations, communicate their
reasoning, and analyze the reasoning
of others.

Item 19

As children use models or drawings,
have them group or circle the ones that
they use to make a ten if necessary.

Mathematical Practices	
MP2	**Reason abstractly and quantitatively.**

Item 19: Children make sense of quantities and their relationships to add
and explain their work.

MP3	**Construct viable arguments and critique the reasoning of others.**

Item 20: Children construct arguments by using drawings or
concrete objects.

OBJECTIVE

Use place-value models, tens and ones charts, number charts, and mental math to find 10 more or 10 less than a number.

ESSENTIAL QUESTION

Introduce the lesson focus by asking children how they can find 1 more or 1 less than a number. Then read aloud the Essential Question and have children discuss strategies they might use to find 10 more or 10 less than a number. Some children may be able to describe similar methods for adding or subtracting 1 or 10.

FLUENCY PRACTICE

Fluency practice is available at **sadlierconnect.com**.

Concept Development

Understand: Find 10 more than a number

■ Models and place-value charts can help children visualize what happens when 10 is added to a number. Children can also use the patterns and relationships on a number chart to add 10.

■ Make sure children use number charts that show ten numbers across. Other number charts that children use, such as month calendars, will not be helpful in showing the changes that occur when 10 is added to or subtracted from a number.

■ Children should understand that, unless the tens digit is 9, when 10 is added to a number only the digit in the tens place changes. The digit in the ones place stays the same.

Lesson 16 — Find 10 More or 10 Less

Essential Question: How can you find 10 more or 10 less than a number?

Guided Instruction

In this lesson you will learn how to find 10 more or 10 less than a number.

Understand: Find 10 more than a number

> Gina has 63 beads. She needs 10 more beads to make a bracelet. How many beads does Gina need to make a bracelet?

What number is 10 more than 63?

Remember!
10 ones = 1 ten

63 = 6 tens 3 ones   To find 10 more, add 1 ten.

 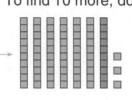

6 tens + 1 ten = 7 tens
7 tens 3 ones = 73
73 is 10 more than 63.

You can use a place-value chart to find 10 more. Look at the tens digit. 10 more is 1 more ten. The ones digit does not change.

73 is 10 more than 63.

tens	ones
6	3

tens	ones
7	3

▷ Gina needs 73 beads to make a bracelet.

Support English Language Learners

English language learners may be confused because the words *more* and *fewer* have meanings that are similar to the meanings of *greater* and *less*. The words *more* and *fewer* are used when groups of things are being compared. Numbers are usually described as being *greater* or *less* than one another, but the words *more* and *fewer* are also often used when numbers are being compared.

Lesson 16

Guided Instruction

Understand: Find 10 less than a number

Gina has 63 beads.
Mark has 10 fewer beads than Gina.
How many beads does Mark have?

What number is 10 less than 63?

63 = 6 tens 3 ones   To find 10 fewer, take away 1 ten.

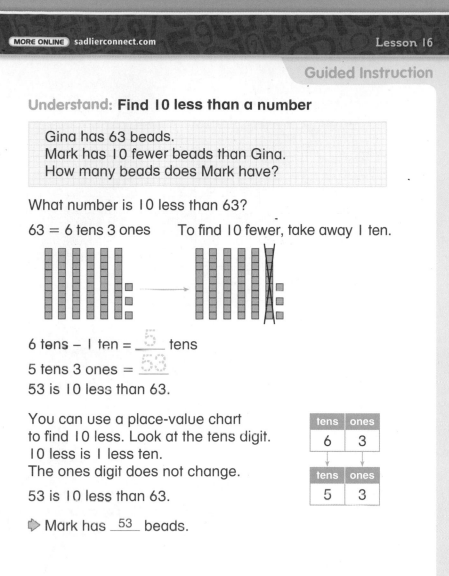

6 tens – 1 ten = __5__ tens

5 tens 3 ones = __53__

53 is 10 less than 63.

You can use a place-value chart
to find 10 less. Look at the tens digit.
10 less is 1 less ten.
The ones digit does not change.

53 is 10 less than 63.

tens	ones
6	3

tens	ones
5	3

▷ Mark has __53__ beads.

Understand: Find 10 less than a number

■ Explain to children that *10 fewer*, *take away 1 ten*, and *10 less than* are ways to describe what happens when subtracting 10 from a number.

■ Write a vertical subtraction on the board to represent the sample problem. Ask children to describe what they have already learned about adding the ones when one of the addends ends with zero. Children should be able to explain that adding zero to a number of ones does not change the number. Point out that in the same way, subtracting zero does not change the number.

■ If necessary, provide connecting cubes for children to use in acting out the problem.

Math-to-Art Connection

Handprints Provide finger paints or other non-toxic art paints and large pieces of art paper for the activity. Have each child make two handprints on a piece of art paper, placing the right and left hands side by side to show 10 fingers in all. If paints are not available, have children draw or trace two hands on art paper. Also prepare smaller pieces of art paper that show a number of fingerprints to represent numbers 1 to 9. Use children's art to display a number of tens on a wall and one of the fingerprint papers to model a two-digit number. Have children identify the number that is modeled, using the handprints as the number of tens and the fingerprints as the number of ones.

Connect: Use patterns on a number chart to find 10 more or 10 less than a number Use this page to help children understand that using a number chart can help them easily identify 10 more and 10 less.

■ Make sure children understand that a number chart shows ten numbers in each row. Have them look at the columns of numbers and explain the patterns that they observe, such as the ones digits remaining the same from the top to the bottom of each column.

■ Children who are proficient in counting patterns may be able to identify consecutive numbers from the top to the bottom of a column as showing *10 more*.

■ Provide additional examples of finding 10 more or 10 less on the number chart if children demonstrate a need for further practice before they go on to the Guided Practice page.

Lesson 16   Find 10 More or 10 Less

Guided Instruction

Connect: Use patterns on a number chart to find 10 more or 10 less than a number

What is 10 more and 10 less than 37?

1	2	3	4	5	6	7	8	9	10
11	12	13	14	15	16	17	18	19	20
21	22	23	24	25	26	27	28	29	30
31	32	33	34	35	36	37	38	39	40
41	42	43	44	45	46	47	48	49	50
51	52	53	54	55	56	57	58	59	60
61	62	63	64	65	66	67	68	69	70

Step 1

Find 37 on the chart. Circle it.
To find the number that is 10 more, find the number below it.

__47__ is below 37.

So 10 more than 37 is __47__.

Remember!
When you look at each column, the number below any number is 10 more than the number.

Step 2

To find the number that is 10 less, find the number above 37.

__27__ is above 37.

So 10 less than 37 is __27__.

▷ __47__ is 10 more than 37. __27__ is 10 less than 37.

Math-to-Camping Connection

Ice Chests of Water Have children pretend that they are going on a camping trip and need to carry water for all of the campers. Tell children that a large ice chest will hold 48 bottles of water, but small ice chests only hold 10 bottles of water each. Have children work together in small groups to make up a story about how many bottles of water they can take in a large and a small ice chest. Next have them discuss how many bottles of water they have if they only take a large ice chest and drink 10 bottles of water.

Lesson 16

Guided Practice

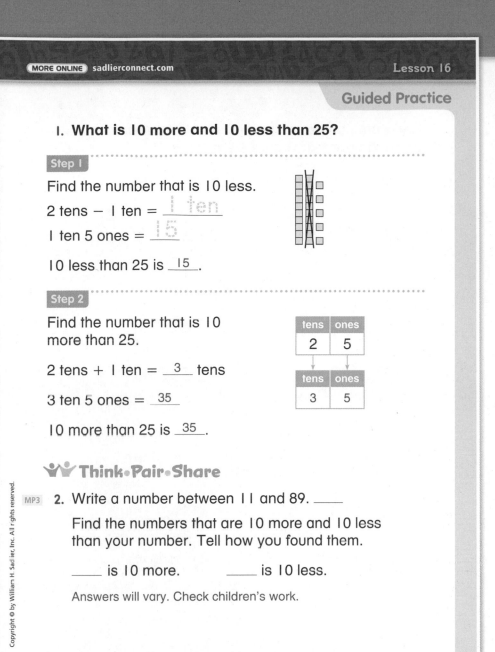

1. **What is 10 more and 10 less than 25?**

Step 1

Find the number that is 10 less.

2 tens − 1 ten = __1 ten__

1 ten 5 ones = __15__

10 less than 25 is __15__.

Step 2

Find the number that is 10 more than 25.

2 tens + 1 ten = __3__ tens

3 ten 5 ones = __35__

10 more than 25 is __35__.

tens	ones
2	5

tens	ones
3	5

👑 Think•Pair•Share

MP3 2. Write a number between 11 and 89. ____

Find the numbers that are 10 more and 10 less than your number. Tell how you found them.

____ is 10 more.   ____ is 10 less.

Answers will vary. Check children's work.

Unit 2 ■ Focus on Number and Operations in Base Ten **139**

Mathematical Practices

Mathematical Practice Standards underline the teaching and understanding of all concepts and skills presented. The emphasis of specific practices is noted throughout the guided and independent practice of this lesson.

MP3	**Construct viable arguments and critique the reasoning of others.**

Item 2: Children justify their conclusions, communicate them to others, and respond to the arguments of others.

Observational Assessment

Use page 139 to assess whether children are able to readily identify numbers that are 10 more and 10 less. Observe whether children need the support of models and charts or if they begin to demonstrate that they can use mental math to add or subtract one ten. Make note of children who seem to need additional practice using hands-on models.

👑 Think•Pair•Share

Peer Collaboration Have children explain how they solved each part of the problem. Prompt peer discussions with questions such as:

- *How did you choose a starting number? Is there more than one choice?*

- *What strategy did you use to find 10 more? 10 less?*

- *How can a place-value chart show that 10 more is the same as adding 1 ten?*

Allow volunteers to share their solution strategies with the class, showing whether they used drawings, models, or charts. If children used mental math, encourage them to explain how they did so.

Return to the Essential Question

Reread the Lesson 16 Essential Question on page 136: *How can you find 10 more or 10 less than a number?*

Tell children to think about what they learned in this lesson to answer this question.

(Possible responses: I can add or take away a tens model. I can add 1 ten to or subtract 1 ten from the starting number. When the ones digit is less than 9, I can add 10 by keeping the ones the same and just changing the number of tens.)

Concept Application

Children may work independently on these pages in the classroom or at home. They may refer to the first four pages of the lesson to revisit the instruction or to see a worked-out example.

Common Errors and **Teaching Tips** may help you support learning either in the classroom or as a follow-up for work done at home.

Common Errors

Item 5

If children incorrectly assume that every answer on the page must be a two-digit number, they may subtract 1 rather than 1 ten from 17. Help them understand that 1 ten take away 1 ten equals 0 tens, but that the 0 does not need to be written in the answer.

Teaching Tips

Item 1

Some children may recognize that adding 10 to a multiple of 10 is similar to counting by tens.

Item 4

Make sure children understand that adding 10 to a one-digit number is done the same way as adding 10 to a two-digit number. In a one-digit number, the number of tens is zero, so zero tens plus 1 ten equals 1 ten.

Read the number in the place-value chart. Write the number that is 10 more.

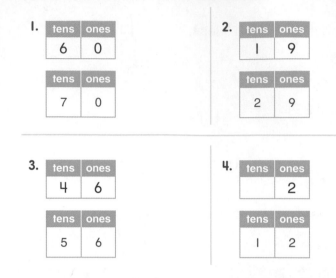

Read the number in the place-value chart. Write the number that is 10 less.

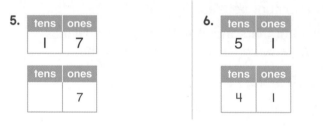

Talking About Math

Ask and Answer Questions Arrange children into small groups to create one math story that involves 10 more and one math story that involves 10 less. Have them prepare a story to tell to the class and ask questions about the number in all or the number left. Allow time for each group to share their questions and for the rest of the class to answer them.

Lesson 16

Independent Practice

Read the number. Write the number that is 10 more and 10 less. Draw models to check your answer.

7. 24

   10 more than 24 is ___34___ .   Check children's models.

   10 less than 24 is ___14___ .

8. 53

   10 more than 53 is ___63___ .

   10 less than 53 is ___43___ .

9. 87

   10 more than 87 is ___97___ .

   10 less than 87 is ___77___ .

10. 18

   10 more than 18 is ___28___ .

   10 less than 18 is ___8___ .

Unit 2 ■ Focus on Number and Operations in Base Ten **141**

Common Errors

Items 7-10

Children who transpose the meanings of *10 more* and *10 less* may write their answers in the wrong blanks. If so, review their answers to problem 7. Have them make the necessary changes, and then tell them to check their other answers again.

Children who write numbers that are *1 more* and *1 less* may benefit from further instruction in how to use tens and ones models.

Teaching Tips

Items 7-10

Point out to children that their drawings do not need to be as detailed as the illustrated models in the lesson. Show them how to draw a line to represent each ten and a dot or small square to represent each one.

Item 10

Be sure that children understand that not every answer must be a two-digit number.

Digital Connection

How-to Videos Use an online search engine to identify available videos that teach and practice adding 10 to and subtracting 10 from a two-digit number. Review these and make a list of the resources that best meet the children's needs.

Teaching Tips

Items 11–12

If children demonstrate confusion about how to approach problem 11, have them use a larger number chart, mask off the part they do not need, and find the missing numbers. Then ask children to try problem 12 without the use of a larger chart, using analysis of the number relationships rather than simply locating numbers.

Items 13–14

Children should be able to identify problem 13 as an addition situation and problem 14 as a subtraction situation. If children seem to hesitate, make sure they can read the problems or provide assistance by reading each problem aloud.

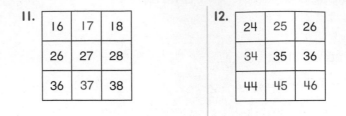

Independent Practice

**Each puzzle below is part of a number chart.
Fill in the missing numbers.**

11.

16	17	18
26	27	28
36	37	38

12.

24	25	26
34	35	36
44	45	46

13. Bonnie's toy chest has 23 toys in it.
The toy chest has room for 10 more toys.
How many toys can fit in Bonnie's toy chest?

___33___ toys can fit in Bonnie's toy chest.

14. Rudy wanted to bring 24 peaches to a party.
When he opened the bag, he found he had
10 fewer peaches than he thought. How many
peaches did he find in the bag?

Rudy found ___14___ peaches in the bag.

Math-to-Literature Connection

Math Storybooks Search online bookstores to gather titles of math storybooks that involve addition and subtraction. Read the synopses of books to identify several that involve two-digit counting or operations. Then look for those books in the school library or other local library and, after reviewing them, provide several of them for children to read and explore. Select one of the books to read aloud to the class, completing the calculations together throughout the story.

Lesson 16

Independent Practice

MP7 **15.** Meg wrote a mystery number.
She gave this clue:
69 is 10 more than my number.
What is her mystery number?
What is 10 less than her number?
Tell how you found her mystery number.

Mystery number: __59__

__49__ is 10 less than her mystery number.

Answers will vary. Check children's work.

MP8 **16.** Fill in the missing numbers on this
number chart puzzle piece. Talk about
how you found the missing numbers.

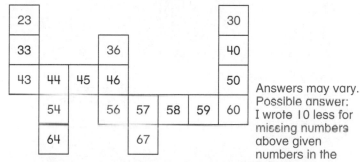

Answers may vary.
Possible answer:
I wrote 10 less for
missing numbers
above given
numbers in the
puzzle and 10 more for missing numbers below given
numbers. I wrote 1 less for missing numbers to the left of
given numbers and 1 more for missing numbers to the right
of given numbers.

Unit 2 ■ Focus on Number and Operations in Base Ten **143**

Common Errors

Item 15
Children may use incorrect reasoning
to identify 79 as the mystery number,
assuming 69 *and* 10 more rather
interpreting the given information as
$69 = \blacksquare + 10$. Help children read the
clues again and identify the error.
Children's explanations of how to find
the mystery number may vary, but
the numbers in the blanks should be
59 and 49.

Teaching Tips

Item 16
Some of the missing numbers can be
identified by adding or subtracting 1,
some can be identified by adding or
subtracting 1 ten, and some of them can
be verified by doing both, depending
on whether they are part of the same
row or same column. Be sure children
understand that the puzzle is part of a
number chart, so the patterns of rows
and columns will be the same as on a
whole number chart that starts at 1 and
has rows of 10 numbers each.

Mathematical Practices	
MP7	**Look for and make use of structure.**

Item 15: Children look closely to discern a pattern and to analyze the
structure of the clue.

MP8	**Look for and express regularity in repeated reasoning.**

Item 16: Children notice if calculation patterns are repeated and look for
general methods and shortcuts.

OBJECTIVE

Use models, place-value charts, and number charts to subtract a multiple of 10 from a multiple of 10.

ESSENTIAL QUESTION

Focus children on the Essential Question by reading it aloud and have children share their answers. Point out that the previous lesson added and subtracted 10 from any two-digit number, but this lesson will focus on two-digit numbers that have 0 in the ones place.

FLUENCY PRACTICE

Fluency practice is available at **sadlierconnect.com**.

Concept Development

Understand: Use place-value models and a place-value chart to help you subtract tens from tens

■ Demonstrate for children what they already know about subtracting one-digit numbers. Use cubes to show that 4 − 1 = 3. Help children apply prior knowledge to this lesson by a demonstration using 10 cubes in each of 4 bags. Ask a volunteer to hold up each bag. Have 1 volunteer turn around to model 4 bags minus 1 bag, pointing out that there are 3 bags left. Help children make the transition to tens by focusing on 10 cubes in each bag. Write on the board 40 − 10 = 30, pointing out that 4 tens minus 1 ten equals 3 tens.

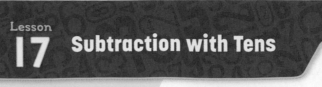

Lesson 17 Subtraction with Tens

Essential Question: How can you subtract tens from tens?

Guided Instruction

In this lesson you will learn how to subtract tens from tens.

Understand: Use place-value models and a place-value chart to help you subtract tens from tens

> A clown wants to blow up 40 balloons. He blows up 10 balloons. How many more balloons does he need to blow up?

Subtract to find how many more.   40 − 10 = ■

Use place-value models.

Remember!
10 ones = 1 ten

40 = 4 tens   Take away 1 ten.

4 tens − 1 ten = 3 tens
3 tens = 30

Write the subtraction in a place-value chart.

40 − 10 = 30

	tens	ones
	4	0
−	1	0
	3	0

▷ The clown needs to blow up 30 more balloons.

Support English Language Learners

Some English language learners have difficulty associating different ways of naming multiples of 10. Explain that people can be named different ways: their first names, their last names, or their first and last names together. Next, tell children that in mathematics, numbers can be named in different ways. For example, five tens can also be named *fifty*. Use the sentence frame and say *I can name (multiple of 10) as _____*. Model different ways to say and write names for the number, having children repeat you. Then, give children different multiples of 10 and ask them to say and write different ways to name the number.

Lesson 17

Guided Instruction

Connect: Use what you know about place value and subtraction facts

Paul has 50 pencils. He gives 30 pencils to Marla. How many pencils does Paul have left?

Subtract to find how many are left. $50 - 30 =$ ▦

Step 1

Think about how many tens are in each number.

$50 = \underline{5}$ tens

$30 = \underline{3}$ tens

Step 2

Think of a subtraction fact that uses the tens digit of each number.

$5 - 3 = \underline{2}$

Step 3

Subtract the tens.
Write the tens as two-digit numbers.

5 tens − 3 tens = $\underline{2}$ tens

50   −   30   = $\underline{20}$

➡ Paul has $\underline{20}$ pencils left.

Unit 2 ■ Focus on Number and Operations in Base Ten **145**

Connect: Use what you know about place value and subtraction facts Use this page to help children strengthen their understanding of subtracting multiples of 10 from multiples of 10.

■ Use drawings or connecting cubes to demonstrate how subtracting 5 ones minus 3 ones is similar to subtracting 5 tens minus 3 tens. Ask volunteers to describe the similarities in their own words.

■ Be sure children can fluently express a number of tens as a two-digit number, as well as expressing a multiple of ten as a number of tens.

■ Provide connecting cubes for children to act out the problem if needed.

■ Proficient children may recognize that they can also apply a strategy that they learned previously, *use a related fact.* For example, if they know that $2 + 3 = 5$, they can reason that 2 tens + 3 tens = 5 tens and that $20 + 30 = 50$ and use this reasoning to solve the subtraction example on page 145.

Math-to-Games Connection

Subtracting Tens Prepare sets of nine index cards. Each of the nine cards will show a different multiple of 10 from 10 to 90. Whether playing in pairs, teams, or as a whole class, provide each group with two sets of prepared index cards. After mixing the two sets together, place them face down and have children draw two cards. Children will use the two cards to write an equation to find the difference between the greater and lesser multiples of 10. If children find the correct difference, lay those two index cards aside, draw two new cards, and find the next difference. If children do not find the correct difference, have them return the cards to the draw pile, draw two new cards, and find the next difference. Have children continue until all cards have been used.

Guided Practice

Observational Assessment

Use pages 146–147 to assess whether children are able to use strategies and patterns to solve problems. Observe whether areas of difficulties seem to indicate problems using a number chart, understanding patterns, recognizing relationships between names of numbers, or applying place-value concepts. Tailor additional practice to one of these specific skills, using models or place-value charts as needed.

Guided Practice

1. Use the patterns in the chart to help you subtract: $80 - 20 = $ ■.

Remember!
Every number on the chart is 10 less than the number just below it.

Step 1

Find 80 on the chart. Circle it.

1	2	3	4	5	6	7	8	9	10
11	12	13	14	15	16	17	18	19	20
21	22	23	24	25	26	27	28	29	30
31	32	33	34	35	36	37	38	39	40
41	42	43	44	45	46	47	48	49	50
51	52	53	54	55	56	57	58	59	60
61	62	63	64	65	66	67	68	69	70
71	72	73	74	75	76	77	78	79	80
81	82	83	84	85	86	87	88	89	90
91	92	93	94	95	96	97	98	99	100

Step 2

To subtract 20, think: $20 = \underline{2}$ tens

Every time you move up a number in a column, you subtract 10.

To subtract 20, you have to move up $\underline{2}$ numbers on the hundred chart.

Start at 80. Move up two numbers.

$\underline{70}$ is 10 less than 80, so $\underline{60}$ is 20 less than 80.

$80 - 20 = \underline{60}$

146 Unit 2 ■ Focus on Number and Operations in Base Ten

Math-to-Money Connection

Budgets Create a list of items with prices that are rounded to the nearest ten dollars. Give each child 9 ten-dollar bills in play money. Have the children make a list of items they will buy with their play money and how much play money they have left. Pair children who choose different items to purchase. Have them discuss their reasoning for purchasing the items on their list.

Lesson 17

Guided Practice

2. $90 - 50 = $ ▪

Step 1

Think about how many tens are in each number.

$90 = \underline{9}$ tens $50 = \underline{5}$ tens

Step 2

Write a subtraction fact using the tens digits in 90 and 50. Use it to solve the problem.

$9 - 5 = \underline{4}$

$90 - 50 = \underline{40}$

👑 Think•Pair•Share

MP7   **3.** Choose one of these numbers: 50, 60, 70, 80, 90. Subtract 40 from that number.

_____ – 40 = _____

Choose a different number from the list. Subtract 40 from that number.

_____ – 40 = _____

Talk about how the subtractions are alike and how they are different. **Answers may vary. Possible answer: The number being subtracted was the same. All the numbers are tens. I was always subtracting tens from tens. The numbers that I was subtracting from were different, so the answers were different. The answer was a greater number when the number I subtracted from was greater.**

Unit 2 ▪ Focus on Number and Operations in Base Ten **147**

👑 Think•Pair•Share

Peer Collaboration Have children explain subtracting ten from a number. Prompt peer discussions with questions such as:

- *How is subtracting 90 – 40 similar to subtracting 9 – 4?*

- *How is subtracting 90 – 40 similar to subtracting 80 – 40?*

- *Will the result of subtracting 80 – 40 be greater than or less than the result of subtracting 90 – 40? How do you know?*

Make sure children are able to summarize how to subtract 9 ones – 5 ones and how to subtract 9 tens – 5 tens. If children know that 4 tens equals 40, they can use that knowledge to write any number of tens up to and including 9 tens as a two-digit number.

Return to the Essential Question

Reread the Lesson 17 Essential Question on page 144: *How can you subtract tens from tens?*

Tell children to think about what they learned in this lesson to answer this question.

(Possible responses: I can use a number chart, models of tens and ones, place-value charts, or mental math to subtract tens from tens.)

Mathematical Practices

Mathematical Practice Standards underline the teaching and understanding of all concepts and skills presented. The emphasis of specific practices is noted throughout the guided and independent practice of this lesson.

MP7	**Look for and make use of structure.**

Item 3: Children look for patterns and relationships as they subtract.

Independent Practice

Concept Application

Children may work independently on these pages in the classroom or at home. They may refer to the first four pages of the lesson to revisit the instruction or to see a worked-out example.

Common Errors and **Teaching Tips** may help you support learning either in the classroom or as a follow-up for work done at home.

Common Errors

Items 1–2

Some children may write two-digit numbers in the first answer row of each of these problems. If so, emphasize that 50 tens is a much greater number than either 5 tens or 50, which is the same as 50 ones.

Teaching Tips

Items 1–2

Provide models or drawing paper for children if needed.

Items 3–5

Children have seen this problem format in each lesson of the unit. Utilize peer tutoring if needed to have one child explain the format to a child who appears to need help understanding the directions.

Independent Practice

Use the models to help you subtract.

1. 50 − 10 = ■

   ___5___ tens − ___1___ ten = ___4___ tens

   50 − 10 = ___40___

2. 70 − 40 = ■

   ___7___ tens − ___4___ tens = ___3___ tens

   70 − 40 = ___30___

Circle the correct answer.

3. 40 − 20 = ■   30   (20)   10

4. 90 − 40 = ■   30   40   (50)

5. 80 − 50 = ■   (30)   20   10

Talking About Math

Math in Storybooks Have children tell about any math storybooks they have read or seen that involve tens. Ask children to identify the main topic of the book, or what the book was mostly about. Encourage children to describe details such as how the tens came up in the story, what types of characters there were, and whether there were math problems included in the book.

Lesson 17

Independent Practice

Subtract.

6. $60 - 60 = \underline{0}$

7. $90 - 70 = \underline{20}$

8. $40 - 30 = \underline{10}$

9. $80 - 30 = \underline{50}$

10. $70 - 40 = \underline{30}$

11. $60 - 40 = \underline{20}$

12. $70 - 70 = \underline{0}$

13. $80 - 20 = \underline{60}$

14. $90 - 80 = \underline{10}$

15. $70 - 20 = \underline{50}$

Unit 2 ■ Focus on Number and Operations in Base Ten **149**

Common Errors

Item 8
If children write 70 as the solution to problem 8, provide a hint that all of the problems on the page represent subtraction rather than addition.

Teaching Tips

Items 6 and 12
Some children may need a reminder that any number minus itself involves a specific subtraction property. Children are not expected to name the property, but they should be able to explain why the answer to problems 6 and 12 must be the same.

Items 6-15
Point out to children that the answers to all of the problems should be numbers only, not a one-digit number followed by the word *tens*. This is because the expected answers typically have the same format as the numbers that are given. However, if children answer with a single digit and *tens*, the answer is not necessarily incorrect. For example, if children write 2 tens as the answer to problem 7, they are technically correct but they also should be able to explain that 2 tens equals 20.

Digital Connection

Patterns Activities Use an Internet search engine to look for math patterns activities that involve numbers or objects. After reviewing the activities, make a list of Web sites for children to visit to practice different types of patterns. After children have become familiar with some of these activities, have the class discuss how patterns of tens, other number patterns, and object patterns are alike and how they are different.

Independent Practice

Teaching Tips

Items 16–18

If needed, allow children to look at a complete number chart to answer problem 16. Then have children work without the chart and use patterns to complete problems 17 and 18.

Items 19–20

Provide drawing paper for children who need to draw a model to answer problem 19. Then tell children to try to answer problem 20 without using a model.

Independent Practice

Each puzzle piece below is part of a hundred chart.

Fill in the missing numbers.

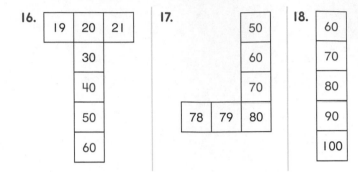

16.

19	20	21
	30	
	40	
	50	
	60	

17.

		50
		60
		70
78	79	80

18.

60
70
80
90
100

Solve each problem. Show your work.

19. Ava has 70 stamps.
She gives away 30 stamps.
How many stamps does
she have left?

Ava has __40__ stamps left.

20. A store has 80 boxes of crayons.
The store sells 60 boxes of crayons.
How many boxes of crayons are left?

There are __20__ boxes of crayons left.

150   Unit 2 ■ Focus on Number and Operations in Base Ten

Math-to-Math Connection

Make Cents from Dimes Children should be able to use what they know about working with tens to work with dimes. Supply each pair of children with 9 dimes in play money or in money stamp cards. Explain that a dime is worth ten cents, so a dime represents 1 ten, or 10. Have children count the dimes by ones and identify the number of dimes that they have, 9. Tell them that just as 9 tens = 90, 9 dimes are worth 90 cents. Ask questions such as *How many cents is 6 dimes? How many cents is 6 dimes minus 4 dimes? How do you know?*

Lesson 17

Independent Practice

MP1 **21.** Celia wrote the number 60.
She said this was her answer when she
subtracted 30 from her number.
What was her number?
Tell how you found her number.

Her number was __90__ .
Answers may vary. Possible answer: I counted on
3 tens from 6 tens to 9 tens, which is 90.

MP8 **22.** Raj says he can subtract 5 tens from his
secret number on the hundred chart.
The answer will be 20.
What is Raj's secret number?

__70__

MP3 **23.** Joan says that the number that is
2 tens less than 90 is the same as
the number that is 3 tens less than 80.
Is Joan correct? Talk about why or why not.

__no__

Answers may vary. Possible answer: 2 tens is the same as 20,
and 20 less than 90 is 70. 3 tens is the same 30, and 30 less
than 80 is 50. 50 and 20 are two different numbers.

Unit 2 ■ Focus on Number and Operations in Base Ten **151**

Teaching Tips

Items 21–23
Review common problem-solving steps
with children to help them approach and
analyze each problem. Encourage them
to start each problem by identifying
what information is given and what they
are being asked to find out.

Return to the

Progress Check

Remind children to return to the
Progress Check self-assessment,
page 93, to check off additional items
they have mastered during the unit.

Mathematical Practices

MP1	Make sense of problems and persevere in solving them.
Item 21: Children analyze problem clues and plan a solution.	
MP3	Construct viable arguments and critique the reasoning of others.
Item 23: Children construct arguments and share reasoning with others.	
MP8	Look for and express regularity in repeated reasoning.
Item 22: Children obtain fluency using patterns and evaluating the reasonableness of answers.	

The Unit 2 Review covers all the standards presented in the unit. Use it to assess your students' mastery of the unit's concepts and skills.

Depth of Knowledge

The depth of knowledge is a ranking of the content complexity of assessment items based on Webb's Depth of Knowledge (DOK) levels. The levels increase in complexity as shown below.

Level 1: Recall and Reproduction
Level 2: Basic Skills and Concepts
Level 3: Strategic Reasoning and Thinking
Level 4: Extended Thinking

Item	DOK
1	1
2	2
3	1
4	2
5	2
6	2
7	1
8	2
9	4
10	3

1. Count on to find how many. Write the number. Mark each object as you count it.

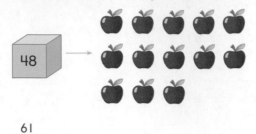

   61

2. Fill in the missing numbers.

81	82	83	84	85	86	87	88	89	90
91	92	93	94	95	96	97	98	99	100
101	102	103	104	105	106	107	108	109	110
111	112	113	114	115	116	117	118	119	120

Read the number name. Circle that number.

3. fifty-two   42   43   (52)

Compare the numbers. Write <, =, or >.

4. 43 (>) 36   5. 70 (<) 80

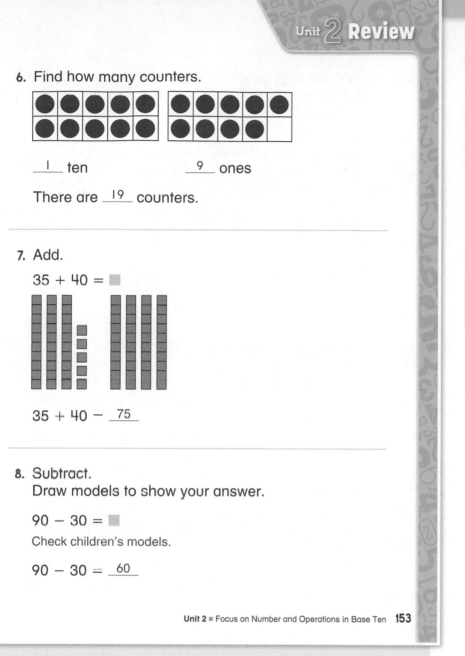

6. Find how many counters.

___1___ ten   ___9___ ones

There are ___19___ counters.

7. Add.

35 + 40 = ▩

35 + 40 — ___75___

8. Subtract.
Draw models to show your answer.

90 − 30 = ▩

Check children's models.

90 − 30 = ___60___

This chart correlates the Unit 2 Review items with the lessons in which the concepts and skills are presented.

Item	Lesson
1	11
2	11
3	12
4	14
5	14
6	13
7	15
8	17
9	13
10	16

Talking About Math

Direct students to respond to the Unit 2 Essential Question. (This can also be found on page 95.)

Essential Question:
How does understanding place value help you add and subtract?

Possible responses:
- Understanding place value helps you use mental math to add 10 to a number or to add tens.
- Place-value models show you how to add ones, make a ten if needed, and then add tens.

Unit Assessment

- Unit 2 Review, *pp. 152–154*
- Unit 2 Performance Task **ONLINE**

Additional Assessment Options

- Performance Task 1, *pp. 155–158*
  ALSO ONLINE

Optional Purchase:

- iProgress Monitor **ONLINE**
- Progress Monitor Student Benchmark Assessment Booklet

Unit 2 Review

MP1 9. I am a 2-digit number.
My tens and ones digits have a sum of 10.
I have 2 more tens than ones.
What number am I?

Write the number in the place-value chart.
Explain how you found the number.

<u>64</u>

tens	ones
6	4

Answers may vary. Possible answer: 6 + 4 = 10 and 6 is 2 more than 4. So there are 6 tens and 4 ones.

MP7 10. Cole wrote a mystery number.
He gave this clue: 47 is 10 more than my number.
What is his mystery number?

Mystery number: <u>37</u>

What is 10 less than his mystery number?

<u>27</u> is 10 less than his mystery number.

Tell how you found his mystery number.

Answers may vary. Possible answer: I know Cole's number is 10 less than 47 because 47 is 10 more than Cole's number. So I subtracted 10 from 47 to find his mystery number.

154 Unit 2 ■ Focus on Number and Operations in Base Ten

Mathematical Practices
MP1   **Make sense of problems and persevere in solving them.**
Item 9: Children analyze given constraints and relationships to identify a two-digit number.
MP7   **Look for and make use of structure.**
Item 10: Children look closely to discern a pattern or structure to add ten and subtract ten.

Performance Task I

Performance Tasks

Performance Tasks show your understanding of the math that you have learned.

Beginning This Task

This is the beginning of a Performance Task. The next three pages have problems for you to solve.

As you work, you will:

1. Show that you can use math skills and concepts.

2. Decide how to solve a problem.

3. Use different ways to model and solve real-world problems.

Tips to help you!

- Read each problem carefully.
- Plan how you will solve the problem.
- Check your work.
- Be ready to show your work or explain your thinking.

ONLINE Customize Performance Task 1

Performance Task 1 in *Progress Mathematics* also provides children with additional practice. You can use the online items of Performance Task 1 to customize the amount and kind of performance task practice based on your ongoing evaluation of your children. You may choose to challenge some children, to give extra experience with a particular kind of task for other children, or to extend exposure to performance assessment for the entire class.

Go to **sadlierconnect.com** to download the following resources for Performance Task 1.

- Additional Items

- Additional Teacher Support

- Additional Scoring Rubrics

Performance Task 1 Overview

Performance Task 1 in *Progress Mathematics* provides children with practice for the types of items that may be found on standardized performance assessments.

Various item formats, including short- and extended-response items and technology-enhanced items, are included in the tasks. All items connect mathematical content correlated to the Mathematical Practices.

Items in Performance Task 1 are based on three primary types of tasks:

Type I Mastery of mathematical concepts, skills and procedures

Type II Using and explaining mathematical reasoning

Type III Modeling problem situations in a real-world context

Performance Task 1 begins with a collection of three self-contained items in the Student Book and continues with additional items online at **sadlierconnect.com**.

Introduce Performance Task 1 Read page 155 to the children. Explain that Performance Task 1 may cover any of the math they have learned in Units 1 and 2. Orient children to each item and communicate helpful reminders that will enable children to approach each item successfully. Once children have completed each item, go over the correct responses with them.

Recommended Pacing Administer Performance Task 1 on Student Book pages 156–158 over three 15-minute sessions.

Teacher Resources For each task, the teacher materials include:

- Item types and purposes

- Correlations to Standards for Mathematical Practice, and Depth of Knowledge (DOK) levels

- Suggested administration procedure

- Scoring Rubric

Item 1: Playground Time

Item	Type	Purpose
1.a.	I	Write an equation to solve a word problem.
1.b.	II	Write a related equation.
1.c.	III	Solve the word problem.
1.d.	II	Explain mathematical reasoning.

Item	MP	DOK
1.a.	2	Level 2
1.b.	4	Level 2
1.c.	1	Level 1
1.d.	3	Level 3

Administering Item 1 (Pacing: 15 minutes)

Ask a volunteer to read the introductory paragraph. Have others describe the situation in their own words.

Item 1.a. (4 minutes)

Read the problem aloud to the class. Guide children to see that the problem is asking them to write either an addition or a subtraction equation. To help children who have difficulty with this task, provide them with counters to help them model the problem.

Item 1.b. (4 minutes)

Tell children that in this problem, they need to write another equation for the problem using a different operation. If they used addition in the previous problem, then they should write a subtraction equation here, and visa versa.

Item 1.c. (3 minutes)

Children should see that they need to solve one of the equations they wrote in Items 1.a. or 1.b.

Item 1.d. (4 minutes)

Children should understand that every addition has a related subtraction, and which operation is chosen is irrelevant.

Playground Time

I. Mrs. Bell's class is on the playground.
There are 11 children playing on the swings.
6 of the children on the swings are girls.
How many children on the swings are boys?

a. Write an equation that can help you solve the problem. Use a ? to stand for the unknown number. Write + or − in the ◯.

____ ◯ ____ = ____   Possible answers:
$6 + ? = 11$ or $11 − 6 = ?$

b. Write another equation using a different operation you can use to solve the problem. Use a ? to stand for the unknown number. Write + or − in the ◯.

____ ◯ ____ = ____   Possible answers:
$11 − 6 = ?$ or $6 + ? = 11$

c. How many children on the swings are boys?

There are __5__ boys on the swings.

d. Does it matter which equation you use to solve? Explain.

No. Answers may vary. Possible answer: Every addition has a related subtraction. Adding some number to 6 makes the sum of 11, so subtracting 6 from 11 will have a difference that is the same as the unknown addend. These are related equations. All three numbers in both equations are the same.

156 Performance Task I

Scoring Rubric

Item	Points	Student Responses
1.a.	2	Correctly writes equation.
	1	Writes equation in illogical order.
	0	Does not write an equation.
1.b.	2	Correctly writes new equation with a different operation.
	1	Uses same operation as in Item 1.a.
	0	Does not write an equation.
1.c.	2	Correctly completes sentence.
	0	Incorrectly completes sentence or does not respond.
1.d.	2	Shows clear understanding of related addition and subtraction.
	1	Shows partial understanding of related addition and subtraction.
	0	Does not write explanation.

Performance Task I

Recycle Time

2. Deborah picks up 28 bottles.
   She puts them in the recycle bin.
   After lunch, she picks up 6 more bottles.

   a. Draw the bottles that Deborah picked up
   after lunch.

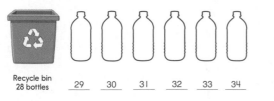

Recycle bin
28 bottles   29   30   31   32   33   34

   b. Start at 28. Count on. Say and write the
   number below the bottles you drew for 2a.

   c. How many bottles did Deborah pick up in all?

   __34__ bottles

   d. Write the number name for the total.

   _____thirty-four_____ bottles

Scoring Rubric

Item	Points	Student Responses
2.a.	2	Draws 6 figures to represent bottles.
	1	Draws more or fewer than 6 bottles.
	0	Does not make a drawing.
2.b.	2	Correctly labels bottles 29 to 34.
	1	Skips or repeats a number 29 to 34.
	0	Does not count on from 28.
2.c.	2	Correctly identifies number in all, 34.
	1	Writes number to match error in Item 2.b.
	0	Writes erroneous number or none.
2.d.	2	Correctly writes thirty-four.
	1	Writes number word to match error.
	0	Does not write a logical number word.

Item 2: Recycle Time

Item	Type	Purpose
2.a.	III	Make a drawing to solve a problem.
2.b.	I	Count on from a given number.
2.c.	I	Interpret the result of counting on.
2.d.	I	Write a number name for a number.

Item	MP	DOK
2.a.	4	Level 1
2.b.	7	Level 1
2.c.	1	Level 2
2.d.	6	Level 1

Administering Item 2 (Pacing: 15 minutes)

Ask a volunteer to read the introductory paragraph. Have others describe the situation in their own words.

Item 2.a. (5 minutes)

Read the question aloud to the class. Children should understand that they need to draw 6 bottles to show the total bottles collected. Suggest that children draw simple circles or rectangles to represent each bottle, in order to save time.

Item 2.b. (4 minutes)

In this item, children need to write numbers under their drawings from Item 2.a. to represent counting on.

Item 2.c. (2 minutes)

Have children complete the sentence to tell how many bottles Deborah picked up in all.

Item 2.d. (4 minutes)

Have children write the number name for the total. Point out that they should check their answers for Item 2.c. before attempting Item 2.d. Some children may need help spelling the number word.

Item 3: Sticker Books

Item	Type	Purpose
3.a.	I	Compare multiples of 10.
3.b.	III	Add 10 to a multiple of 10.
3.c.	III	Subtract 20 from a multiple of 10.

Item	MP	DOK
3.a.	2	Level 2
3.b.	7	Level 2
3.c.	4	Level 1

Administering Item 3 (Pacing: 15 minutes)

Ask a volunteer to read the introductory paragraph. Have others describe the situation in their own words.

Item 3.a. (5 minutes)

In this problem, children need to use comparison symbols to compare two powers of ten. To help children who have difficulty with this task, provide place-value manipulatives that they can use to model the problem.

Item 3.b. (4 minutes)

Children need to first identify the number of Hector's stickers from the problem stem at the top of the page. Then they will choose the operation to find a number that is 10 more.

Item 3.c. (6 minutes)

Explain to children that they need to find Jess' number of stickers from the problem stem. Then they will choose the operation to find a number that is 20 less.

Sticker Books

3. Hector and Jess collect stickers.
   Hector has 20 stickers.
   Jess has 40 stickers.

   a. Compare the number of stickers each child has. Use <, =, or >.

   ____ ○ ____   20 < 40 or 40 > 20

   b. Hector gets 10 more stickers.
      How many stickers does Hector have now?

      _30_ stickers

   c. Jess gives away 20 of her stickers.
      How many stickers does Jess have left?
      Draw a picture to check your answer.

      _20_ stickers
      Check children's drawings.

Scoring Rubric

Item	Points	Student Responses
3.a.	2	Correctly writes comparison.
	1	Writes correct numbers but incorrect symbol.
	0	Does not write a comparison.
3.b.	2	Correctly identifies sum of 20 + 10.
	1	Finds addends but subtracts to find 10.
	0	Writes random or no number.
3.c.	2	Correctly subtracts 40 − 20.
	1	Finds numbers but adds to find 60.
	0	Writes random or no number.

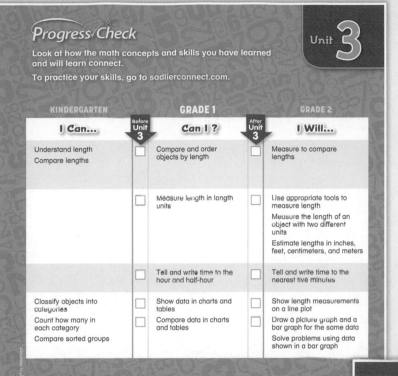

Progress Check

Look at how the math concepts and skills you have learned and will learn connect.

To practice your skills, go to sadlierconnect.com.

KINDERGARTEN		GRADE 1		GRADE 2
I Can...	**Before Unit 3**	**Can I ?**	**After Unit 3**	**I Will...**
Understand length Compare lengths	☐	Compare and order objects by length	☐	Measure to compare lengths
	☐	Measure length in length units	☐	Use appropriate tools to measure length Measure the length of an object with two different units Estimate lengths in inches, feet, centimeters, and meters
	☐	Tell and write time to the hour and half-hour	☐	Tell and write time to the nearest five minutes
Classify objects into categories	☐	Show data in charts and tables	☐	Show length measurements on a line plot
Count how many in each category Compare sorted groups	☐	Compare data in charts and tables	☐	Draw a picture graph and a bar graph for the same data Solve problems using data shown in a bar graph

Unit 3 ■ Focus on Measurement and Data

Student Page 159

Progress Check

Progress Check is a self-assessment tool that children can use to gauge their own progress. Research shows that when children take accountability for their learning, motivation increases.

Before children begin work in Unit 3, have them check any items they know they can do well. Explain that it is fine if they don't check any of the boxes; they will have the opportunity to learn and practice all the standards through the course of the unit.

Let children know that at the end of the unit they will review their checklists to check their progress. After children have completed the last lesson of the unit, before they begin the Unit 3 Review, you will be prompted to have children revisit this page. Remind them to keep this page in a safe place where they can find it later.

HOME ◆ CONNECT...

The Home Connect feature is a way to keep parents or other adult family members apprised of what their children are learning. The key learning objectives are listed, and some ideas for related activities and discussions are included.

Explain to children that they can share the Home Connect page at home with their families. Let children know there is an activity connected to their classroom learning that they can do with their families.

Encourage children and their parents to share their experiences using the suggestions on the Home Connect. You may wish to invite children to share this work with the class.

HOME ◆ CONNECT...

In this unit your child will:

- Compare and order lengths.
- Measure length in length units.
- Tell time on the hour and half hour.
- Learn the value of coins (Optional)
- Use tables.

An exciting concept that your child will learn in first grade is how to tell time by reading both an analog and a digital clock. In this unit, your child will learn how to tell time to the hour and to the half hour.

hour minutes

hour hand   minute hand

You can ask your child to help tell time at home. Make note of the hour and half-hour times that you begin or end activities, like starting sports practice, eating dinner, or reading a book.

Activity: In this unit, your child will learn to measure the length of objects using shorter objects called length units. For example, they will measure the length of a piece of ribbon using paper clips as the length unit. They will place paper clips end to end with no gaps or overlap and record the length by writing how many paper clips long the object is. Provide your child with paper clips or choose some other length unit. Ask him or her to measure the length of objects in your home such as the length of a table, the width of a chair, and so on.

Ways to Help Your Child

Playing games with your child is a wonderful way to practice math skills. Board games and card games that use counting are a fun way to help your child build his or her skills.

Look for opportunities to emphasize the importance of measurement and data in daily life. Understanding the news, reading a magazine article, and evaluating the truth of a TV ad often require knowing about data and how to interpret it. When working on home repairs, cooking, sewing, building, planting, or following a hobby—the ability to successfully complete a project can depend on the ability to measure accurately.

ONLINE
For more Home Connect activities, continue online at sadlierconnect.com

160   Unit 3 ■ Focus on Measurement and Data

Student Page 160

UNIT PLANNER

Lesson	Objective
18 Compare and Order Lengths	Compare and order the lengths of objects by aligning the objects or using a third object as the standard for comparison.
19 Measure with Same-Size Length Units	Measure the length of objects as a whole number using nonstandard units.
20 Tell Time	Tell and write the time to the nearest half hour that is shown on an analog or digital clock.
21 Money	Find the value of a group of coins containing pennies, nickels, dimes, and quarters.
22 Use Tables	Use tables to record information and make comparisons.

Essential Question	Words to Know
How can you compare and order the lengths of objects?	length
How can you measure the length of objects?	unit
How can you tell time?	clock hour hand hour minute hand minutes half hour
How do you find the value of a group of coins?	penny cent nickel dime quarter
How do you use a table to make comparisons?	data table tally mark

Unit Assessment

- Unit 3 Review, *pp. 202–204*
- Unit 3 Performance Task ⬭ONLINE⬭

Additional Assessment Options

Optional Purchase:

- iProgress Monitor ⬭ONLINE⬭
- Progress Monitor Student Benchmark Assessment Booklet

⬭ONLINE⬭ Digital Resources

- Home Connect Activities
- Unit Performance Tasks
- Additional Practice
- Fluency Practice
- Teacher Resources
- iProgress Monitor (optional purchase)

Go to SadlierConnect.com to access your Digital Resources.

For more detailed instructions see page T3.

LEARNING PROGRESSIONS

This page provides more in-depth detail on the development of math concepts and skills across the grade levels. See also the unit Progress Check page in the Student Edition for a roadmap of the Learning Progressions.

Grade K

- Students describe and discuss measurable attributes of objects, such as weight or length.
- Students compare two objects based on a measurable attribute.
- Students classify objects into ten or fewer categories, count how many objects are in each category, and sort the categories by their counts.

Grade 1

- Students order three objects by length and compare the lengths of two objects indirectly by using a third object as a benchmark.
- When measuring the length of an object with multiple copies of a shorter object (the length unit) students must be careful not to leave gaps or create overlaps.
- Students tell and write time to the hour and half-hour using analog and digital clocks.
- Students organize, represent, and interpret categorical data (up to three categories). They ask and answer questions about the number of data points in each category, how many more or less are in one category than in another, and the total number of data points.

Grade 2

- Students measure the lengths of objects using appropriate tools.
- Students measure the length of an object twice, using different length units, and describe how the two measurements relate to size of the chosen units.
- Students estimate length using inches, feet, centimeters, and meters.
- Students measure to determine how much longer one object is than another, expressing the difference in terms of standard length units.
- Students tell and write time to the nearest five minutes, from both analog and digital clocks. They understand and use A.M. and P.M.
- Students generate measurement data by measuring objects to the nearest whole unit, and display the measurements on a line plot marked off in whole number units.
- Students draw a picture graph and a bar graph (with a single-unit scale) to represent a data set of up to four categories. They solve simple problems (put-together, take-apart, and compare) using information in a bar graph.

Focus on Measurement and Data

Unit 3

Essential Question:
How can you tell what
time it is?

Unit 3 ■ Focus on Measurement and Data **161**

As children become involved with the Essential Question they will use analog and digital clocks to identify time to the hour and half hour. In this unit, children will also explore length measurement, tally marks and tables, and coin values.

Conversation Starters

Have children discuss the photograph. Ask question such as: *What are the objects that are shown? How are they used in everyday life? Where have you seen objects like these before?*

Ask children to compare the clocks in the photograph. *How are these clocks alike?* (All of them have at least one number showing. The faces of the clocks are round. All of them have at least two hands.) *How are the clocks different?* (Some of them have more than two hands. Some of them have numbers and marks for the missing numbers. They are different sizes, designs, and colors.)

Have children identify any times that are shown on clocks that they already know how to read. Ask children to find clocks that match particular clues such as: *Which clock has a long hand that points to 12 and a shorter hand that points to 1?* (the bright yellow clock) *The yellow clock shows one o'clock. Can you find the clock that shows five o'clock? It is like one o'clock, but the shorter hand points to 5.* (the orange clock at the top right of the picture)

Ask children to share what they know about telling time and whether they have seen a clock that looks different from the ones in the photograph. Display an analog and a digital clock for children to compare.

Activity

Materials: drawing paper, crayons, markers
Have a whole-class discussion about how children know when to get up in the morning. Ask them whether they wake up to an alarm clock or if someone wakes them up. Tell children to draw a picture of what they do before school, such as eating breakfast, combing their hair, or brushing their teeth. If time allows, ask children to turn their pictures over and draw something about their afternoon on the back, such as what they do after school.

Conclude the activity by naming a daily event and asking children to tell whether it happens in the morning or in the afternoon.

OBJECTIVE

Compare and order the lengths of objects by aligning the objects or using a third object as the standard for comparison.

ESSENTIAL QUESTION

Read aloud the Essential Question and ask children to tell what they think it means. Prompt discussion about the difference between comparing the lengths of two objects and ordering the lengths of three or more objects from shortest to longest.

PREREQUISITE SKILLS

Use Foundational Skills Handbook page 255, *Measurement,* to review the concepts of longer and shorter.

FLUENCY PRACTICE

Fluency practice is available at **sadlierconnect.com**.

Concept Development

Understand: Comparing the lengths of objects

■ As children use the illustrations to complete the page, have them look for similar classroom objects to use in comparing lengths.

■ Be sure children understand that comparing lengths is easier if they first align the objects as shown on the page.

Lesson 18

Compare and Order Lengths

Guided Instruction

In this lesson you will learn how to compare and order the lengths of objects.

Understand: Comparing the lengths of objects

Which is longer? Which is shorter?

Compare the length of the paintbrush and the length of the marker.

Line up the left ends of the objects.

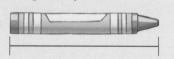

The right end of the paintbrush is farther from the line, so it is longer.

The right end of the marker is closer to the line, so it is shorter.

▷ The paintbrush is longer than the marker. The marker is shorter than the paintbrush.

Words to Know

length: how long an object is

Example:

Glossary can be found on pp. 261–272.

Lesson 18

Guided Instruction

Understand: **Ordering objects by length**

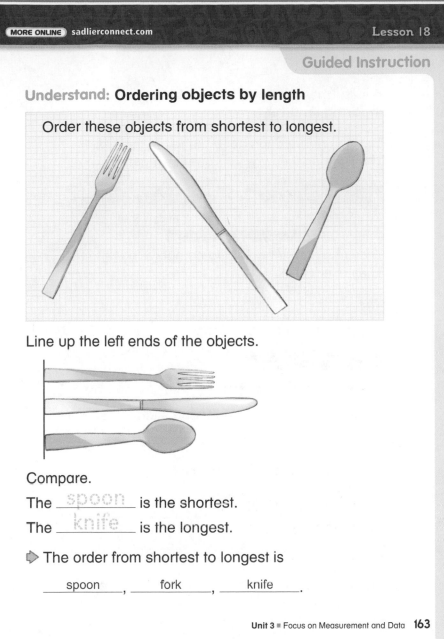

Order these objects from shortest to longest.

Line up the left ends of the objects.

Compare.

The _spoon_ is the shortest.

The _knife_ is the longest.

▷ The order from shortest to longest is

___spoon___ , ___fork___ , ___knife___ .

Understand: **Ordering objects by length**

■ Measurement skills are limited to focusing on the underlying concepts of length such as comparing the lengths of objects with respect to being *shorter, longer, shortest,* or *longest;* ordering three objects by their comparative lengths; and understanding length as a number of equal-sized units. Measurement concepts that involve standard units such as inches or centimeters are not covered until Grade 2.

■ Emphasize to children the importance of aligning objects at one end so that they can accurately compare the lengths of the objects. Ask children questions such as: *Which picture, the one at the top or the one at the bottom, is easier to use in deciding how to order the lengths of the fork, knife, and spoon?*

Support English Language Learners

There are many meanings for the word *length* in the English language, which may be confusing to English language learners. For example, the length of a school day refers to the amount of time the school day lasts; the length of a child's report refers to the number of pages or the number of words that make up the report; a *lengthy* discussion refers to a discussion that goes on for a long time; and the length of an object refers to the distance from one end of the object to the other. Children should understand that it is this last meaning of *length* that is the focus of this lesson. When they compare the length of two objects, they are finding how much longer or shorter one object is than the other.

Connect: Use what you know about comparing lengths Use this page to help children understand how to compare the lengths of objects when the objects are in different locations and therefore cannot be directly compared.

■ One part of this standard is to use one object to indirectly measure two other objects. The stick in this example is used as the unit of measure. When one shelf is shorter than the stick and one shelf is longer than the stick, a conjecture can be made that the first shelf is shorter than the second shelf. Children learn to use the stick as a tool when using direct comparison of the lengths of the two shelves is not possible.

■ Some children may recognize that the stick is similar to a ruler because it sets a standard. However, be sure children understand that they are not calculating the actual length of either shelf.

Guided Instruction

Connect: Use what you know about comparing lengths

Tim and Andre each have a shelf in their room. They want to know which one is longer.

Tim's Shelf   Andre's Shelf

They use another object to compare the lengths. They use a stick.

Step 1

Compare Tim's shelf to the stick.

Tim's shelf is ___shorter___ than the stick.

Step 2

Compare Andre's shelf to the stick.

Andre's shelf is ___longer___ than the stick.

▷ Andre's shelf is ___longer___ than Tim's shelf.

Math-to-Physical Education Connection

Mats in the Gym Children who are familiar with yoga, tumbling, and other gymnastics activities may recognize the different types of floor mats that are used for safety. Have children describe some of the mats they have seen or used. If school gym equipment is available, display two different size mats side-by-side. If mats are not available, use wrapping paper to model two side-by-side mats of different lengths. Using a jump rope to measure the mats, have children compare the lengths of the mats to each other and to the length of the rope. Then have them discuss how the rope was used to indirectly measure the lengths of the mats.

Lesson 18

Guided Practice

1. Which is longer, the length across the window or the length across the door?

Step 1

Put the end of a stick on one side of the window.

Make a red mark on the stick to show the length across the window.

Step 2

Now put the end of the stick on one side of the door.

Look at the mark on the stick.

The mark is past the side of the door.

The length across the ___window___ is longer.

⚊ Think•Pair•Share

MP5 **2.** Use a string to compare the length across the classroom door and the length across your desk.

Which is shorter? Explain how you know.

Check children's work.

Unit 3 ■ Focus on Measurement and Data **165**

Mathematical Practices

Mathematical Practice Standards underline the teaching and understanding of all concepts and skills presented. The emphasis of specific practices is noted throughout the guided and independent practice of this lesson.

MP5   Use appropriate tools strategically.

Item 2: Children use a tool to compare the lengths across two objects that cannot be aligned with one another.

Observational Assessment

Use page 165 to assess whether children are able to use the pictures to understand how the window and door are compared using an indirect method. For children who need further conceptual understanding, use a broomstick to compare the length across a door and the length across a nearby window or whiteboard.

⚊ Think•Pair•Share

Peer Collaboration Have pairs of children explain the methods they used to compare lengths and verify their answers. Provide strings of various lengths from which children may choose. Prompt the discussions with questions such as:

- *Which item did you compare first to the string?*

- *Was the first item longer than or shorter than the string?*

- *How did the second item compare to the length of the string?*

- *What did you do if both items were shorter than the string or longer than the string?*

Some children may choose a different string to make the comparisons again and verify their answers.

Return to the Essential Question

Reread the Lesson 18 Essential Question on page 162: *How can you compare and order the lengths of objects?*

Tell children to think about what they learned in this lesson to answer this question.
(Possible responses: I can line up two objects on the left to tell which one is shorter or longer. I can use a stick or a string to compare the lengths of objects that I can't line up.)

Have children share other measurement methods they learned in this lesson.

Concept Application

Children may work independently on these pages in the classroom or at home. They may refer to the first four pages of the lesson to revisit the instruction or to see a worked-out example.

Common Errors and **Teaching Tips** may help you support learning either in the classroom or as a follow-up for work done at home.

Teaching Tips

Items 1-3

Read aloud the directions to children and make sure they understand that they need to do two things to each problem. For children who struggle with multi-step directions, tell them that they can first circle the longer object in all three problems. Then they can underline the shorter object in each problem.

Be sure children understand that they are comparing two objects at a time, not comparing all six objects for the longest and shortest of them all.

Circle the object that is longer.
Underline the object that is shorter.

1.
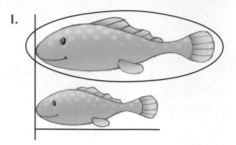

2.
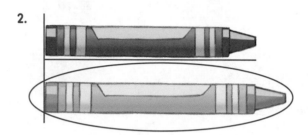

3.
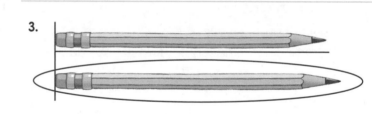

Talking About Math

Use Details to Create Clues Have pairs of children whose desks are close by work together for this discussion. Tell one person in each pair to find and show a pencil on his or her desk. Then have this child make a comparison of something that is not shown. Clues should include the word *longer* or *shorter* and should include another clue to help identify the object, such as, *I have something to write with that is shorter than my pencil.* Then tell the second child in each pair to find an object that fits the clue. Have children take turns choosing an object from their desks, providing clues, and finding objects that fit the clues.

MORE ONLINE sadlierconnect.com

Lesson 18

4. List the objects in order from longest to shortest.

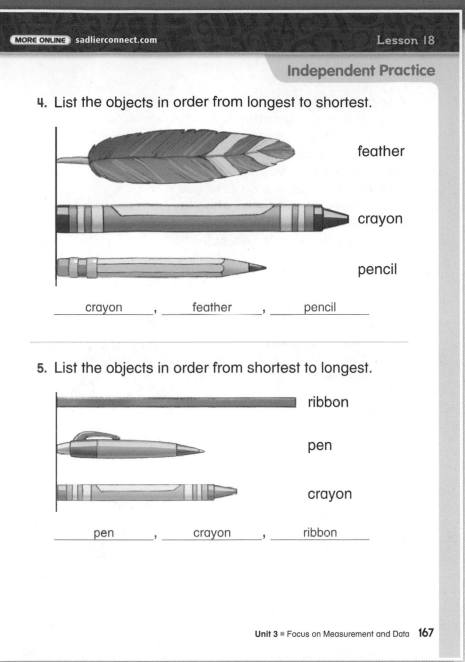

feather

crayon

pencil

___crayon___ , ___feather___ , ___pencil___

5. List the objects in order from shortest to longest.

ribbon

pen

crayon

___pen___ , ___crayon___ , ___ribbon___

Common Errors

Items 4-5

If children write their answers in the opposite order, have them reread the direction lines and explain their errors.

Teaching Tips

Items 4-5

Point out to children that in each problem they will make three comparisons rather than two, making clear the distinction between the terms *shorter* and *shortest* as well as the terms *longer* and *longest.*

Digital Connection

Length Comparison Activities Search online for free math games or activities that are grade-level specific and involve length comparisons of two and three objects. After your review, bookmark appropriate measurement activities or measurement games for children to use in applying what they have learned about length.

Teaching Tips

Items 6–7

Read the directions to children at least two times and make sure children understand what they are to do. It may help children remember what to do if they circle the word *longer* in the second-to-last sentence and underline the word *shorter* in the last sentence.

To save time and efficiently organize the activity, precut the paper strips for children to use. Each strip should be narrow, white, and about 4 inches long for ease of use.

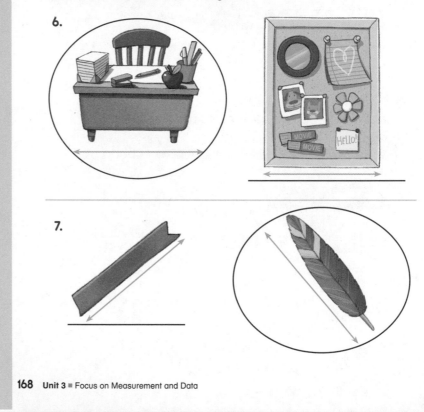

For problems 6 and 7, use a strip of paper to compare the lengths of the two objects. The green lines show the lengths. Make a red mark on the strip to show the length of one object. Use the mark on the strip to see if the other object is longer or shorter. Circle the longer object. Underline the shorter object.

6.

7.

Math-to-Sports Connection

Bats and Rackets Some children may not realize that bats and rackets come in different lengths. Collect several examples to display for children. Have two volunteers choose two bats to compare. Ask the class to guess which bat they think is longer. Then have the volunteers align the bats to compare them. If they are equal, have children state that they are the same length. Then ask two more volunteers to choose two rackets, not necessarily two that are used for the same sport. Again, ask the class to make a prediction and then have children verify the results. Continue with additional examples if available.

Lesson 18

Independent Practice

MP3 **8.** Sam says the crayon is longer than the scissors.
Do you agree with Sam? Tell why or why not.

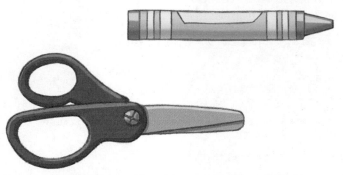

No. Answers may vary. Possible answer: The left ends are not
lined up. If Sam had used a strip of paper and marked off the
length of the crayon, then compared that length to the scissors,
he would have seen that the scissors is longer than the crayon.

MP6 **9.** Find three objects in the classroom.
Put them in order from shortest to longest.
Explain how you put them in order.

Answers will vary. Check children's work.

Unit 3 ■ Focus on Measurement and Data **169**

Teaching Tips

Item 8
Children may reuse their paper strips
from the previous lesson page, make
their own paper strips, or use other
methods to solve the problem.

Check that the explanations clearly
support the conclusions. Help children
recognize that a visual guess in this
situation is not a valid way to solve
the problem.

Item 9
Children can use the actual objects to
demonstrate the comparisons or trace
each object to make a drawing to show
their work. Be sure children can clearly
state or write their explanations.

Mathematical Practices	
MP3	**Construct viable arguments and critique the reasoning of others.**
Item 8: Children critique the given reasoning and explain how to make a better comparison.	
MP6	**Attend to precision.**
Item 9: Children order lengths of objects accurately and formulate explanations.	

OBJECTIVE

Measure the length of objects as a whole number using nonstandard units.

ESSENTIAL QUESTION

Read aloud the Essential Question. Ask children to describe what they know about finding the length of an object. Tell them that in this lesson they will explore how to measure objects by counting the number of equal units to find the lengths of the objects.

FLUENCY PRACTICE

Fluency practice is available at **sadlierconnect.com**.

Concept Development

Understand: Measure objects using other objects

■ Children develop underlying concepts of measurement by using equal-sized units to show the length of an object.

■ Point out that the first paper clip is placed so that it aligns with the left end of the pencil.

■ Ask children how they know when to stop adding paper clips. Children should recognize that the length of the line of paper clips is close to the length of the pencil.

■ Remind children that the paper clips should touch each other, but not overlap. Also, in real life, the length of the line of paper clips probably will not exactly correspond to the length of the object.

Lesson 19 — Measure with Same-Size Length Units

Essential Question: How can you measure the length of objects?

Words to Know
unit

In this lesson you will learn how to measure the length of objects.

Understand: Measure objects using other objects

How long is the pencil?

Use a paper clip as a unit of measurement.

Place a paper clip at one end of the pencil.

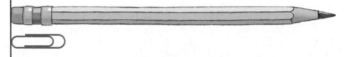

Add paper clips one at a time.

Make sure they touch but do not overlap.

Stop when you get to the end of the pencil.

Count how many paper clips you used.

▷ The pencil is 6 paper clips long.

Words to Know

unit: used to measure length

Example:

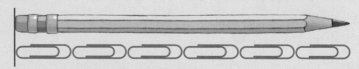

The pencil is 6 paper-clip units long.

Glossary can be found on pp. 261–272.

Guided Instruction

Understand: **Use different units to measure**

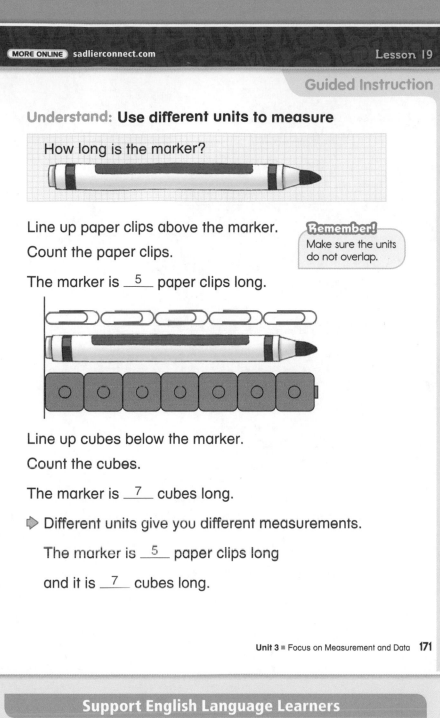

How long is the marker?

Line up paper clips above the marker.

Count the paper clips.

Remember!
Make sure the units do not overlap.

The marker is __5__ paper clips long.

Line up cubes below the marker.

Count the cubes.

The marker is __7__ cubes long.

▷ Different units give you different measurements.

The marker is __5__ paper clips long

and it is __7__ cubes long.

Understand: **Use different units to measure**

■ Learning about different unit objects in Grade 1 prepares children for specific units of measure in Grade 2 such as inches and centimeters.

■ In Grade 1, children are not required to use a ruler for measurement.

■ Point out that using different unit objects may result in different unit measurements. When comparing measurements, each object should be measured by using the same unit object.

■ Make sure children understand the importance of placing the units in a row so that they touch end-to-end, but do not overlap.

Support English Language Learners

In some languages, the word for *one* is similar to the word *unit,* such as *uno, un, una,* and *unu.* The prefix *uni-* appears in many English words that mean "one of something." For example, a unicycle has one wheel; a unicorn has one horn, and the word *unique* means one of a kind. Help children understand the meaning of *unit* by relating it to one part of an object or set, a single thing, or a single person who is part of a group. If an object is three paper clips long, the unit of measurement is one paper clip.

Unit 3 ■ Focus on Measurement and Data   171

Connect: What you know about measuring length Use this page to help children understand how to measure an object by counting its unit lengths.

■ Ask children to count the number of unit cubes shown in the picture. Ask how many of those cubes are used to measure the length of the crayon. Children should be able to explain that two cubes at the right are not part of the measurement of the crayon because they extend beyond the end of the crayon.

■ Show the class a smaller unit length, such as a small bead or a dot of paper from a hole-punch. Ask children to predict whether the measurement using the new unit would be greater or less than the measurement using the cubes. Children should be able to predict that the smaller the unit length, the greater the number of units that would be used to measure an object. Allow children to use the new unit length to measure the crayon on this page.

Connect: **What you know about measuring length**

How many cubes long is the crayon?

Step 1

Check that the cubes start at one end of the crayon.

Step 2

Find where the crayon ends.

Step 3

Count how many cubes are between the two ends of the crayon.

There are __6__ cubes.

▷ The crayon is __6__ cubes long.

Math-to-Math Connection

Nonstandard Units Before children understand standard unit measurement, they explore naming lengths using various nonstandard units. Have children choose a nonstandard unit to measure something in the classroom. You may have children measure the length or width of the classroom by walking heel-to-toe. Children will likely count different numbers of units for the same distance. Ask them to discuss what might have been the cause of the different measurements. Children may express the differences in shoe sizes or leaving spaces between each shoe length.

Lesson 19

Guided Practice

I. How long is the feather?

Step 1

Start at one end. Line up paper clips one by one.
Make sure they do not overlap.

Step 2

Count how many paper clips there are.

There are __4__ paper clips.

The feather is __4__ paper clips long.

👑 Think•Pair•Share

MP3 **2.** Clay and Alli use paper clips to measure
a pencil case.

Clay uses large paper clips.
Alli uses small paper clips.
Will they get the same measurement?
If not, who will get a greater number? Explain.

No; Alli; Answers may vary. Possible answer. Alli's unit is smaller,
so she will need more of them to cover the same length.

Unit 3 ■ Focus on Measurement and Data **173**

Mathematical Practices

Mathematical Practice Standards underline the teaching and understanding of all concepts and skills presented. The emphasis of specific practices is noted throughout the guided and independent practice of this lesson.

MP3	**Construct viable arguments and critique the reasoning of others.**

Item 2: Children construct arguments by using drawings or concrete objects and analyze and compare reasoning.

Observational Assessment

Use page 173 to assess whether children are able to recognize length as the number of equal units needed to find the length of an object. Observe whether children have difficulty understanding that units having different lengths result in different answers.

👑 Think•Pair•Share

Peer Collaboration Have pairs of children explain their answers to one another. Prompt the discussions with questions such as:

- *Do Clay and Alli use the same size paper clips? How do you know?*

- *How does the size of the paper clips change the measurement?*

- *What method can you use to check your reasoning?*

Some children may struggle to comprehend that a smaller unit results in a greater number of units or that a larger unit results in a lesser number of units. If the pencil case is used as a single unit, then the pencil case is one unit long. Several paper clips will be needed to equal the length of the pencil case, so it takes more smaller units (paper-clip unit) to equal the length of one larger unit (pencil-case unit).

Return to the Essential Question

Reread the Lesson 19 Essential Question on page 170: *How can you measure the length of objects?*

Tell children to think about what they learned in this lesson to answer this question.
(Possible responses: I can line up equal objects end-to-end with no overlaps or gaps. Then I can count the number of objects to tell the length of the item using the object as the unit of measure.)

Independent Practice

Concept Application

Children may work independently on these pages in the classroom or at home. They may refer to the first four pages of the lesson to revisit the instruction or to see a worked-out example.

Common Errors and **Teaching Tips** may help you support learning either in the classroom or as a follow-up for work done at home.

Teaching Tips

Items 2-3

If children have difficulty keeping track of the number of paper clips in the row, suggest they number each paper clip consecutively to find the total.

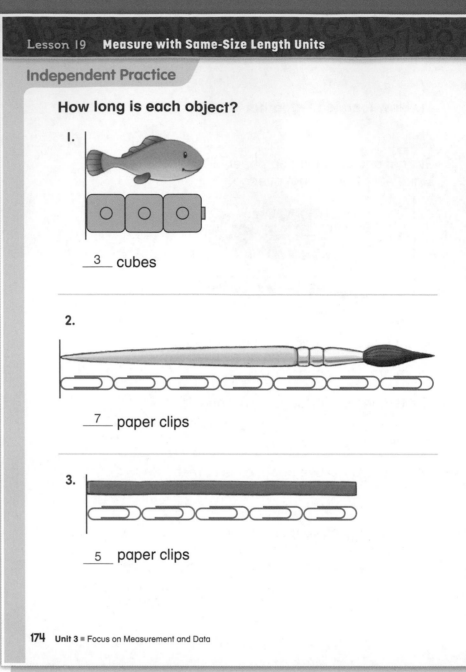

Independent Practice

How long is each object?

1.

__3__ cubes

2.

__7__ paper clips

3.

__5__ paper clips

174   Unit 3 ▪ Focus on Measurement and Data

Talking About Math

Fact or Fiction Ask children whether they are familiar with any storybook about a character that is extra large or extra small. For example, some traditional stories include tales of a giant at the top of a beanstalk or stories of a boy or girl no bigger than a thumb. Have children tell whether the stories are fact or fiction and how they know. Then ask children to identify each of the following story titles as fact or fiction and explain their reasoning.

- The Dog Who is 3 Paper Clips Long
- The Crayon That is 30 Cubes Long
- The Football That is 12 Cubes Long

Lesson 19

Independent Practice

How long is each object?

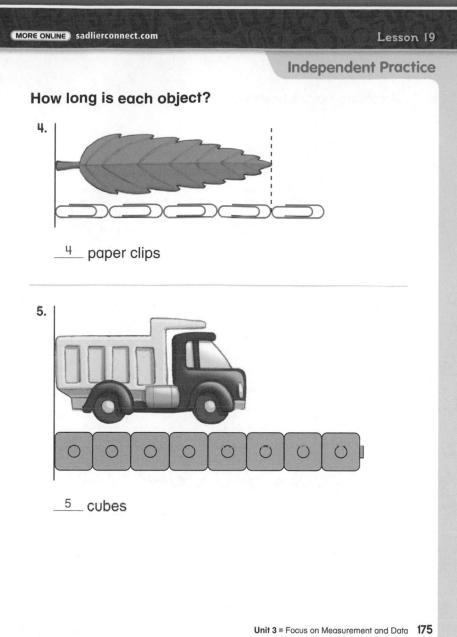

4.

_____4_____ paper clips

5.

_____5_____ cubes

Unit 3 ■ Focus on Measurement and Data **175**

Common Errors

Items 4-5

Children may count the total number of units to name the length of the object. Remind them that the length of an object is from one end to the other. Any units that extend beyond the object are not counted as part of the measurement.

Teaching Tips

Items 4-5

Make sure children can explain that the purpose of the solid red line at the left of each picture is to show the start of the measurement. The dashed red line to the right of the leaf shows the end of the measurement. Ask children where the dashed red line should be on the picture of the toy dump truck.

Digital Connection

Line Them Up Use an interactive whiteboard to complete a drag and drop activity. Select an electronic marker or paintbrush to draw a straight, horizontal line of any length across the board. Then demonstrate how to select a nonstandard unit and drag and drop it below the line. Make sure the first nonstandard units aligns with the left end of the line. Continue placing nonstandard units end-to-end without overlapping until they extend a little past the line. Have children count the number of units to name the length of the line. Repeat the activity using a different nonstandard unit and compare the two measurements.

Independent Practice

Teaching Tips

Items 6-8

Help children point to and read each choice. Two of the answer choices show the correct number of units, but one of those choices has an incorrect unit label. Make sure children understand the correlation between the illustrations and the labels of the correct answer choices.

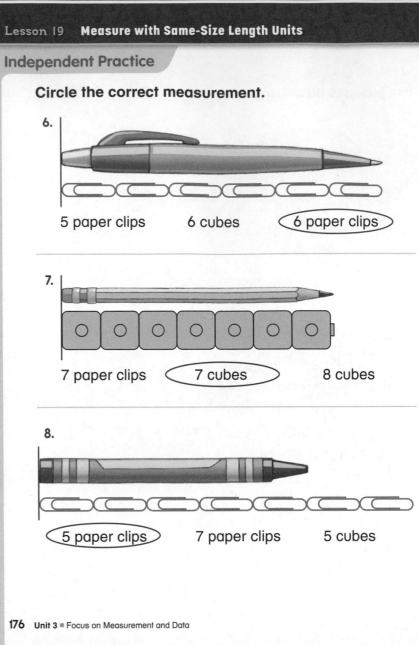

Independent Practice

Circle the correct measurement.

6.

5 paper clips　　6 cubes　　（6 paper clips）

7.

7 paper clips　　（7 cubes）　　8 cubes

8.

（5 paper clips）　　7 paper clips　　5 cubes

Math-to-Transportation Connection

Train Lengths by Cars Ask children to describe any trains they have seen, including real trains or model trains. Encourage a few comments about children's personal experiences with trains. Have children share information about what trains do and what they carry. Then ask children whether they have ever counted train cars as they watched a train pass by a railroad crossing. Point out that this is a real-world example of measuring length by the number of units.

Independent Practice

MP6   **9.** Sue, Brandon, and Ana measured a straw.

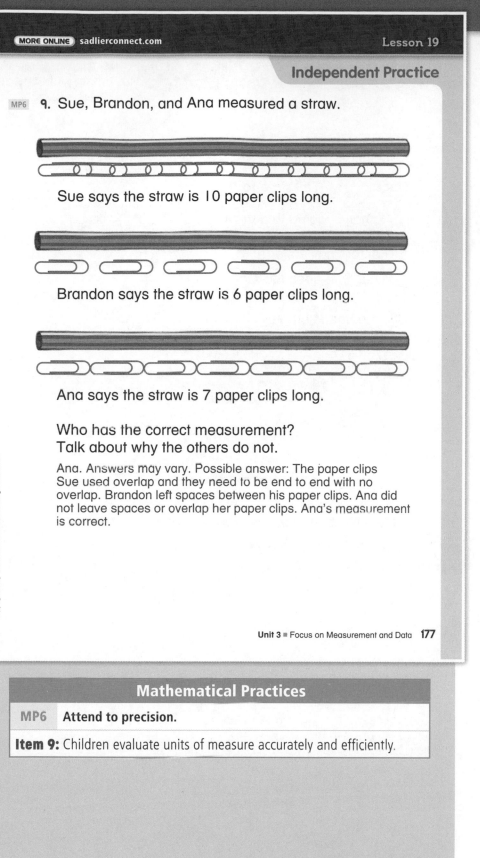

Sue says the straw is 10 paper clips long.

Brandon says the straw is 6 paper clips long.

Ana says the straw is 7 paper clips long.

Who has the correct measurement?
Talk about why the others do not.

Ana. Answers may vary. Possible answer: The paper clips
Sue used overlap and they need to be end to end with no
overlap. Brandon left spaces between his paper clips. Ana did
not leave spaces or overlap her paper clips. Ana's measurement
is correct.

Common Errors

Item 9

Children who state that Sue is correct may not be able to visualize that the paper clips are overlapping. Direct their attention to Ana's work. Point out that her paper clips are touching but not overlapping. Compare Ana's work to Sue and Brandon's work.

Teaching Tips

Item 9

Have children discuss what is correct or incorrect about each illustration.

Mathematical Practices

MP6	Attend to precision.

Item 9: Children evaluate units of measure accurately and efficiently.

OBJECTIVE
Tell and write the time to the nearest half hour that is shown on an analog or digital clock.

ESSENTIAL QUESTION
Read aloud the Essential Question. Ask children to tell about events that happen at particular times: lunch is at noon, bedtime is at 9:00, or Father gets home from work at 5:30. Have them discuss what they know about telling time and how it is done. Tell children that this lesson will help them understand how to tell time to the hour and half hour.

FLUENCY PRACTICE
Fluency practice is available at **sadlierconnect.com**.

Concept Development

Understand: Tell time to the hour

■ Children have explored sequencing skills in kindergarten and first-grade reading programs.

■ Children have already had lessons to compare *shorter* and *longer*. Help children recall these concepts of length by focusing on which clock hand is shorter or longer. It may help them remember that the hour hand is shorter.

Lesson 20 Tell Time

Essential Question: How can you tell time?

Words to Know
clock
hour hand
hour
minute hand
minutes
half hour

In this lesson you will learn how to tell time.

Understand: Tell time to the hour

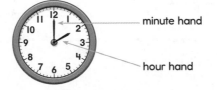

Nathan is going to a movie. The clock shows the time that the movie starts.

What time does the movie start?

Use the hands on a clock to tell time.

minute hand

hour hand

The shorter hand is the hour hand. It points to the hour. The hour hand points to 2.

The longer hand is the minute hand.

When the minute hand points to 12, no minutes have passed the hour, so you say o'clock.

Read the time: two o'clock
Write the time: 2:00

▷ The movie starts at two o'clock, or 2:00.

Words to Know

clock: a tool used to tell the time

hour hand: the shorter hand on a clock, shows the hour

Example:

hour hand

hour: There are 60 minutes in 1 hour.

Lesson 20

Guided Instruction

Understand: Tell time to the half hour

The clock shows the time Amber's music class starts. What time does her music class start?

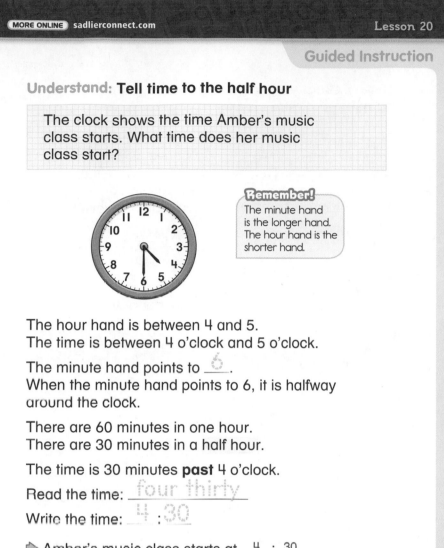

> **Remember!**
> The minute hand is the longer hand. The hour hand is the shorter hand.

The hour hand is between 4 and 5.
The time is between 4 o'clock and 5 o'clock.

The minute hand points to __6__.
When the minute hand points to 6, it is halfway around the clock.

There are 60 minutes in one hour.
There are 30 minutes in a half hour.

The time is 30 minutes **past** 4 o'clock.

Read the time: _four thirty_

Write the time: _4_ : _30_

➡ Amber's music class starts at _4_ : _30_.
   4:30 is also 30 minutes **before** 5 o'clock.

Unit 3 ■ Focus on Measurement and Data **179**

Understand: Tell time to the half hour

■ Have children recall which is the hour hand and which is the minute hand. Have children discuss how the positions of the hands shown on this clock differ from the previous clock. This clock shows the minute hand is pointing down, but on the other clock, it was pointing up. The hour hand on this clock is between two numbers, but on the other clock, the hour hand points to the 2.

■ Make sure children understand the term *halfway*. Point out that in one whole hour, the minute hand starts at 12 and moves all the way around the clock until it is pointing back at 12. Have children demonstrate the movement of the minute hand on the clock illustration. Explain that *halfway* is the point that is as far from the start as it is from the end. The halfway point on a clock face is 6.

■ Children may be used to hearing time expressed verbally while having no real context for meaning of the numbers they are hearing. Tell children that when telling time, the first number said represents the hour and the second number said represents the minutes. Have children listen as you say aloud the time shown on the clock. Ask them to tell the hour. Again, say aloud the time and ask children to tell the minutes.

Words to Know

minute hand: the longer hand on a clock, shows the minutes

Example:

—minute hand

minutes: There are 60 minutes in 1 hour.

half hour: There are 30 minutes in a half hour.

Glossary can be found on pp. 261–272.

Connect: What you know about telling time and using a digital clock Use this page to help children connect the meanings of the displays on an analog and a digital clock.

■ Review which hand on the analog clock is the hour hand and which is the minute hand. Tell children that the two dots shown on the digital clock are called a colon. The colon separates the hour from the minutes.

■ Have children point to both the hour shown on the analog clock and the digits to the left of the colon on the digital clock. Ask children to say the hour.

■ Have children repeat the process for the minutes. Point out that when the minute hand points to 12, it means there are no minutes past the hour. The digital clock says no minutes by showing 0s to the right of the colon.

■ Point out that the hour is read first on both clocks, and the way to say the time is *ten o'clock.*

Connect: What you know about telling time and using a digital clock

You know how to read the time shown by clock hands. The time shown on the clock below is 10:00.

A digital clock does not have clock hands. Read and write the time shown on the digital clock below.

hour   minutes

Step 1

What is the hour? __10__

Step 2

How many minutes have passed? __0__

Read the time as __ten__ o'clock.

Write the time as __10__ : __00__.

▷ The time on the digital clock is __ten__ o'clock,

or __10__ : __00__.

Support English Language Learners

The terms *hour* and *minute* are abstract to many children. Help English language learners first understand that *hour* and its homophone *our* are not the same words. Build understanding of the former by asking children to name some activities that take about an hour to complete. Then point out that people often use the phrase *just a minute* to tell someone that they will do something or respond to a request in a quick amount of time. Contrast activities that take about an hour or about a minute until children demonstrate the basic understanding that a minute goes by much more quickly than an hour. Avoid using the term *short* to describe a minute in order to avoid confusion about the length of the hands on a clock.

1. **What time is it?**

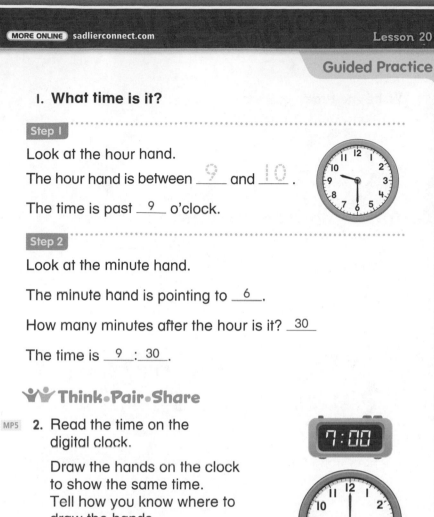

Step 1

Look at the hour hand.

The hour hand is between _9_ and _10_ .

The time is past _9_ o'clock.

Step 2

Look at the minute hand.

The minute hand is pointing to _6_ .

How many minutes after the hour is it? _30_

The time is _9_ : _30_ .

Think·Pair·Share

MP5 2. Read the time on the digital clock.

7:00

Draw the hands on the clock to show the same time. Tell how you know where to draw the hands.

Answers may vary. Possible answer: The time is seven o'clock, or 7:00. The hour hand points to 7 and the minute hand, which is longer, points to 12.

Unit 3 ■ Focus on Measurement and Data **181**

Mathematical Practices

Mathematical Practice Standards underline the teaching and understanding of all concepts and skills presented. The emphasis of specific practices is noted throughout the guided and independent practice of this lesson.

MP5 **Use appropriate tools strategically.**

Item 2: Children demonstrate that they understand the connection between a digital time display and drawing the time on an analog clock.

Observational Assessment

Use page 181 to assess whether children are able to tell and write time to the hour and half hour when the time is shown on analog and digital clocks. Observe whether children need additional help telling time. Use manipulative clocks to allow children additional practice.

Think·Pair·Share

Peer Collaboration Children may work in pairs to display and describe the hands that they drew on the clock. Prompt the discussions with questions such as:

- *Which clock hand did you draw first? Was it the longer or the shorter hand?*

- *Which clock hand points to the hour? Which points to the minutes?*

- *What time is shown on the clocks?*

For children who do not correctly draw the hands of the clock, help them find and use examples from the lesson to correct their work.

Return to the Essential Question

Reread the Lesson 20 Essential Question on page 178: *How can you tell time?*

Tell children to think about what they learned in this lesson to answer this question.

(Possible responses: I can read the numbers on a digital clock to tell time. On analog clocks, the short hand tells the hour and the long hand tells minutes.)

Have children share any strategies they use to remember what part of the time each clock hand tells.

Independent Practice

Concept Application

Children may work independently on these pages in the classroom or at home. They may refer to the first four pages of the lesson to revisit the instruction or to see a worked-out example.

Common Errors and **Teaching Tips** may help you support learning either in the classroom or as a follow-up for work done at home.

Common Errors

Items 1–4

Children may write the number the minute hand is pointing to on the clock face for the minutes. Remind children that when the minute hand points to 12, there are no minutes past the hour. When the minute hand points to the 6, it is half past the hour, or 30 minutes past the hour.

Items 3–4

Children may reason that, since the hour hand is no longer pointing to a number, it cannot be that hour anymore. For example, in item 3, explain that the time is between 2 o'clock and 3 o'clock, but the hour is still 2 o'clock.

Teaching Tips

Items 1–4

Remind children that just as the hour is said first when telling time aloud, the hour is written first, followed by a colon and the minutes.

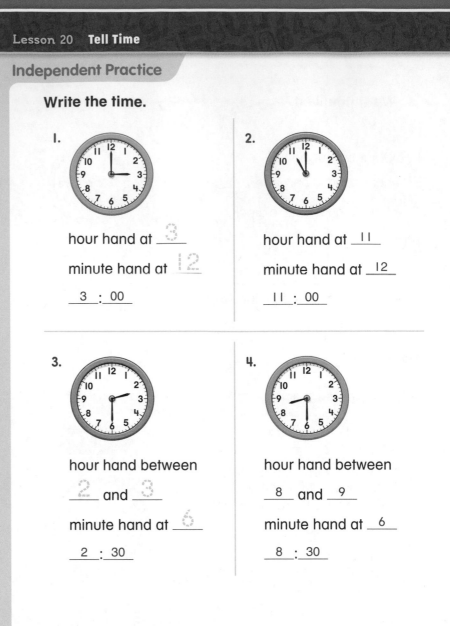

Independent Practice

Write the time.

1.

hour hand at ___3___

minute hand at _12_

__3__ : __00__

2.

hour hand at _11_

minute hand at _12_

_11_ : __00__

3.

hour hand between

___2___ and ___3___

minute hand at ___6___

__2__ : __30__

4.

hour hand between

__8__ and __9__

minute hand at __6__

__8__ : __30__

Talking About Math

Describe Settings Have children describe what they might be doing during one or more of the times shown on the clocks. Encourage them to describe where they might be, whether they are outside or inside, or whether they are describing an event on a weekday or weekend. Children at this level are not expected to describe the concepts of A.M. or P.M., but they can describe different activities for morning and evening hours.

MORE ONLINE sadlierconnect.com

Lesson 20

Independent Practice

Draw lines to match the clocks that show the same time.

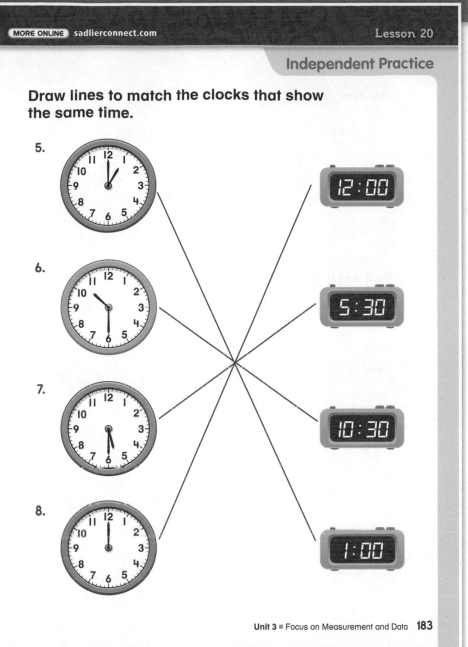

5.

6.

7.

8.

12:00

5:30

10:30

1:00

Unit 3 ■ Focus on Measurement and Data **183**

Common Errors

Item 8

If children state that the clock for problem 8 is missing one of the hands, use a manipulative clock to demonstrate both hands pointing at the 12 and to describe what that means.

Teaching Tips

Items 5–8

Try challenging more proficient children by having them cover the digital clocks with a sheet of paper. Then ask them to write the digital time for each analog clock. They may use the matching activity to check their answers and reveal any problem areas.

Digital Connection

Matching Clocks Use an Internet search engine to identify time-telling games and activities that are appropriate for Grade 1. Review available resources and make a list of the materials that the children can use. Tailor the lists for specific children's needs, limiting resources to time to the hour for children having difficulty and perhaps including time-telling concepts beyond the lesson for children who are already proficient reading analog and digital clocks.

Independent Practice

Common Errors

Item 11

If children record this time as 12:30, review the meaning of each hand. Have them circle the smaller hand and ask them to name the hour. Ask them to recall what it means when the minute hand points to 12.

Item 12

If children write 1:30, it might be because they reason that the counting number 1 comes before the counting number 12. Explain that when a clock rotates past 12, the numbers start over again. Therefore, 1 comes after 12 when telling time.

Teaching Tips

Items 9 and 11

If children question why they should write two zeros after the hour rather than one, explain that minutes are always written using two digits.

Items 10 and 12

Remind children to find the numbers before and after the hour hand, and then write the one that is before.

Independent Practice

Write the time.

9.

  9 : 00

10.

  6 : 30

Solve each problem.

11. The clock shows the time that Gayle eats dinner. What time does she eat dinner?

  6 : 00

12. The clock shows the time the soccer game starts. What time does the soccer game start?

  12 : 30

Math-to-Careers Connection

Time for Work Explain to children that many jobs begin on an hour or half hour. For example, a teacher may need to be at school at 7:30 in the morning. A doctor's office may open at 9:00 in the morning. Have children ask several adults they know what time to the nearest half hour they have to be at work. Ask children to record the responses and bring the list back to school. Allow time for children to read the times from their lists and write them on the board for the class to see.

MORE ONLINE sadlierconnect.com

Independent Practice

MP1 **13.** Louis draws the hour hand on the clock between the 1 and the 2. Then he draws a minute hand pointing to the 6.

What time does his clock show? Draw hands on the clock to help. Talk about how you found the time.

___1___ : __30__

Answers may vary. Possible answer: I drew the hands on the clock the same way Louis did. Then I read the time from the clock. Since the hour hand is between 1 and 2, the hour is after 1 and before 2. Since the minute hand points to 6, it is 30 minutes after 1, or 1:30.

MP4 **14.** Find the mystery time. It is 30 minutes past the hour. The hour hand is between 5 and 6.

Draw the hands on the clock. Explain how you found the mystery time.

___5___ : __30__

Answers may vary. Possible answer: I used the clues to draw the hands on the clock. Then I was able to tell the time.

Unit 3 ▪ Focus on Measurement and Data **185**

Mathematical Practices

MP1	Make sense of problems and persevere in solving them.

Item 13: Children use pictures to help conceptualize and solve a problem.

MP4	Model with mathematics.

Item 14: Children use diagrams to analyze and draw conclusions about information.

Teaching Tips
Items 13–14
Be sure children understand different ways to describe time to the half hour. If children struggle to follow the descriptions in either of these problems, have them explain *hour* and *half hour* in their own words, relating those concepts to an analog clock. Then assist children in transferring that understanding as they reread and solve the problems.

OBJECTIVE
Find the value of a group of coins containing pennies, nickels, dimes, and quarters.

ESSENTIAL QUESTION
Read aloud the Essential Question and ask children to tell what they know about coins. Explain that in this lesson, children will learn the names and values of some coins. They will also practice counting to find the total value of a group of coins.

FLUENCY PRACTICE
Fluency practice is available at **sadlierconnect.com**.

Concept Development

Understand: Identify coins and compare their values

■ All of the coins pictured in the lesson show the obverse side (heads) and are the current national United States coins. Explain to children that their coins may not always show the same design. Make sure children understand that like coins have the same value regardless of which designs they show.

■ Point out that the size of a coin does not determine its relative value. The dime is the smallest of all U.S. coins in circulation today, but its value is greater than both the penny and the nickel.

■ Make sure children can readily identify the value of each coin and compare the values accurately before going to the next page, combining coins.

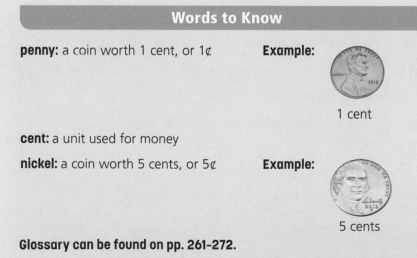

Lesson

21 Money

Guided Instruction

Essential Question:
How do you find the value of a group of coins?

Words to Know
penny
cent
nickel
dime
quarter

In this lesson you will learn about coins and their values.

Understand: Identify coins and compare their values

penny	nickel	dime	quarter
1¢	5¢	10¢	25¢
1 cent	5 cents	10 cents	25 cents

Jamie has these two coins. Which coin is worth more?

This is a dime.
It is worth 10 cents.

This is a _nickel_.
It is worth _5_ cents.

10 cents is more than 5 cents.

Remember!
10 is greater than 5.

⇨ The _dime_ is worth more than the _nickel_.

186 Unit 3 ■ Focus on Measurement and Data

Words to Know

penny: a coin worth 1 cent, or 1¢   **Example:**

1 cent

cent: a unit used for money

nickel: a coin worth 5 cents, or 5¢   **Example:**

5 cents

Glossary can be found on pp. 261–272.

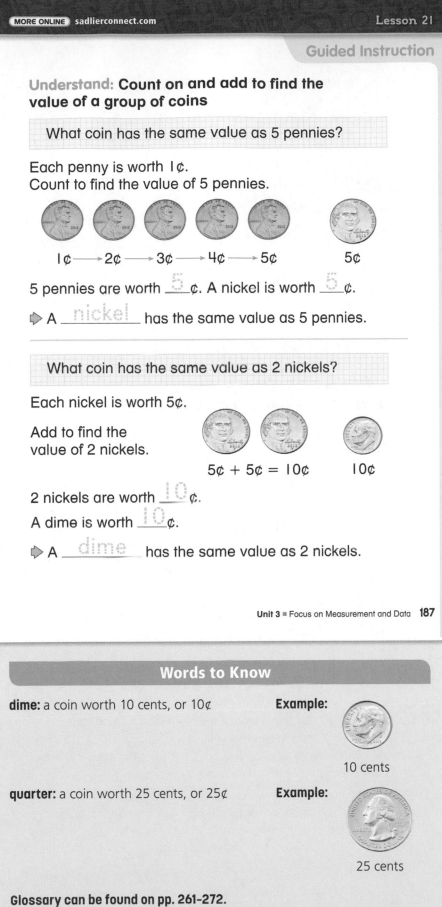

Understand: Count on and add to find the value of a group of coins

What coin has the same value as 5 pennies?

Each penny is worth 1¢.
Count to find the value of 5 pennies.

1¢ ⟶ 2¢ ⟶ 3¢ ⟶ 4¢ ⟶ 5¢   5¢

5 pennies are worth __5__ ¢. A nickel is worth __5__ ¢.

➡ A __nickel__ has the same value as 5 pennies.

What coin has the same value as 2 nickels?

Each nickel is worth 5¢.

Add to find the
value of 2 nickels.

5¢ + 5¢ = 10¢   10¢

2 nickels are worth __10__ ¢.

A dime is worth __10__ ¢.

➡ A __dime__ has the same value as 2 nickels.

Unit 3 ■ Focus on Measurement and Data **187**

Understand: Count on and add to find the value of a group of coins

■ Explain that counting the value of coins is different than counting the number of coins. When counting the value of any group of coins, start counting with the value of the first coin, and then count on the values of each remaining coin.

■ If children struggle to find the value of two nickels, suggest they use a basic addition fact or the doubles strategy.

Words to Know

dime: a coin worth 10 cents, or 10¢   **Example:**

10 cents

quarter: a coin worth 25 cents, or 25¢   **Example:**

25 cents

Glossary can be found on pp. 261–272.

Connect: **What you know about the values of coins** Use this page to help children understand how to combine coin values to find the number of cents in all.

■ If children struggle to identify the value of each coin, suggest they refer back to page 186 for help.

■ Throughout the Guided Instruction and Guided Practice pages, children may need to refer to a chart showing illustrations of coins and their values. If a classroom chart is not available, display an enlarged copy of the top of page 186 for children to use.

■ Have children discuss some strategies they might use for solving the problems. In Step 2, they may prefer to write the additions vertically, adding the ones and then adding the tens. They may find the count-on strategy, starting with the greatest value and counting on by ones an easier method to use in adding Ken's coins. Other children may demonstrate other strategies, such as drawing a picture.

Connect: **What you know about the values of coins**

Anna has these two coins. How many cents are they worth in all?

Step 1

Name each coin and its value.

dime 10¢   nickel __5__¢

Step 2

Add the coin values.

10¢ + 5¢ = __15__¢

▷ Anna's coins are worth __15__¢ in all.

Ken has two pennies and a nickel. How much money does Ken have?

Each penny is worth 1¢.
The nickel is worth 5¢.

Add the coin values.

1¢ + 1¢ + 5¢ = __7__¢

Ken has __7__¢ in all.

Support English Language Learners

The word *cent* may be difficult for English language learners because it is a multiple-meaning word and it also has more than one homophone. The word can be defined as a monetary unit or as the symbol ¢. In colloquial usage, the word often is used as a synonym for penny, although this usage is not entirely accurate.

The homophones for *cent* include *scent* and *sent*. The homonyms for *cents* are *scents* and *since,* possibly adding further confusion as children begin to work with money amounts. Display these words and define each for children. Circle *cent* to help children focus on the terms that refer to coin values.

Lesson 21

Guided Practice

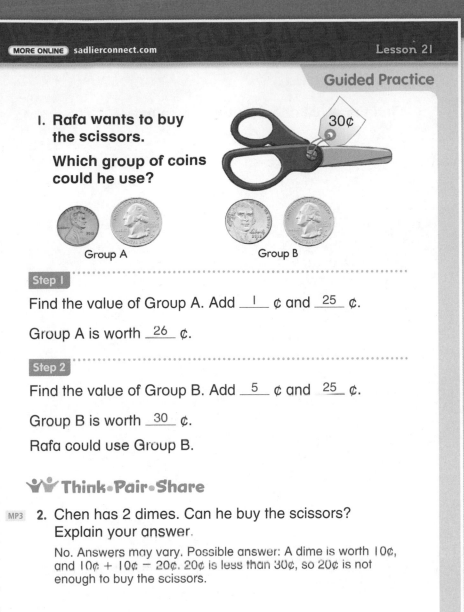

I. Rafa wants to buy the scissors.

Which group of coins could he use?

30¢

Group A   Group B

Step 1

Find the value of Group A. Add __I__ ¢ and __25__ ¢.

Group A is worth __26__ ¢.

Step 2

Find the value of Group B. Add __5__ ¢ and __25__ ¢.

Group B is worth __30__ ¢.

Rafa could use Group B.

👑 Think•Pair•Share

MP3 **2. Chen has 2 dimes. Can he buy the scissors? Explain your answer.**

No. Answers may vary. Possible answer: A dime is worth 10¢, and 10¢ + 10¢ = 20¢. 20¢ is less than 30¢, so 20¢ is not enough to buy the scissors.

Unit 3 ■ Focus on Measurement and Data **189**

Mathematical Practices

Mathematical Practice Standards underline the teaching and understanding of all concepts and skills presented. The emphasis of specific practices is noted throughout the guided and independent practice of this lesson.

MP3	**Construct viable arguments and critique the reasoning of others.**

Item 2: Children analyze a problem situation and use reasoning to support their solutions.

Observational Assessment

Use page 189 to assess whether children are able to identify the values of coins and combinations of coins. Have children use play money coins if they need further practice.

👑 Think•Pair•Share

Peer Collaboration Have children analyze the problem independently and then work in pairs to explain their answers to one another. Prompt the discussions with questions such as:

- *What is the value of two dimes?*

- *How did you find out whether this was enough money to buy the scissors?*

- *Did you explore how much more Chen needs? If so, explain how you found out.*

Children should indicate that Chen does not have enough to buy the scissors, but their approaches to the question may vary greatly. Some children may compare the total values, and some may compare the numbers of dimes needed. Encourage children to discuss varying solution methods.

Return to the Essential Question

Reread the Lesson 21 Essential Question on page 186: *How do you find the value of a group of coins?*

Tell children to think about what they learned in this lesson to answer this question.
(Possible responses: First I need to know the value of each coin. Then I can count on or use addition to find the value in all.)

Encourage children to tell about something new they learned about coins or a different strategy they tried for combining coin values.

Concept Application

Children may work independently on these pages in the classroom or at home. They may refer to the first four pages of the lesson to revisit the instruction or to see a worked-out example.

Common Errors and **Teaching Tips** may help you support learning either in the classroom or as a follow-up for work done at home.

Common Errors

Items 1–5

Incorrect answers that are off by five cents or a multiple of five may indicate that children transposed the values of dimes and nickels. Correct children's thinking by explaining that the coins are not ordered in value by their size.

Teaching Tips

Items 1–3, and 5

Children are likely to use count on or a combination of strategies to answer these problems. Suggest children begin counting with the coin that has the greatest value.

If children struggle in their solution approach, suggest they write the value above each coin before they begin.

Items 2 and 5

Children may not be able to use mental math strategies to add the value of a quarter and other coins. Other possible strategies include writing the values of the coins as vertical additions or using patterns on a number chart to solve.

Lesson 21   **Money**

Independent Practice

Find the value of each group of coins.

1. _11_ ¢

2. _30_ ¢

3. _11_ ¢

4. _15_ ¢

5. _35_ ¢

6. _3_ ¢

Talking About Math

Ask and Answer Questions Ask children to discuss the ways that they use coins in their daily lives. Have small groups of children work together to create and answer questions about coin values, whether one coin has more or less value than another, and what group of coins could total a given value. Some children may benefit from using play coins to find and count values. Allow time for groups to share one of their questions with the rest of the class and to check the answers that are given.

Lesson 21

Independent Practice

Circle the group of coins that has the value shown.

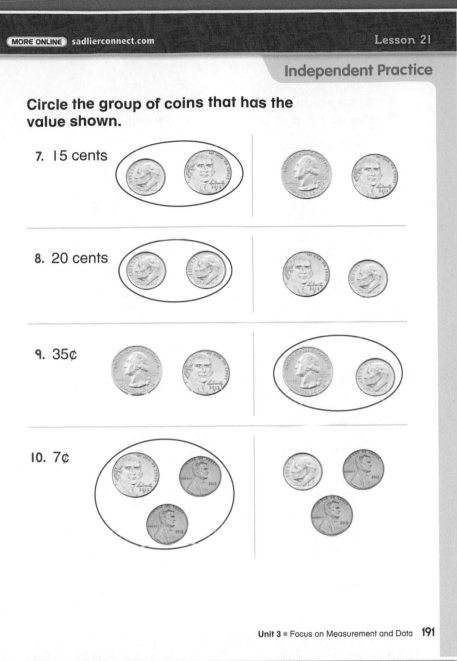

7. 15 cents

8. 20 cents

9. 35¢

10. 7¢

Unit 3 ■ Focus on Measurement and Data **191**

Teaching Tips
Items 7-10
Make sure children understand the format of the page before they begin. Point out that the value shown is not a label for the first group of coins; rather, children will choose whether the amount labels the first or second group of coins.

Digital Connection

Groups of Coins Select math software or online games for children to practice combining groups of coins. For children who need basic practice, recommend activities that are limited to coin recognition, the value of each coin, and comparing two coins. For children who are ready for a challenge, select coin activities recommended for Grade 2 or introduce them to the value of a half dollar.

Teaching Tips

Items 11–14

To simplify the layout of the page, have children use a sheet of paper to cover the right-hand column as they complete the left-hand column. Then have them remove the sheet of paper and match their answers to the objects with equivalent price tags. In this way, the page becomes self-checking if all of the answers do not match up.

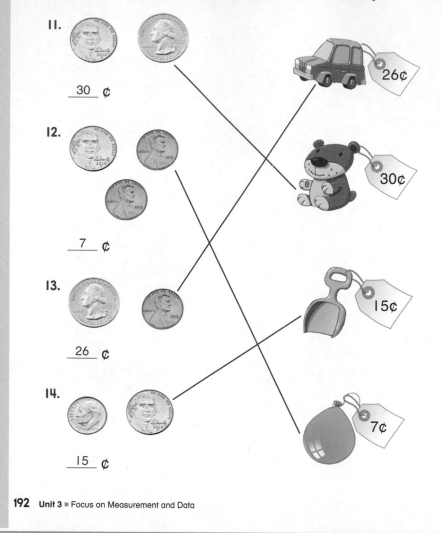

**Write the value of each group of coins.
Match each group of coins to the toy it will buy.**

11. _____ 30 ¢

12. _____ 7 ¢

13. _____ 26 ¢

14. _____ 15 ¢

26¢

30¢

15¢

7¢

Math-to-Shopping Connection

Simulated Store Have each child draw a picture of an inexpensive toy, trinket, or school supply. Tell them to draw a price tag beside the object and write a price that is between 7¢ and 30¢. Collect the drawings and have children pretend that they are real objects in a store. Provide play coins for children to select the amount needed to buy the object that they choose. Encourage children to choose an item other than their own. Have children work in pairs and take turns acting as the buyer or seller, counting out the coins, and checking one another's work.

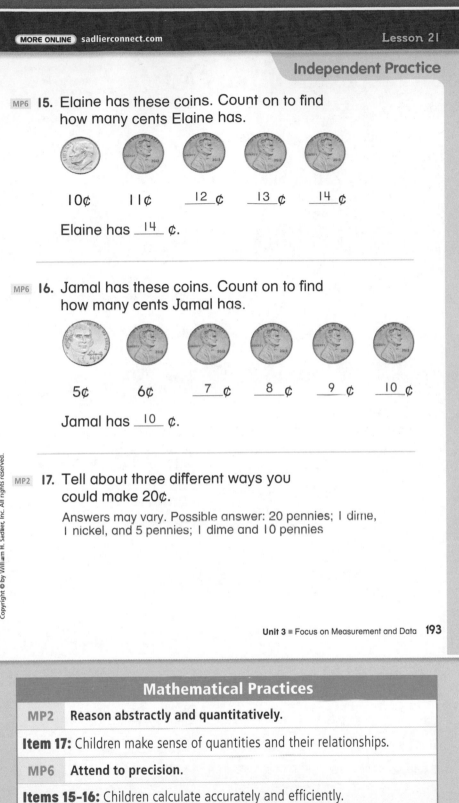

MP6 15. Elaine has these coins. Count on to find how many cents Elaine has.

10¢   11¢   _12_ ¢   _13_ ¢   _14_ ¢

Elaine has _14_ ¢.

MP6 16. Jamal has these coins. Count on to find how many cents Jamal has.

5¢   6¢   _7_ ¢   _8_ ¢   _9_ ¢   _10_ ¢

Jamal has _10_ ¢.

MP2 17. Tell about three different ways you could make 20¢.

Answers may vary. Possible answer: 20 pennies; 1 dime,
1 nickel, and 5 pennies; 1 dime and 10 pennies

Teaching Tips

Items 15–16
Be sure children count on from the previous number rather than starting their counting from 1.

Item 17
Provide play coins to help children model and think about the various combinations of coins or whether they can use only one type of coin to make 20¢.

Mathematical Practices

MP2	**Reason abstractly and quantitatively.**

Item 17: Children make sense of quantities and their relationships.

MP6	**Attend to precision.**

Items 15–16: Children calculate accurately and efficiently.

OBJECTIVE
Use tables to record information and make comparisons.

ESSENTIAL QUESTION
Read aloud the Essential Question and ask children to tell what they know about using a table to show information. Explain that a data table is different than a table having a flat surface that is supported by three or four legs.

FLUENCY PRACTICE
Fluency practice is available at **sadlierconnect.com**.

Concept Development

Understand: Use tally marks to show data in a table

■ Children are not introduced to tally marks in kindergarten and may be unfamiliar with them. Demonstrate how to draw one to four tally marks, making sure children understand that these marks do not represent numerals, particularly 1 and 11. Then demonstrate how to make a cross mark for a bundle of five.

■ Make sure children understand that tally marks are not bundled by place value as in the tens and ones models used previously. The fives are bundled simply to make counting the marks easier.

Lesson
22 Use Tables

Guided Instruction

Essential Question: How do you use a table to make comparisons?

Words to Know
data
table
tally mark

In this lesson you will learn how to use a table.

Understand: Use tally marks to show data in a table

The children in Keri's class are using these toys. Use a table to show how many of each toy the children are using.

To show data in a table:
Look at the names of the toys in the table.

Look at the pictures. In the table, make a tally mark for each picture next to its name.

Draw a line through four tally marks to make a bundle of five.

Toy	Number of Toys
Car	ЖІІ
Train	ІІІІ
Plane	ЖІІІ

▷ The children are using 7 cars, 4 trains, and 8 planes.

Words to Know

data: factual information, the facts shown in a data table

table: a visual way to show data

Example:

Favorite Sport	Number of Children
Soccer	ЖІ ЖІ ІІ
Basketball	ІІІ
Baseball	ЖІ ІІІ

tally mark: marks used to show how many

Example: І means 1   ЖІ means 5

Glossary can be found on pp. 261–272.

Lesson 22

Guided Instruction

Understand: **Use a table to find how many in all**

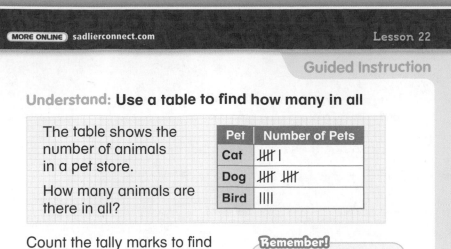

The table shows the number of animals in a pet store.

How many animals are there in all?

Pet	Number of Pets
Cat	ЖЖ I
Dog	ЖЖ ЖЖ
Bird	IIII

Count the tally marks to find how many of each animal.

There are 6 cats, 10 dogs, and 4 birds.

Add to find the total number of animals.

$6 + 10 + 4 = 20$

➪ There are 20 animals in all.

> **Remember!**
> A line through four tally marks shows a bundle of 5: ЖЖ

Understand: **Use a table to compare**

Does the table above show that there are more birds or more cats? How many more?

There are 6 cats and 4 birds. 6 is greater than 4. There are more cats than birds.

Subtract to find how many more. $6 - 4 = 2$

➪ There are 2 more cats than birds.

Understand: Use a table to find how many in all

■ Make sure children understand that the tally marks beside each pet tell the total number of that kind of pet. Have children point to each kind of pet and count the number of tally marks in that row.

■ Tell children that they can count the number of cats by counting the bundle as 5 and then counting on the number of individual marks. Children can count the number of dogs by counting the first bundle as 5 and then counting on by ones. They can count the number of birds by counting by ones.

Understand: Use a table to compare

■ Have children discuss whether the tally marks make it easier to compare the numbers of the different kinds of pets.

■ Point out that tally marks makes it easier to see when there are bundles of 5. For example, it is easy to see that there are more dogs than cats because 2 bundles of 5 shows more animals than 1 bundle of 5.

Support English Language Learners

Children learning to speak English often struggle with homographs, words that are spelled alike but are different in meaning or pronunciation. The language is further complicated by words that simply have more than one pronunciation, often depending on regional accents or specific settings. Children may hear the word *data* pronounced more than one way and incorrectly think that it is two different words. Dictionaries vary in designating the more common pronunciation, *day-ta,* with a long a sound, or *dat-a,* with a short a sound. Some sources point out that *day-ta* is the more common pronunciation among data processing professional settings. Children may pronounce the word either way as long as they understand both pronunciations as the same word.

Connect: **What you know about showing data in a table** Use this page to help children gather and record information from an illustration.

■ Children may count all of the yellow stickers as happy faces because the suns all show a smile. Clarify the distinction between the suns and happy faces prior to beginning the page.

■ If children struggle to count each type of sticker accurately, suggest they cross off each sticker in the group as they count.

■ Remind children to check their answers by comparing the number of tally marks they drew with the number of stickers in the illustration.

Connect: **What you know about showing data in a table**

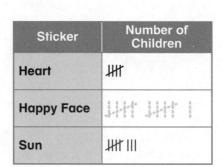

Rosa has these stickers in her album.

Use a table to show how many of each sticker Rosa has.

Step 1

List the kinds of stickers. Look at the pictures.

Make a tally mark for each sticker.

Draw a line through four tally marks to make a bundle of 5.

Sticker	Number of Children
Heart	卌
Happy Face	卌 卌 I
Sun	卌 III

Step 2

Count the tally marks for each kind of sticker.

▷ Rosa has __5__ heart stickers, __11__ happy face stickers, and __8__ sun stickers.

Math-to-Current Events Connection

Reporting the News Tell children that data tables are often shown in newspapers and magazines to share important or interesting information. Research and provide several real-world examples of data charts and tables found in news sources geared toward children. Talk about the different kinds charts and tables and explain what information can be learned from them. If tally marks are used to record the data, ask children to talk about and make comparisons between the different values.

Lesson 22

Guided Practice

I. **The table shows the favorite sport of some children.**

Sport	Number of Children
Soccer	ⅢⅡ
Baseball	Ⅲ Ⅲ Ⅰ
Basketball	ⅠⅠⅠⅠ

How many more children chose soccer than chose basketball?

Step 1

How many children chose soccer? __7__ children

How many children chose basketball? __4__ children

Step 2

Subtract to compare. __7__ − __4__ = __3__

__3__ more children chose __soccer__.

🤴 Think・Pair・Share

MP3 2. **Use the table about some children's favorite sport. Write a question that you would use addition to solve.**

Tell how you would solve the problem.
Sample answer: How many children in all chose soccer or baseball? I would use the table to find how many children chose soccer and how many chose baseball. I would add the two numbers to find the answer.

Unit 3 ■ Focus on Measurement and Data **197**

Mathematical Practices

Mathematical Practice Standards underline the teaching and understanding of all concepts and skills presented. The emphasis of specific practices is noted throughout the guided and independent practice of this lesson.

MP3	**Construct viable arguments and critique the reasoning of others.**

Item 2: Children construct and solve a problem related to the data.

Observational Assessment

Use page 197 to assess whether children are able to follow the step-by-step analysis of the information displayed in the table.

🤴 Think・Pair・Share

Peer Collaboration Have pairs of children share the questions that they created and explain the processes they used. Prompt the discussions with questions such as:

- *What data from the table did you decide to use?*

- *What question did you choose to answer about the data?*

- *How did you use addition to answer the question?*

Make sure children understand that there are many ways to solve the problem. They only need to use the data accurately to write and solve a question by using addition.

Return to the Essential Question

Reread the Lesson 22 Essential Question on page 194: *How do you use a table to make comparisons?*

Tell children to think about what they learned in this lesson to answer this question.
(Possible responses: I can use tally marks to show the number of objects in each group. I can use and compare the data by looking at the number of tally marks.)

Have children share specific ways they can use data in a table.

Independent Practice

Concept Application

Children may work independently on these pages in the classroom or at home. They may refer to the first four pages of the lesson to revisit the instruction or to see a worked-out example.

Common Errors and **Teaching Tips** may help you support learning either in the classroom or as a follow-up for work done at home.

Common Errors

Item 1

Children may miscount due to skipping beads or counting them more than once. As they count each bead, have children draw a mark through the bead and then draw a tally mark in the table in the correct row.

Teaching Tips

Item 1

Remind children that every fifth bead is marked in the chart by using a diagonal line through the four preceding tallies.

Independent Practice

Pat has red, green, and blue beads.

1. Count the beads to complete the table.

Beads	Number of Beads
Red	‖‖‖ ‖‖‖ I
Green	‖‖‖ ‖‖‖ IIII
Blue	‖‖‖ ‖‖‖ ‖‖‖

2. Are there more red beads or blue beads?

   _____blue_____ beads

3. How many green beads are there?

   __14__ green beads

4. Which color bead does Pat have the greatest number of? _____blue_____

Talking About Math

Clarify the Meaning of Words Ask children to identify tables (the kind with legs) that they see in the classroom. Encourage them to name other places where they might see such tables, such as at the library, at home, or in the cafeteria. Point out that tables of a different kind are sometimes used to display models that provide information. Have children discuss ways that a data table shows information. Ask children to work in small groups to describe one way to use a furniture table to show a collection of objects and one way to use a data table to show information about those objects.

Lesson 22

Independent Practice

Each child at the school fair was given one balloon. The table shows how many balloons of each color were given out.

Color	Number of Balloons
Red	卌 卌
Blue	卌 I
Green	III

5. How many children were given blue balloons?

   __6__ children

6. Which color balloon was given to the most children?

   __red__

7. How many more children were given blue balloons than were given green balloons?

   __3__ children

8. How many children were given either a red balloon or a green balloon?

   __13__ children

Unit 3 ■ Focus on Measurement and Data **199**

Common Errors
Items 7-8
Children may not correctly identify the mathematical operation needed to answer the problems. Having children use colored pencils to draw the balloons may help them clarify their thinking.

Teaching Tips
Items 7-8
Point out that these problems require more than one step to solve. Remind children to first identify the important data shown by the tally marks. Then have them decide whether to add or subtract to solve the problem.

Digital Connection

Online Activities Use an Internet search engine to look for grade-appropriate data displays, searching topics such as *tally marks, tallies, tables,* and *data.* Display the illustrations and ask children to tell about what the data shows.

Teaching Tips

Item 9

Make sure children understand that they will count the number of names in each sentence to identify the how many tally marks they need to make.

Item 12

If children show they are having difficulty in how they approach the solution, prompt them to restate the question and then describe whether the solution requires addition or subtraction.

---

9. **Complete the table to show what some children ate for breakfast.**

Food	Number of Children
Hot cereal	III
Cold cereal	IIII
Eggs	IIII

Kyle, Lex, and Sammy ate hot cereal for breakfast. Make tally marks for these children in the table.

Jenny, Maria, Pablo, Nate, and Rob ate cold cereal for breakfast. Make tally marks for these children.

Ana, Luke, Bella, and Zach ate eggs for breakfast. Make tally marks for these children.

Use the table for problems 10–12.

10. **Which food did the most children eat for breakfast?**

   cold cereal

11. **How many more children ate eggs than hot cereal?**

   I more

12. **How many children ate cereal in all?** __8__ children

Math-to-Reading Connection

Stories and Data Displays Choose a picture book that includes groups of objects. Before reading to the class, draw a table to record data from the book as you read. Allow children to make suggestions about how to record the data in the table. Encourage them to identify the data within the story and explain where to record it in the table. After completing the story, use the tally marks to ask questions about information gathered from the story. Allow children to use the data to pose their own questions for the rest of the class to answer.

Lesson 22

Independent Practice

MP1 **13.** Color some stars blue. Color the rest yellow.

Use your stars. Make tally marks to complete the table.

Color	Number of Stars
Blue	
Yellow	

14. Are there more blue stars or yellow stars?

_____ stars

15. How many more are there?

_____ more Check children's work.

Teaching Tips

Item 13
Point out that there are many acceptable ways to solve the problem. Children can color any number of the stars blue. Each table will correspond to that particular group of colored stars.

Items 14–15
Answers to these problems will vary. Have children work together in pairs to explain their work and justify their answers.

Return to the

Progress Check

Remind children to return to the Progress Check self-assessment, page 159, to check off additional items they have mastered during the unit.

Mathematical Practices
MP1 **Make sense of problems and persevere in solving them.**
Item 13: Children create a data set and record the data in a table.

The Unit 3 Review covers all the standards presented in the unit. Use it to assess your students' mastery of the unit's concepts and skills.

Depth of Knowledge

The depth of knowledge is a ranking of the content complexity of assessment items based on Webb's Depth of Knowledge (DOK) levels. The levels increase in complexity as shown below.

Level 1: Recall and Reproduction
Level 2: Basic Skills and Concepts
Level 3: Strategic Reasoning and Thinking
Level 4: Extended Thinking

Item	DOK
1	2
2	2
3	2
4	1
5	1
6	2
7	2
8	2
9	2
10	4

Unit 3 **Review**

1. Nick and Ella use a ribbon to compare the length across their books. Nick marks the ribbon with a red line to show the length across his Science book. Ella uses the same ribbon to show the length across her Math book.

   Circle the book that has the longer length across. Mark an X on the book that has the shorter length across.

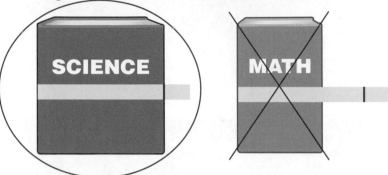

2. Put the objects in order from shortest to longest.

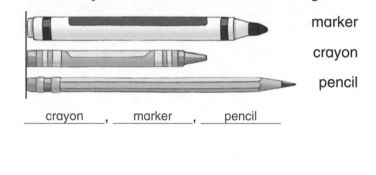

marker

crayon

pencil

____crayon____ , ____marker____ , ____pencil____

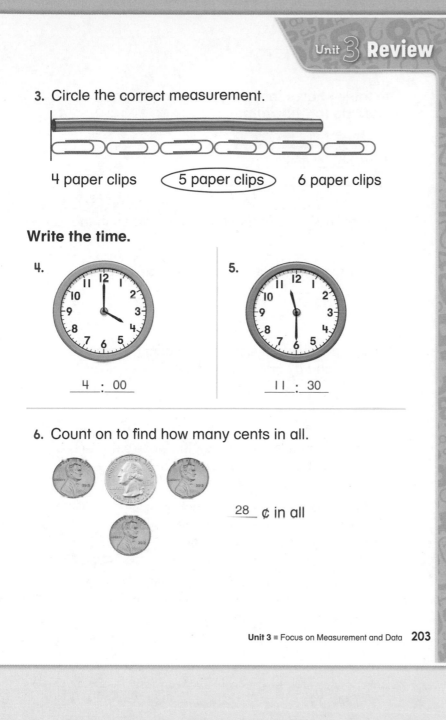

Unit 3 Review

3. Circle the correct measurement.

4 paper clips   ⬭5 paper clips⬬   6 paper clips

Write the time.

4.

_4_ : _00_

5.

_11_ : _30_

6. Count on to find how many cents in all.

_28_ ¢ in all

This chart correlates the Unit 3 Review items with the lessons in which the concepts and skills are presented.

Item	Lesson
1	18
2	18
3	19
4	20
5	20
6	21
7	22
8	22
9	22
10	20

Talking About Math

Direct students to respond to the Unit 3 Essential Question. (This can also be found on page 161.)

Essential Question:
How can you tell what time it is?

Possible responses:
- On clocks that have hands, the hour hand points to the hour and the minute hand points to the number of minutes past that hour.
- Digital clocks show three or four digits that name the time.

Unit Assessment

- Unit 3 Review, *pp. 202–204*
- Unit 3 Performance Task ONLINE

Additional Assessment Options

Optional Purchase:
- iProgress Monitor ONLINE
- Progress Monitor Student Benchmark Assessment Booklet

Unit **3** Review

The table shows the camps that children signed up for this summer.

Camp	Number of Children
Soccer	ЖЖ ЖЖ II
Dance	ЖЖ I

7. Alex, Ava, Sam, and Julia also signed up for Dance camp. Add tally marks for these children in the table.

8. How many children in all signed up for camp?

   __18__ children

9. Did more children sign up for Soccer camp or Dance camp? How many more?

   _____ Soccer camp; 6 more _____

MP1 10. Kyle draws the hour hand on the clock between the 3 and the 4. Then he draws the minute hand pointing to the 6.

What time does his clock show? Draw hands on the clock to help. Explain how you found the time.

   __3__ : __30__

Answers may vary. Possible answer: I drew the hands on the clock the same way Kyle did. Then I read the time on the clock as three-thirty.

Mathematical Practices	
MP1	Make sense of problems and persevere in solving them.

Item 10: Children make conjectures about the meaning of a solution and plan pathways to complete their explanations.

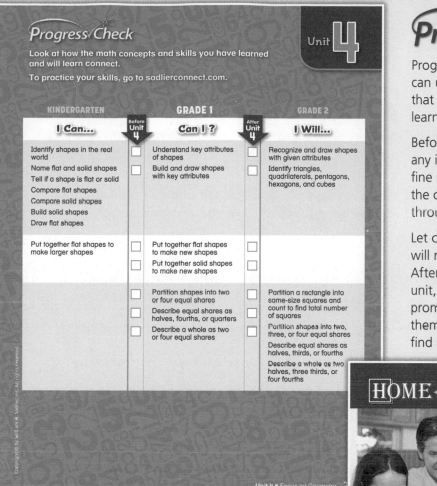

Progress Check

Progress Check is a self-assessment tool that children can use to gauge their own progress. Research shows that when children take accountability for their learning, motivation increases.

Before children begin work in Unit 4, have them check any items they know they can do well. Explain that it is fine if they don't check any of the boxes; they will have the opportunity to learn and practice all the standards through the course of the unit.

Let children know that at the end of the unit they will review their checklists to check their progress. After children have completed the last lesson of the unit, before they begin the Unit 4 Review, you will be prompted to have children revisit this page. Remind them to keep this page in a safe place where they can find it later.

HOME ◆ CONNECT...

The Home Connect feature is a way to keep parents or other adult family members apprised of what their children are learning. The key learning objectives are listed, and some ideas for related activities and discussions are included.

Explain to children that they can share the Home Connect page at home with their families. Let children know there is an activity connected to their classroom learning that they can do with their families.

Encourage children and their parents to share their experiences using the suggestions on the Home Connect. You may wish to invite children to share this work with the class.

HOME ◆ CONNECT...

Your child will identify flat (two-dimensional) and solid (three-dimensional) shapes. They will also make new shapes by combining flat and solid shapes.

Your child will identify a flat shape by its sides and its corners.

- A closed flat shape with 3 straight sides and 3 corners is a triangle.
- A closed flat shape with 4 straight sides and 4 square corners is a rectangle.
- A closed flat shape with 4 straight sides that are the same length and 4 square corners is a square.

Your child will also learn how to partition circles and rectangles into two and four equal parts or shares.

In this unit your child will:

- Identify and compose two-dimensional shapes and three-dimensional shapes.
- Make equal shares.

Ways to Help Your Child

Using literature is a great way to make connections between reading and math. Your local library will contain wonderful resources for books that involve math for first graders. Children's books with math themes are readily available and can enhance what your child is learning in the classroom.

Take advantage of every chance to point out flat and solid shapes in daily life. Encourage your child to notice these shapes both at home and when shopping or doing other chores outside the home. Vacations also provide an excellent opportunity to spot new and unusual flat and solid shapes not normally seen in the family's day-to-day environment.

Activity: Play "I Spy a Shape." Challenge your child to find the two-dimensional (flat) or three-dimensional (solid) shapes you describe to them. You might say, "I spy a closed, flat shape with three sides." (Triangle) Since shapes are everywhere, you can play this game whether you are taking a walk, shopping for groceries, or just driving around town.

ONLINE
For more Home Connect activities, continue online at sadlierconnect.com

206 Unit 4 ■ Focus on Geometry

UNIT PLANNER

Lesson	Objective
23 Identify Shapes	Identify characteristics of triangles or rectangles.
24 Compose Flat Shapes	Combine two-dimensional shapes to make new shapes and identify the shapes that make up composite shapes.
25 Compose Solid Shapes	Combine three-dimensional shapes and identify the shapes that make composite solid shapes.
26 Partition Shapes into Equal Shares	Use drawings to make equal shares of halves and fourths.

Essential Question	Words to Know
How do you identify triangles and rectangles?	sides corners triangle rectangle square trapezoid
How do you put shapes together to make new shapes?	hexagon
How do you put solid shapes together to make a new solid shape?	flat shape cube solid shape faces rectangular prism
How do you make equal shares?	equal share halves half fourth quarter

Unit Assessment

- Unit 4 Review, *pp. 240–242*
- Unit 4 Performance Task ONLINE

Additional Assessment Options

- Performance Task 2, *pp. 243–246*
  ALSO ONLINE

Optional Purchase:

- iProgress Monitor ONLINE
- Progress Monitor Student Benchmark Assessment Booklet

ONLINE Digital Resources

- Home Connect Activities
- Unit Performance Tasks
- Additional Practice
- Fluency Practice
- Teacher Resources
- iProgress Monitor (optional purchase)

Go to SadlierConnect.com to access your Digital Resources.

For more detailed instructions see page T3.

LEARNING PROGRESSIONS

This page provides more in-depth detail on the development of math concepts and skills across the grade levels. See also the unit Progress Check page in the Student Edition for a roadmap of the Learning Progressions.

Grade K

- Students identify objects in the environment using names of shapes and describe their relative positions using terms such as *above, below, beside, in front of, behind,* and *next to.* They correctly name shapes regardless of their orientation or overall size.
- Students identify shapes as two-dimensional or three-dimensional, using words such as "flat" and "solid."
- Students analyze and compare two- and three-dimensional shapes, in different sizes and orientations, using informal language to describe their similarities, differences, parts, and other attributes.
- Students model shapes by building them from components (e.g., sticks, clay balls) and by drawing them.
- Students put together simple shapes to form larger shapes.

Grade 1

- Students distinguish between attributes that define shapes (e.g., number of sides) and non-defining attributes (e.g., color, size, orientation). They build and draw shapes to match given defining attributes.
- Students compose two-dimensional shapes or three-dimensional shapes to create a composite shape, and compose new shapes from the composite shape.
- Students partition shapes into two or four equal shares, describe the shares as *halves, fourths,* and *quarters,* and use the phrases *half of, fourth of,* and *quarter of.* They describe a whole as two halves, four fourths, or four quarters, and understand that partitioning the same shape into more equal shares creates smaller shares.

Grade 2

- Students identify and draw shapes with specified attributes, such as a given number of angles or a given number of equal faces.
- Students identify triangles, quadrilaterals, pentagons, hexagons, and cubes.
- Students partition rectangles into rows and columns of same-size squares and count to find the total number of squares.
- Students partition circles and rectangles into two, three, or four equal shares and describe them as halves, thirds, and fourths. They describe a whole as two halves, three thirds, or four fourths. They recognize that equal shares of identical wholes need not have the same shape.

Focus on Geometry

Unit 4

Essential Question:
What shapes do you see?

Unit 4 ■ Focus on Geometry **207**

As children become involved with the Essential Question they will identify and combine flat shapes and identify and combine solid shapes.

Conversation Starters

Have children discuss the photograph. Ask question such as: *What kinds of shapes do you see? Can you name any of the shapes? Can you point to two shapes that are the same shape in different colors?*

Many children will already know the word *triangle.* Explain that triangles have three straight sides. Have children look for triangles in the photograph. *Are all of the triangles alike?* (no) *How are some of them different?* (There are different colors of triangles. Some are long and skinny, but some have sides that look like the same lengths.) *Are all of the kites the same shape? How can you describe them?* (The kites are different shapes. One of them is round with streamers. One is almost a triangle. The big kite looks like a star.)

Have children work in pairs to count triangles that are the same color. Then have the pairs of children share the color and number of triangles they counted.

Activity

Materials: attribute shapes or paper shapes (circles, triangles, and rectangles)

Give each child three shapes: a circle, a triangle, and a rectangle. Arrange children in equal groups of three to five members. Explain that you will give clues about a shape that you see in the photograph on this page and that all members of the groups must hold up a shape that matches the clues. The first group in which all children show the correct answer wins a point. Provide attribute clues such as: *I see a big round shape; I see a shape that has three straight sides; I see a shape that has four straight sides.* Remind children to work together to make sure their entire group can find the correct shapes. Tell them that the colors do not need to match. Continue the game until children can readily identify shapes that match the clues.

OBJECTIVE
Identify characteristics of triangles or rectangles.

ESSENTIAL QUESTION
Read the Essential Question aloud and ask children to discuss what they already know about triangles and rectangles. Tell children that the lesson will help them identify these shapes by looking at their sides and corners.

PREREQUISITE SKILLS
Use Foundational Skills Handbook page 256, *Geometry and Data,* to review sorting shapes based on the number of sides in each figure.

FLUENCY PRACTICE
Fluency practice is available at **sadlierconnect.com**.

Concept Development

Understand: Use sides and corners to identify a triangle

■ Explain that a side is a line that shows the outer edge of a shape.

■ Point out that corners are formed where two sides meet. Have children point to each corner of the triangle.

■ Children may not understand that a figure can have sides and corners but not be a closed shape. For example, if the left and right sides of the triangle did not meet to form a corner, the shape would not be closed and it would not be a triangle.

■ Children will be introduced to four shapes in this lesson. Provide index cards for children to use in drawing and labeling examples of the shapes as they learn about them.

Lesson
23 Identify Shapes

Essential Question:
How do you identify triangles and rectangles?

Words to Know
sides
corners
triangle
rectangle
square
trapezoid

Guided Instruction

In this lesson you will learn to identify triangles and rectangles.

Understand: Use sides and corners to identify a triangle

Sophia drew this shape. What is the shape called?

You can identify this shape by its sides and its corners.

side →

← corner

This shape has 3 straight sides and 3 corners.

It is a closed shape. There are no gaps in the sides.

A closed shape with 3 straight sides and 3 corners is a triangle.

▷ Sophia drew a triangle.

Words to Know

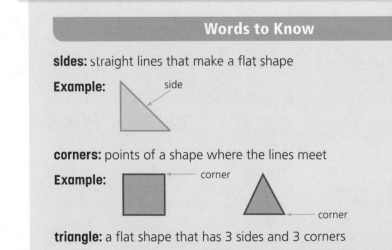

sides: straight lines that make a flat shape

Example: side

corners: points of a shape where the lines meet

Example: corner   corner

triangle: a flat shape that has 3 sides and 3 corners

Understand: Use sides and corners to identify a rectangle and a square

May drew these two shapes. What are they called?

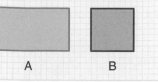

A   B

Shape A has 4 straight sides. It has 4 square corners, like the corners of this page. It is closed.

A closed shape with 4 straight sides and 4 square corners is a rectangle.

Shape A is a rectangle.

Shape B also has 4 straight sides and 4 square corners. All 4 sides are the same length. It is closed.

A closed shape with 4 straight sides that are the same length and 4 square corners is a square.

Shape B is a square. A square is a special rectangle.

May drew a rectangle and a ___square___.

Understand: Use sides and corners to identify a rectangle and a square

■ Point out the difference between the corners of a triangle and the corners of rectangles and squares. Rectangles and squares have special *square* corners. Every square corner looks the same. They all have the same shape.

■ By definition, the opposite sides of a rectangle are parallel and are the same length, and each of the four angles are equivalent, measuring 90°. The square is a special rectangle having four sides that are all the same length.

■ If children struggle with the difference between a square and a rectangle that is not a square, have them draw each shape on grid paper. Have them cut the two shapes out and place the square on top of the rectangle. Ask children to describe the ways in which the shapes are the same and different. They both have square corners, and their opposite sides match up. The rectangle that is a square has four equal sides. The rectangle that is not a square has two longer equal sides and two shorter equal sides.

■ Model how to fold paper figures in half diagonally. If the figure is a square, both halves will align. If the figure is a rectangle that is not a square, the halves will not align.

Words to Know

rectangle: a flat shape with 4 sides and 4 square corners

square: a flat shape with 4 equal sides and 4 square corners

trapezoid: a flat shape with 4 sides, 2 sides are parallel

Glossary can be found on pp. 261–272.

Guided Instruction

Connect: What you know about identifying shapes Use this page to help children understand how to differentiate between shapes by their attributes.

■ Ask children to explain how they know that both shapes are closed. Children should be able to express that they are closed shapes because there are no gaps in the lines that form the sides of the shapes.

■ Although the example of a trapezoid shown on the page does not have any square corners, point out that some trapezoids may have square corners.

■ Some children may describe the trapezoid shown on the page as being similar to a triangle with the top part cut off.

Guided Instruction

Connect: What you know about identifying shapes

Natalie cut out a rectangle and a trapezoid.

rectangle

trapezoid

How are the shapes alike?
How are they different?

Step 1

Tell how the rectangle and the trapezoid are alike.

Both shapes are _____closed_____.

Both shapes have 4 sides and __4__ corners.

Step 2

Tell how the shapes are different.
Look at the corners.

The rectangle has 4 ___square___ corners.

The trapezoid does not have square corners.

▷ Both shapes are closed. Both shapes have 4 sides and 4 corners. The trapezoid does not have square corners.

210 Unit 4 ■ Focus on Geometry

Support English Language Learners

An understanding of common prefixes often helps English language learners take apart words to figure out what they mean. For example, *bicycle* means "two wheels" and *tricycle* means "three wheels." Children who are familiar with these words may quickly grasp that *triangle* means "three of something." Display the words *triangle* and *rectangle*. Explain that the word *angle* is one way to describe a corner of a shape, so *triangle* means "three corners." Tell children to find the word *angle* in *rectangle*. Explain that the prefix *rect-* tells that the angles are square, so *rectangle* means "square corners."

Lesson 23

Guided Practice

1. **Which of these shapes are triangles?**

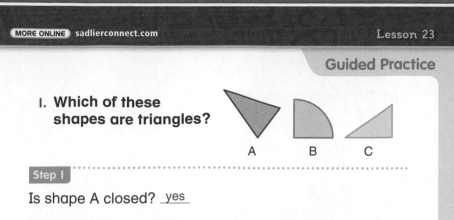

A   B   C

Step 1

Is shape A closed? _yes_

Does it have 3 straight sides and 3 corners? _yes_

Is shape A a triangle? _yes_

Step 2

Does shape B have 3 straight sides? _no_

Is shape B a triangle? _no_

Step 3

Is shape C closed? _yes_

Does it have 3 straight sides and 3 corners? _yes_

Is shape C a triangle? _yes_

♛ Think•Pair•Share

MP3 2. **Shape A and shape C are both triangles. Talk about how they are different.**
Answers may vary. Possible answer: Shapes A and C are different colors, different sizes, and they are turned in different ways. Triangles can be any color, turned in any direction, and be different sizes. They are still triangles as long as they are closed and have 3 sides and 3 corners.

Unit 4 ■ Focus on Geometry **211**

Mathematical Practices

Mathematical Practice Standards underline the teaching and understanding of all concepts and skills presented. The emphasis of specific practices is noted throughout the guided and independent practice of this lesson.

MP3	**Construct viable arguments and critique the reasoning of others.**

Item 2: Children construct arguments by using drawings.

Observational Assessment

Use page 211 to assess whether children are able to analyze examples and counterexamples of triangles. Observe children who demonstrate confusion about shape B and review the meaning of straight sides.

♛ Think•Pair•Share

Peer Collaboration Allow children to work in pairs to explain their answers to one another. Prompt the discussions with questions such as:

- *How do you know that shapes A and C are triangles?*

- *Are they alike in size? Shape? The way they are turned?*

- *Does the color of a shape make it a triangle?*

- *How do you know whether the shapes are closed shapes?*

Children may answer problem 2 in various ways as they demonstrate an understanding of the non-defining attributes such as size, color, and orientation of the triangles.

Return to the Essential Question

Reread the Lesson 23 Essential Question on page 208: *How do you identify triangles and rectangles?*

Tell children to think about what they learned in this lesson to answer this question.
(Possible responses: If a closed shape has 3 sides and 3 corners, it is a triangle. If a closed shape has 4 sides and 4 square corners, it is a rectangle.)

Have children share other concepts they learned in this lesson, such as how squares and rectangles that are not squares are alike and how they are different.

Concept Application

Children may work independently on these pages in the classroom or at home. They may refer to the first four pages of the lesson to revisit the instruction or to see a worked-out example.

Common Errors and **Teaching Tips** may help you support learning either in the classroom or as a follow-up for work done at home.

Common Errors

Item 4

Children who name this shape as a rectangle are correct, but they should recognize that this shape has a more specific name. Make sure children understand that squares are a specific kind of rectangle.

Teaching Tips

Items 1 and 6

Make sure children understand that the names of shapes do not change when the shapes are turned a different direction.

Item 3

Children may have difficulty identifying this shape. Ask questions about the shape of the corners or the number of the sides to help eliminate incorrect answers. Since the figure does not have square corners, it cannot be a rectangle or a square. Since it has more than three sides, it cannot be a triangle. The only remaining choice is the trapezoid.

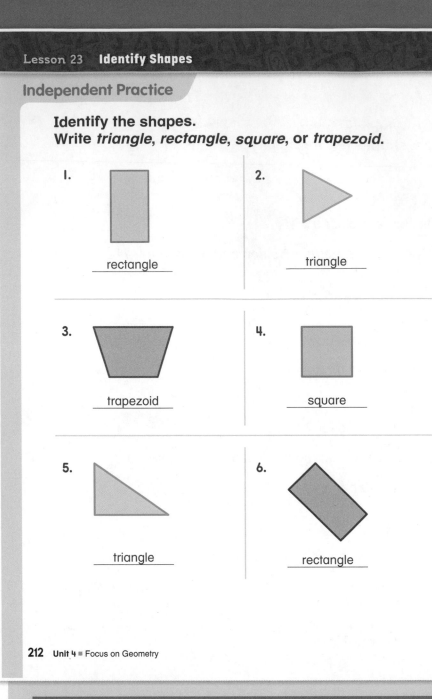

Identify the shapes.
Write *triangle*, *rectangle*, *square*, or *trapezoid*.

1. rectangle

2. triangle

3. trapezoid

4. square

5. triangle

6. rectangle

Talking About Math

Ask and Answer Questions Arrange children in small groups for an activity creating or answering riddles. Ask each child to draw a shape and cover it so that no one can see it. Then have children take turns saying a clue about the shape that they drew and asking others to guess the name of the shape. Remind children not to use non-defining attributes, such as color, size, or position, as clues. If time allows, have children discuss when one clue was enough and when more than one clue was needed.

Independent Practice

The robot is made of different shapes. Use the robot for problems 7, 8, and 9.

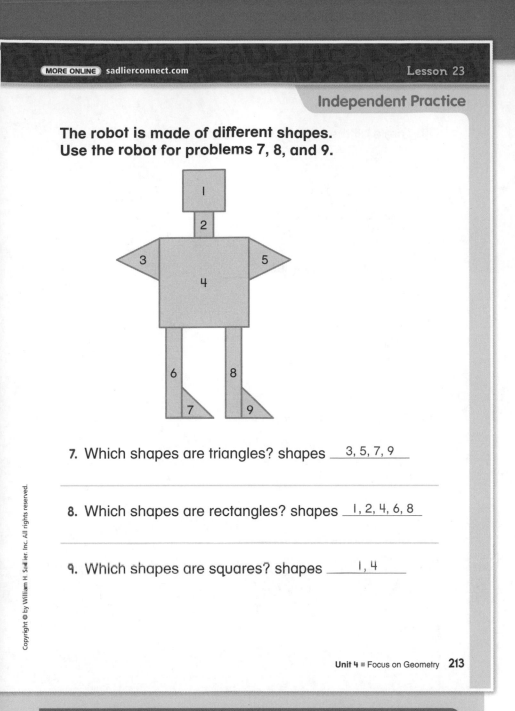

7. Which shapes are triangles? shapes _3, 5, 7, 9_

8. Which shapes are rectangles? shapes _1, 2, 4, 6, 8_

9. Which shapes are squares? shapes _1, 4_

Unit 4 ■ Focus on Geometry **213**

Common Errors

Item 8

Some children may correctly identify figures 1 and 4 as squares but fail to identify them as rectangles as well. Make sure children understand that all squares are also rectangles.

Teaching Tips

Items 7–9

Children may need to mark each shape as they list it to make sure they identify all of the shapes.

Digital Connection

Sorting Shapes Use an interactive whiteboard to display a mixed collection of triangles, rectangles, squares, and trapezoids. Have children drag and drop the shapes to sort them by different attributes or names. For children who need to practice at a basic level, limit the sorting to two categories, such as shapes having 3 sides or 4 sides. Children who are ready for a challenge may sort the shapes into examples and counterexamples, such as triangles and shapes that are not triangles.

Independent Practice

Teaching Tips

Items 10–13

Have children recall that sides are straight and that two sides meet to form corners. One shape in each of these exercises includes at lease one side that is not straight.

Encourage children to demonstrate fluency by explaining why they circled each correct shape in each row and did not circle the incorrect shapes.

Independent Practice

10. Circle all the rectangles.

11. Circle all the triangles.

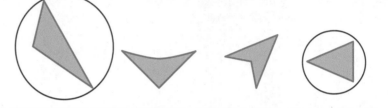

12. Circle all the squares.

13. Circle all the trapezoids.

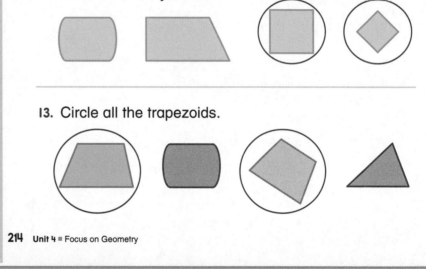

Math-to-Reading Connection

Books About Shapes There are many good trade books for early readers learning their basic shapes. Some of them include pop-out shapes to use as part of a reading and math activity. Select a book to read to the class and provide paper cutout shapes for children to display as you read. As you name each shape in the book, have children hold up their corresponding shape. Follow up the activity by having pairs of children use the illustrations to tell the story again, drawing examples of the shapes they see.

Independent Practice

MP4 **14.** Describe an example of a rectangle and a square in the classroom. Answers may vary.

How did you identify the rectangle?

Answers may vary. Answer should include that the rectangle has 4 straight sides and 4 square corners.

How did you identify the square?

Answers may vary. Answer should include that the square has 4 straight sides that are the same length and 4 square corners.

Draw a rectangle and a square.

Check children's work.

MP4 **15.** Draw a triangle and a trapezoid.

Check children's work.

Jada also drew a triangle and a trapezoid. What must be the same about your shapes and Jada's shapes?

The triangle must have 3 straight sides and 3 corners. The trapezoid must have 4 straight sides and 4 corners.

What could be different about your shapes and Jada's shapes?

Answers may vary. Possible answer: They could be different sizes, different shapes, and different colors. They could be turned in different directions.

Unit 4 ■ Focus on Geometry **215**

Teaching Tips

Item 14

Children who recognize two-dimensional shapes in three-dimensional objects demonstrate readiness for upcoming Lesson 25 concepts.

Item 15

If children hesitate in their approach to the problem, draw a counterexample to prompt analysis of each shape's defining attributes.

Mathematical Practices		
MP4	**Model with mathematics.**	

Item 14: Children analyze shapes and draw conclusions.

Item 15: Children use diagrams to model a solution.

OBJECTIVE

Combine two-dimensional shapes to make new shapes and identify the shapes that make up composite shapes.

ESSENTIAL QUESTION

Read aloud the Essential Question. Ask children to tell what it means to put shapes together. Explain that the lesson will show them how shapes can be combined or taken apart.

FLUENCY PRACTICE

Fluency practice is available at **sadlierconnect.com**.

Concept Development

Understand: Use two squares of the same size to make a rectangle

■ Children deepen their understanding of squares and rectangles by manipulating shapes to relate the two figures.

■ Some children may also recognize that a square can be cut apart horizontally or vertically to make two rectangles. If the square is cut exactly in half, the rectangles will be the same size.

Essential Question:
How do you put shapes together to make new shapes?

Words to Know
hexagon

In this lesson you will learn how to put shapes together to make new shapes.

Understand: Use two squares of the same size to make a rectangle

These two squares are the same size, so all the sides match each other.
What shape can you make by joining two sides of these squares?

Put the two squares next to each other.

Join two sides to make a new shape.
The new shape is a rectangle.

You can also put one square above the other.

Then join two sides to make a new shape. This new shape is also a rectangle.

▷ If two squares are the same size, you can join any two sides of the squares to make a rectangle.

Words to Know

hexagon: a flat shape with 6 sides and 6 corners

Example:

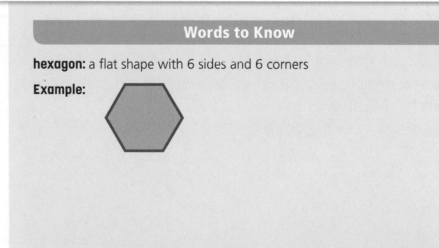

Glossary can be found on pp. 261–272.

Lesson 24

Guided Instruction

Understand: Use two triangles of the same size to make new shapes

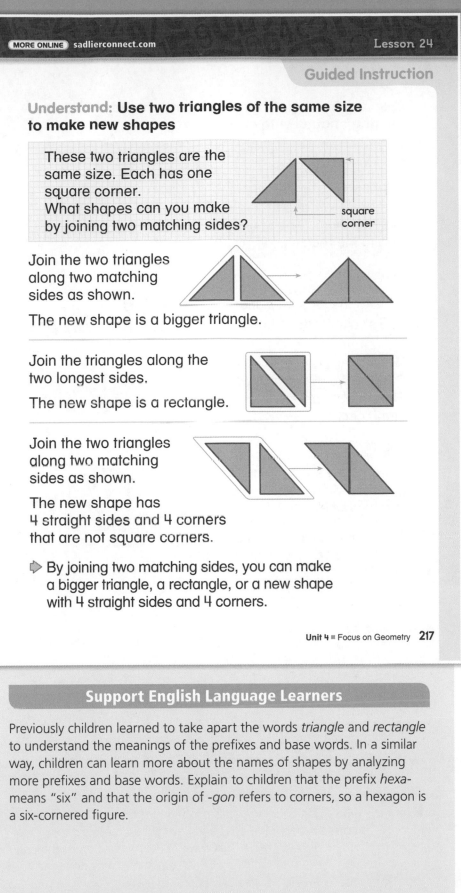

These two triangles are the same size. Each has one square corner.
What shapes can you make by joining two matching sides?

square corner

Join the two triangles along two matching sides as shown.

The new shape is a bigger triangle.

Join the triangles along the two longest sides.

The new shape is a rectangle.

Join the two triangles along two matching sides as shown.

The new shape has 4 straight sides and 4 corners that are not square corners.

▷ By joining two matching sides, you can make a bigger triangle, a rectangle, or a new shape with 4 straight sides and 4 corners.

Unit 4 ■ Focus on Geometry **217**

Understand: Use two triangles of the same size to make new shapes

■ Have children discuss why the triangles must be the same size to be combined as shown on the lesson page.

■ Provide paper right triangles for children to model combining the shapes as shown on this page. Children who demonstrate fluency may enjoy exploring how to combine two identical triangles that are not right triangles.

Support English Language Learners

Previously children learned to take apart the words *triangle* and *rectangle* to understand the meanings of the prefixes and base words. In a similar way, children can learn more about the names of shapes by analyzing more prefixes and base words. Explain to children that the prefix *hexa*- means "six" and that the origin of *-gon* refers to corners, so a hexagon is a six-cornered figure.

Connect: **Making shapes with straight sides and making shapes with curved sides** Use this page to help children understand how to combine more shapes.

■ Demonstrate for children how the shapes with straight and curved sides are part of a circle. Fold a cutout paper circle in half and then in half again. Unfold the circle to demonstrate how each section includes the curved outer edge and two straight lines that meet to form a square corner. Each part of the folded circle looks like one of the curved shapes at the top of page 218.

Connect: **Making shapes with straight sides and making shapes with curved sides**

The two curved shapes are parts of a circle. Put them together to make a larger part of the circle. Then put that shape together with the rectangle to make a new shape.

Step 1

Look at the straight sides. The straight sides match.

Step 2

Put the straight sides together. The new shape is a larger part of the circle.

Step 3

Put the new shape from Step 2 together with the rectangle to make a new shape.

➪ The new shape has a curved part and some straight sides.

Math-to-History Connections

Stained-Glass Windows Stained glass has been around for almost a thousand years. The colorful combinations of glass and paint have been used to record historic events, mythology, and natural scenes. Stained glass is even used to make lampshades, jewelry, and ornaments. Show children pictures of a variety of stained-glass windows that incorporate geometric shapes. Find coloring pages of stained-glass windows on the Internet. Print out a variety of images and have children use colored pencils to create their own stained-glass panel. Allow children to share their completed pictures, identifying and talking about how different shapes were used in their pictures.

1. **What shapes can you make using the two triangles and the rectangle?**

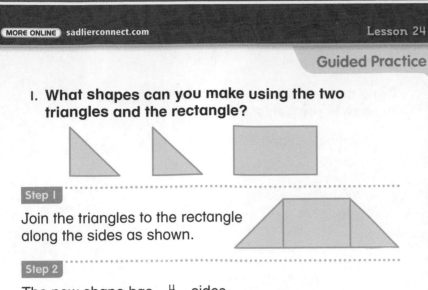

Step 1

Join the triangles to the rectangle along the sides as shown.

Step 2

The new shape has __4__ sides.

Is the new shape a square, a rectangle, or a trapezoid?

The new shape is a ___trapezoid___.

👐 Think·Pair·Share

MP1   2. **You can also make this shape from the triangles and the rectangle.**

How is this new shape like the trapezoid above? How is it different from the trapezoid above?

Answers may vary. Possible answer: Like: Both shapes have 4 straight sides and 4 corners. Both shapes have at least 2 sides that are the same length. Both shapes have no square corners. Different: The top and bottom of the trapezoid are not the same length. The top and bottom of the new shape are the same length.

Observational Assessment

Use page 219 to assess whether children understand how shapes can be put together to make a new shape. If children struggle to recognize the combined shape, suggest they use a bright marker to outline the exterior sides.

👐 Think·Pair·Share

Peer Collaboration Have pairs of children describe their comparisons to one another. Prompt the discussions with questions such as:

- *How many sides does each shape have?*

- *How many corners does each shape have?*

- *What smaller shapes are used to make the larger shapes?*

- *How could you change the second shape to make it look like the first shape?*

If children name the new shape as rectangle, review the characteristics of a rectangle and ask them if this shape has those characteristics.

Return to the Essential Question

Reread the Lesson 24 Essential Question on page 216: *How do you put shapes together to make new shapes?*

Tell children to think about what they learned in this lesson to answer this question.

(Possible responses: I can put squares that are the same size together to make a rectangle. I can put triangles that are the same size and shape together to make bigger triangles or rectangles. I can put shapes together to make other new shapes. I can put the same shapes together in different ways.)

Encourage children share other combinations of shapes that they explored in this lesson.

Mathematical Practices

Mathematical Practice Standards underline the teaching and understanding of all concepts and skills presented. The emphasis of specific practices is noted throughout the guided and independent practice of this lesson.

MP1   **Make sense of problems and persevere in solving them.**

Item 2: Children analyze the relationships of given shapes and explain their similarities and differences.

Concept Application

Children may work independently on these pages in the classroom or at home. They may refer to the first four pages of the lesson to revisit the instruction or to see a worked-out example.

Common Errors and **Teaching Tips** may help you support learning either in the classroom or as a follow-up for work done at home.

Teaching Tips

Items 1–2

If children have trouble identifying the new shape, have them draw lines to match each original shape to a part of the new shape.

Independent Practice

Draw a circle around the correct new shapes to answer problems 1 and 2.

1. Use these shapes.

Which new shape can you make?

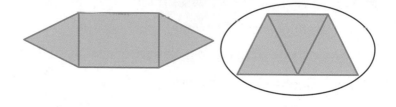

2. Use these shapes.

Which new shape can you make?

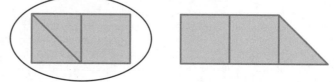

Talking About Math

Describe Details in an Illustration Have groups of children describe or list details in the illustrations of combined shapes on page 220. Prompt children to compare the sizes of each shape in the composite shapes, the lengths of sides that meet, and whether there are gaps. Have children distinguish between the details that matter, such as the defining attributes, and those that do not, such as color.

Independent Practice

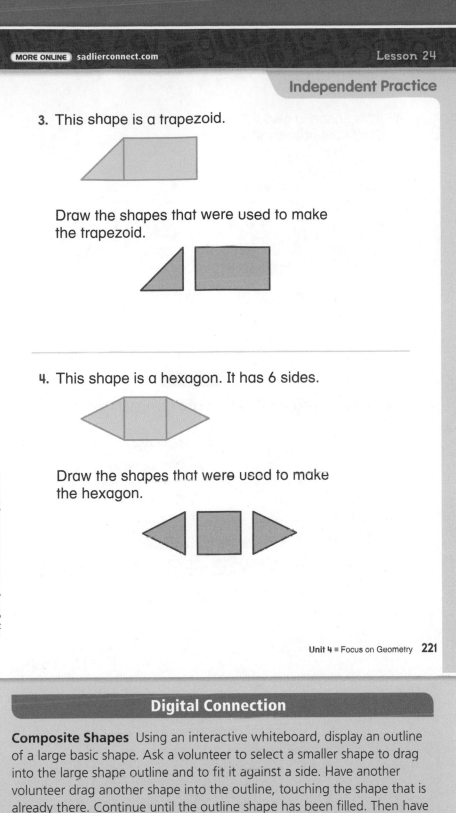

3. This shape is a trapezoid.

Draw the shapes that were used to make the trapezoid.

4. This shape is a hexagon. It has 6 sides.

Draw the shapes that were used to make the hexagon.

Common Errors

Item 4

Some children may break apart only one triangle from the hexagon, resulting in a pentagon and a triangle. Be sure that children understand that the pentagon can be broken into two additional basic shapes. Provide a set of shape manipulatives for children to use as they model how to break the bigger shape into smaller shapes.

Teaching Tips

Item 3

In the previous lesson, the trapezoid model did not have any square corners. Point out that this shape is also a trapezoid. A trapezoid may or may not have square corners. Children should understand that, although having square corners is a defining characteristic of squares and rectangles, it is not a defining characteristic for trapezoids.

Item 4

Children are probably most familiar with a regular hexagon. Explain that a hexagon is any closed figure that has six sides.

Digital Connection

Composite Shapes Using an interactive whiteboard, display an outline of a large basic shape. Ask a volunteer to select a smaller shape to drag into the large shape outline and to fit it against a side. Have another volunteer drag another shape into the outline, touching the shape that is already there. Continue until the outline shape has been filled. Then have children describe all of the shapes that made the larger shape. Continue with other large shape outlines as time allows.

Independent Practice

Teaching Tips

Item 5

Instruct children to circle a shape for every shape in the composite figure rather than circling one of each kind of shape used. Suggest they check their answers by counting the number of shapes in the hexagon and making sure they have circled the same number of shapes below.

Item 6

Provide cutout paper shapes or shape blocks for children who struggle with visual thinking and reasoning.

Independent Practice

5. This shape is also a hexagon. Circle the shapes that were used to make this hexagon.

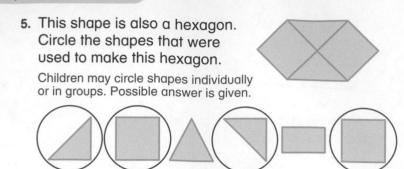

Children may circle shapes individually or in groups. Possible answer is given.

6. Jill has these 3 shapes.

Circle the shapes Jill can make using all 3 shapes.

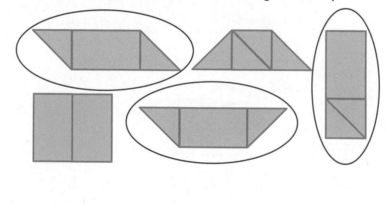

Math-to-Math Connection

Tangrams Provide pairs of children with a set of tangram tiles. Display a completed tangram picture that shows the outlines of the individual tiles. Encourage children to name the object that the combined shapes represent. Have pairs work together to build a replica of the picture by combining the individual tangram tiles. Discuss how the same set of seven shapes can be combined in many different ways to create many different shapes. If children need additional support, print out full-size outlines of tangram pictures. Children can build the shape by matching their tiles to the outlines shown on their papers. Then have partners switch papers.

Teaching Tips

Item 7
Allow children to trace the model and cut apart the squares to explore ways to rearrange the squares to make a different shape.

Item 8
If children struggle in their approach, talk about the similarities and differences between squares and other rectangles. Ask children which parts of the square can be separated and which cannot.

Independent Practice

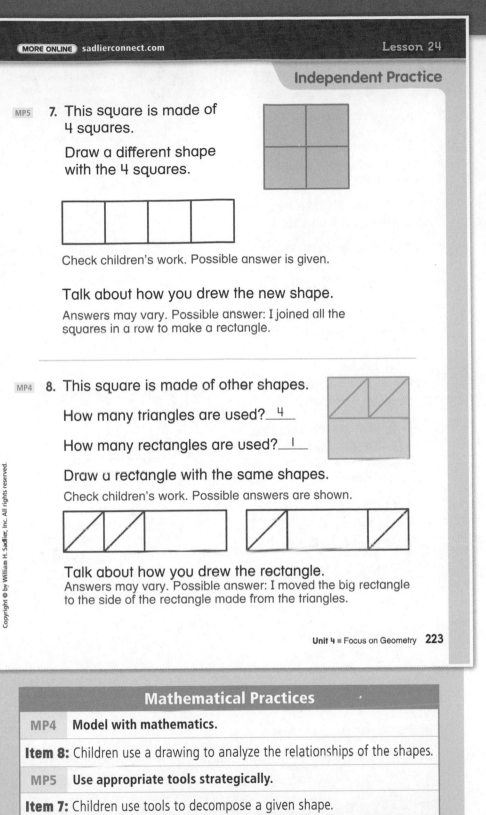

MP5 **7.** This square is made of 4 squares.

Draw a different shape with the 4 squares.

Check children's work. Possible answer is given.

Talk about how you drew the new shape.
Answers may vary. Possible answer: I joined all the squares in a row to make a rectangle.

MP4 **8.** This square is made of other shapes.

How many triangles are used? __4__

How many rectangles are used? __1__

Draw a rectangle with the same shapes.
Check children's work. Possible answers are shown.

Talk about how you drew the rectangle.
Answers may vary. Possible answer: I moved the big rectangle to the side of the rectangle made from the triangles.

Mathematical Practices

MP4	Model with mathematics.
Item 8: Children use a drawing to analyze the relationships of the shapes.	
MP5	Use appropriate tools strategically.
Item 7: Children use tools to decompose a given shape.	

OBJECTIVE

Combine three-dimensional shapes and identify the shapes that make composite solid shapes.

ESSENTIAL QUESTION

Ask children to describe and give examples of how flat shapes and solid shapes are the same and different. Explain that in this lesson children will learn about parts of solid shapes and how to combine and take apart the shapes.

FLUENCY PRACTICE

Fluency practice is available at **sadlierconnect.com**.

Concept Development

Understand: Use two cubes to make a new solid shape

■ Allow children to hold examples of cubes and discuss the attributes.

■ Ask children to compare the number of corners in a square to the number of corners in a cube.

■ Have children name the shape of the front of the rectangular prism. Point out that the name of the shape represents the combined shape, not just the two squares.

■ Have children name the shape of the end of the rectangular prism. Ask why the shape of one side of the solid shape is a rectangle and the shape of the other side is a square.

■ Children should recognize from previous work that two squares form a rectangle, but there is only one square on the end of the rectangular prism, so the shape on the end is a square.

Essential Question: How do you put solid shapes together to make a new solid shape?

Words to Know
flat shape
cube
solid shape
faces
rectangular prism

Guided Instruction

In this lesson you will learn how to put solid shapes together to make a new solid shape.

Understand: Use two cubes to make a new solid shape

A square is a flat shape. A cube is a solid shape that has 6 square faces.

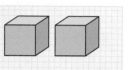

square   cube

> What new solid shapes can you make by joining two faces of these cubes?

Put the cubes next to each other. Put the faces together.

The new solid shape is a rectangular prism. All of its faces are rectangles. Some of the faces are squares.

Remember!
A square is a special kind of rectangle.

Put one cube above the other. The new shape is also a rectangular prism.

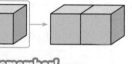

▷ When two faces of same-size cubes are joined, the new solid shape is a rectangular prism.

Words to Know

flat shape: a shape that has length and width

Example:

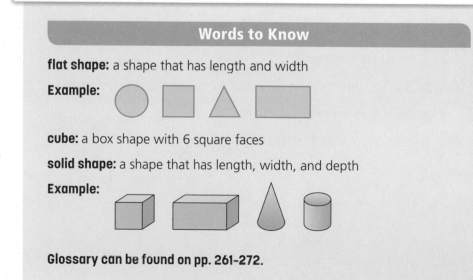

cube: a box shape with 6 square faces

solid shape: a shape that has length, width, and depth

Example:

Glossary can be found on pp. 261–272.

Lesson 25

Guided Instruction

Understand: Use a cube and a rectangular prism to make a new solid shape

What solid shape can you make by putting together these solid shapes?

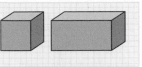

Match two faces that have the same shape.
Put the two faces together.
All the faces of the new solid shape are rectangles.

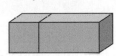

➡ The new solid shape is a rectangular prism.

Understand: Use curved solid shapes to make a new solid shape

These solid shapes have three flat faces.
The flat faces are same-size circles. What new solid shape is made by joining two of these faces?

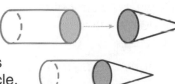

Put the two faces together.

➡ The new solid shape has one flat face that is a circle.

Understand: Use a cube and a rectangular prism to make a new solid shape

■ Make sure children understand that adding more cubes or rectangular prisms like the ones shown will continue to make new, larger rectangular prisms.

■ Have children use three-dimensional shape blocks to explore how cubes do and do not match the sides of rectangular prisms.

Understand: Use curved solid shapes to make a new solid shape

■ Point out to children that curved solid shapes are shapes that will roll.

■ Have children explore cylinders and cones to see how the circular faces can be combined.

■ Explain that the parts of these solid shapes that roll are not considered faces because they are not flat.

Words to Know

faces: the flat sides of a solid shape

Example:

face

rectangular prism: a solid shape that has 6 faces that are rectangles

Glossary can be found on pp. 261–272.

Connect: What you know about using solid shapes to make new shapes Use this page to help children combine cubes in various ways, noting that some of the combinations do not make rectangular prisms.

■ Point out that the adjoining faces of the different solid shapes are the same size and shape.

■ Have children use informal language to describe the shapes that they can make using six same-size cubes.

■ Provide cubes for children to use as they explore combining solid shapes in different ways.

Connect: What you know about using solid shapes to make new solid shapes

Linda made these two shapes out of cubes.

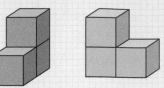

What new shapes can she make with these shapes?

Make the new shapes by putting the ___faces___ together in different ways.

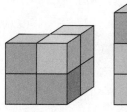 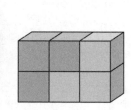

➡ These are some of the shapes Linda can make.

How many cubes are used in each new shape?

__6__ cubes

Support English Language Learners

Help English language learners understand that the word *face* has more than one meaning. When used as a verb, *face* can refer to looking a certain direction or turning to a particular position. The most common usage of the term is the noun that means a person's image from the forehead to the chin. Connect this meaning of *face* to the *face* of a solid figure. Use chalk to draw eyes and a smiling mouth on one face of a wooden block or box that is a cube. Have children think of the surface as the face of the block. Then rub away the eyes and mouth and ask a volunteer to draw eyes and a mouth on another surface of the block. Point out to children that there are six possible places on the block to draw a face, so the cube has six faces.

Lesson 25

Guided Practice

1. **Orlando built this solid shape with cubes. How many cubes did he use?**

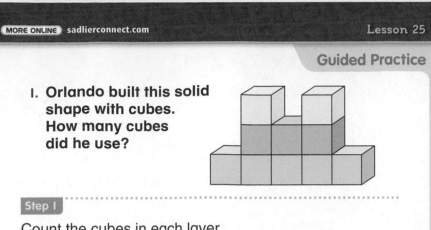

Step 1

Count the cubes in each layer.

How many cubes are in the top layer? _2_

How many cubes are in the middle layer? _3_

How many cubes are in the bottom layer? _5_

Step 2

Add to find the total number of cubes.

_2_ + _3_ + _5_ = _10_

Orlando used _10_ cubes to build the solid shape.

♛ Think•Pair•Share

MP6 2. Orlando also made this shape. Talk about how this shape is like the other shape. Talk about how it is different.
Answers may vary. Possible answer: This shape also uses 10 cubes. It is as wide as the first shape. It has only two layers of cubes. It is not as tall as the first shape.

Unit 4 ■ Focus on Geometry **227**

Observational Assessment

Use page 227 to assess whether children are able to use visual reasoning to analyze composite shapes. Observe whether children have difficulty identifying the number of combined solid shapes.

♛ Think•Pair•Share

Peer Collaboration Have pairs of children explain their answers to one another. Prompt the discussions with questions such as:

- *How many cubes did Orlando use in the first solid shape? In the second?*

- *How are the rows of cubes different in the two solid shapes?*

- *How long and how tall are the two solid shapes?*

Remind children that the color of the cubes is not important. All the cubes are the same size and shape.

Return to the Essential Question

Reread the Lesson 25 Essential Question on page 224: *How do you put solid shapes together to make a new solid shape?*

Tell children to think about what they learned in this lesson to answer this question.
(Possible responses: I can put cubes together to make rectangular prisms. I can put the circular faces of curved shapes together to make towers. I can put solid shapes together in different ways to make new solid shapes.)

Mathematical Practices

Mathematical Practice Standards underline the teaching and understanding of all concepts and skills presented. The emphasis of specific practices is noted throughout the guided and independent practice of this lesson.

MP6	**Attend to precision.**

Item 2: Children communicate with precision to compare the structures of two solid shapes.

Concept Application

Children may work independently on these pages in the classroom or at home. They may refer to the first four pages of the lesson to revisit the instruction or to see a worked-out example.

Common Errors and **Teaching Tips** may help you support learning either in the classroom or as a follow-up for work done at home.

Common Errors

Items 1–2

Children may miscount the number of solid shapes to combine. Suggest they draw a mark on each solid shape as they count the top group of solids and the new combined solid shape.

Teaching Tips

Items 1–2

Have children use connecting cubes to explore how they can combine solid shapes to model the new shapes shown.

Independent Practice

1. Look at these solid shapes.

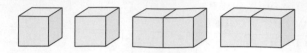

Circle the new solid shape below that can be made by using all the solid shapes above.

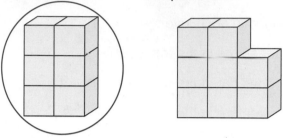

2. Look at these cubes.

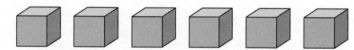

Circle the new solid shape below that can be made by using all the cubes above.

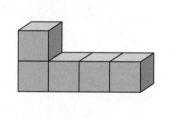
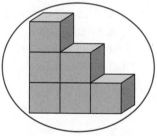

Talking About Math

Compare and Describe Details Use the answer choices in problems 1 and 2 to generate a discussion about how each pair of composite shapes is alike and different. Point out to children that they can count the number of rectangular prisms in each figure, but that answers can vary. For example, descriptions of the yellow shape that shows 6 cubes can be described as 2 vertical rectangular prisms or 3 horizontal rectangular prisms. It can also be described as 6 cubes or as a combination of cubes and rectangular prisms.

Lesson 25

Independent Practice

3. Look at these solid shapes.

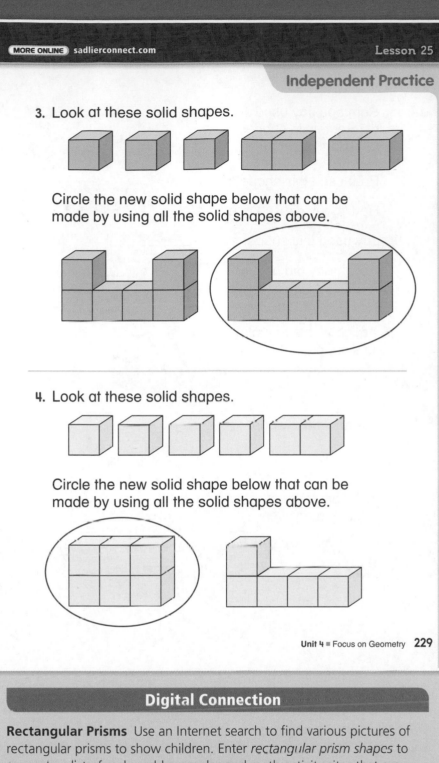

Circle the new solid shape below that can be made by using all the solid shapes above.

4. Look at these solid shapes.

Circle the new solid shape below that can be made by using all the solid shapes above.

Unit 4 ■ Focus on Geometry **229**

Teaching Tips

Items 3–4
Suggest children draw a line connecting each solid shape in the top group to the corresponding solid shape in the new combined shape below.

Digital Connection

Rectangular Prisms Use an Internet search to find various pictures of rectangular prisms to show children. Enter *rectangular prism shapes* to generate a list of real-world examples and math activity sites that are available. Display enough examples for children to be able to understand that some rectangular prisms have at least two square faces, but some have none. Include images of very thin rectangular prisms, such as the shape of a pack of gum.

Common Errors

Item 5

Children may mistakenly count the cubes in the solid shapes to the right of each blank. Make sure they understand that first model represents the solid shape that both Pam and Jay made. Pam used the second solid shape shown to make her model. Jay used the third solid shape shown to make his model.

Teaching Tips

Item 5

If children struggle to visualize each combination of solid shapes, have them trace the shape of Pam's solid shape onto the combined solid shape and count the number of shapes she used in all. Then have children trace the shape of Jay's solid shape onto the combined solid shape and count the number of shapes he used in all.

Item 6

Children may need hints for this complex visual reasoning problem that includes a hidden cube (bottom layer, left back corner). Provide connecting cubes and guide children as they construct the two given solid shapes that Jacob has. Then have children build each of the shapes shown as possible solutions and encourage them to use each shape to try to complete the solid shape that Jacob wants to make.

Lesson 25   **Compose Solid Shapes**

Independent Practice

5. Pam and Jay used different solid shapes to build this shape.

Pam used this shape.

How many did she use? __2__

Jay used this shape.

How many did he use? __4__

6. Jacob wants to make this shape.

He has these shapes.

What other shape does he need? Circle the answer.

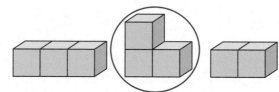

Math-to-Science Connection

Understanding Prisms In mathematics, a prism is a solid shape consisting of faces that are polygons. A prism has one pair of congruent, parallel opposite faces. In science, prisms are transparent, angular solid shapes. As white light, or sunshine, passes through it, the prism refracts, or bends, the light, separating it into bands of color. Under certain conditions, raindrops can act as prisms, reflecting sunshine back into the sky as a spectrum of light we call a rainbow. Bring a prism into the classroom and allow children to explore how sunlight enters the shape as white light and exits the shape in a burst of rainbow light. If a real prism is not available, use the Internet to view examples of prisms in action.

Lesson 25

Independent Practice

MP7 **7.** Look at these solid shapes.

Solid A   Solid B

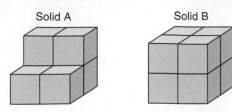

Talk about how these solid shapes are alike and how they are different.

Answers may vary. Possible answer: Both solids are made from cubes. They both have 4 cubes on the bottom. They have a different number of cubes on top. Solid A has 2 cubes on top. Solid B has 4 cubes on top. Solid A is made from 6 cubes in all. Solid B is made from 8 cubes in all.

MP2 **8.** This solid shape is made from 4 cubes.

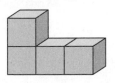

Talk about how you could move the cubes to make two other solid shapes.

Answers may vary. Possible answer: I could move one of the bottom cubes to the top so there are 2 cubes on top and 2 on the bottom. I could move the top cube to the bottom so there is a row of 4 cubes.

Unit 4 ■ Focus on Geometry **231**

Teaching Tips

Item 7
Remind children that sometimes not all of the cubes are visible in the picture. Ask questions to help them reason that the base in each figure must have four cubes in order to support the cubes that are on top.

Item 8
Make sure children understand that the altered shapes must show the cubes without gaps and that there are different possible solutions.

Mathematical Practices

MP2	Reason abstractly and quantitatively.

Item 8: Children analyze and describe different ways of transforming a solid shape into a new solid shape.

MP7	Look for and make use of structure.

Item 7: Children discuss geometric shapes in terms of their similarities and differences.

OBJECTIVE
Use drawings to make equal shares of halves and fourths.

ESSENTIAL QUESTION
Read aloud the Essential Question and ask children to tell what they know about sharing something equally or fairly. Explain that the lesson will help them understand how to show when the shares are equal or not equal.

FLUENCY PRACTICE
Fluency practice is available at **sadlierconnect.com**.

Concept Development

Understand: Make equal shares of a circle

■ Have children discuss the meaning of *equal*. They may give examples or draw pictures of things that are equal. Point out that *equal shares* has the same meaning. All of the pieces are the same size.

■ Ask children whether there are other ways to cut the circle to make equal shares. Drawing any diagonal line or a horizontal line through the center of the circle will also make equal shares.

■ Discuss whether it is possible to cut the circle so the shares are not equal. Demonstrate that any line that does not pass through the center of the circle makes shares that are not equal.

Lesson 26 Partition Shapes into Equal Shares

Essential Question: How do you make equal shares?

Words to Know
equal share
halves
half
fourth
quarter

In this lesson you will learn how to make equal shares.

Understand: Make equal shares of a circle

This circle has the same shape as a whole pizza.

How can 2 friends share the pizza equally?

Cut the whole circle into 2 equal parts. Each equal part is an equal share of the circle.

The circle is cut into halves. Each equal share is one half of the circle. There are 2 halves in the whole circle.

▷ Two friends can share the pizza equally when it is cut into 2 halves.

Words to Know

equal share: one part of an object that has been divided equally

halves: two equal parts that make one whole object

Glossary can be found on pp. 261–272.

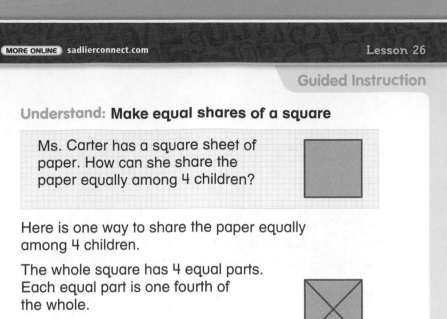

Lesson 26

Guided Instruction

Understand: **Make equal shares of a square**

Ms. Carter has a square sheet of paper. How can she share the paper equally among 4 children?

Here is one way to share the paper equally among 4 children.

The whole square has 4 equal parts. Each equal part is one fourth of the whole.

A fourth is also called a quarter. There are 4 quarters in a whole.

Here is another way to share the paper equally among 4 children.

The whole square has 4 equal parts. Each equal part is one fourth, or one quarter, of the whole. There are 4 fourths, or 4 quarters, in the whole.

⇨ Ms. Carter can use either way to share the paper equally among 4 children. Each child will get 1 fourth of the whole sheet of paper.

Unit 4 ■ Focus on Geometry **233**

Understand: **Make equal shares of a square**

■ Provide two cutout paper squares for each child to use as the class explores ways to fold their squares in four equal parts. Have each child fold one square twice diagonally and the other square horizontally and vertically. Point out that to make equal shares, the edges of the paper must align for each fold. This introduction to the page will help children build a hands-on understanding of fourths, or quarters.

■ Have children circle the base word *four* in the word *fourths*. Explain that making equal shares of fourths means making four parts that are exactly the same size.

■ Be sure children understand that the terms *fourth* and *quarter* have the same meaning.

Words-to-Know

half: one out of two equal parts of an object

fourth: one out of four equal parts of an object

quarter: one out of four equal parts of an object

Glossary can be found on pp. 261–272.

Guided Instruction

Connect: **What you know about equal shares** Use this page to help children relate equal shares of one half to halves and one fourth to fourths.

■ Children do not need to understand fractional notations at this level, but they build the understanding that *one half* means *one out of two equal shares* and that *one fourth* means *one out of four equal shares.*

■ Make sure children understand that the parts described as one half or one fourth are one part of a shape divided into equal shares.

■ Clarify that shapes can be cut into two or four pieces and not be cut into halves or quarters. Not all shares are equal shares. If one or more of the pieces is greater than the others, the shares are not equal, and the parts cannot be called halves or fourths.

Guided Instruction

Connect: **What you know about equal shares**

The two rectangles are cut into equal shares.

Rectangle A   Rectangle B

How many halves are in rectangle A?
How many fourths are in rectangle B?

Step 1

How many equal shares is rectangle A cut into? __2__

Each share is __1 half__ of the whole.

Color 1 half of rectangle A. **Check children's work.**

▷ There are __2__ halves in rectangle A.

Step 2

How many equal shares is rectangle B cut into? __4__

Each share is __1 fourth__ of the whole.

Color 1 fourth of rectangle B. **Check children's work.**

▷ There are __4__ fourths in rectangle B.

234 Unit 4 ■ Focus on Geometry

Support English Language Learners

Most English words can easily be changed from singular to plural forms by simply adding -s or -es. Exceptions to this convention often prove confusing to English language learners. As children work with equal shares, fourths, and quarters, the plural and singular forms of the words are easy to learn. The plural form of half is more difficult to master. Write *half* and *halves* on the board. Have children compare the words, share their observations, and use each word in a sentence.

Lesson 26

Guided Practice

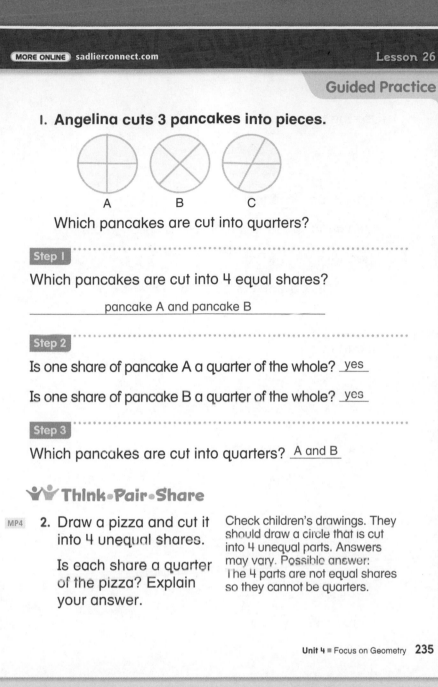

I. Angelina cuts 3 pancakes into pieces.

A   B   C

Which pancakes are cut into quarters?

Step 1

Which pancakes are cut into 4 equal shares?

pancake A and pancake B

Step 2

Is one share of pancake A a quarter of the whole? __yes__

Is one share of pancake B a quarter of the whole? __yes__

Step 3

Which pancakes are cut into quarters? __A and B__

Think•Pair•Share

MP4 2. Draw a pizza and cut it into 4 unequal shares.

Is each share a quarter of the pizza? Explain your answer.

Check children's drawings. They should draw a circle that is cut into 4 unequal parts. Answers may vary. Possible answer: The 4 parts are not equal shares so they cannot be quarters.

Unit 4 ■ Focus on Geometry **235**

Mathematical Practices

Mathematical Practice Standards underline the teaching and understanding of all concepts and skills presented. The emphasis of specific practices is noted throughout the guided and independent practice of this lesson.

MP4   Model with mathematics.

Item 2: Children analyze relationships of parts of a model.

Observational Assessment

Use page 235 to assess whether children are able to demonstrate an understanding of equal shares and fourths. Observe whether children have difficulty recognizing equal shares in different orientations. Remind children to compare the sizes of the shares rather than the position of the shares.

Think•Pair•Share

Peer Collaboration Have pairs of children display and explain their drawings to one another. Prompt the discussions with questions such as:

* *Did you draw a pizza that is a circle or some other shape?*

* *How did you decide on the first line to draw?*

* *Did the first line on your figure make equal halves or unequal shares?*

* *How many lines did you draw in all?*

Although most pizzas are circles, children may choose to draw a rectangle or a square. Ask children to describe whether they drew two lines that passed through the center of their figures or whether they drew unequal shares in a different way.

Return to the Essential Question

Reread the Lesson 26 Essential Question on page 232: *How do you make equal shares?*

Tell children to think about what they learned in this lesson to answer this question.
(Possible responses: I can cut shapes into halves or quarters to make equal shares. Using halves or quarters means that each of the pieces in the cut shape are the same size.)

Have children discuss how they know when two shares are not halves or four shares are not fourths, or quarters.

Independent Practice

Concept Application

Children may work independently on these pages in the classroom or at home. They may refer to the first four pages of the lesson to revisit the instruction or to see a worked-out example.

Common Errors and **Teaching Tips** may help you support learning either in the classroom or as a follow-up for work done at home.

Common Errors

Items 1–2

If children use the plural forms of half, quarter, or fourth to complete the second sentence in either problem, read the whole sentence aloud to emphasize that *each equal share* means one part of the whole shape.

Teaching Tips

Items 1–2

Make sure children understand that coloring half or a quarter means coloring only one equal share in each figure.

Item 2

Ask children to verbally recall the other possible answer for the second sentence. Point out that *quarter* and *fourth* are equally correct responses.

Independent Practice

I. Use the rectangle.

There are __2__ equal shares.

Each equal share is a __half__ of the whole rectangle.

There are __2__ halves.

Color half of the rectangle. Check children's work.

2. Use the circle.

There are __4__ equal shares.

Each equal share is a __quarter or fourth__ of the whole circle.

There are __4__ fourths.

There are __4__ quarters.

Color a quarter of the circle. Check children's work.

236 Unit 4 ■ Focus on Geometry

Talking About Math

Retell Stories Group children into pairs to retell a story of how they have shared a food item with someone. Have them write or draw to tell about who was involved, what they ate, and whether they each received an equal share. Ask children to draw a picture that shows how the food item was cut. If time allows, have children share their drawings with the class.

Draw lines to cut each shape into halves.
Answers may vary. Possible answers are shown.

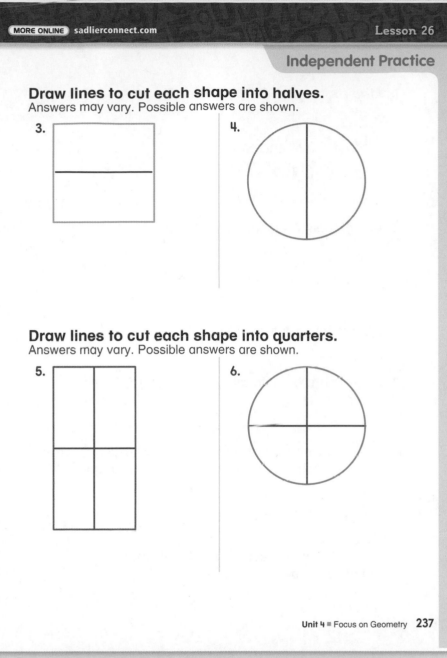

3.

4.

Draw lines to cut each shape into quarters.
Answers may vary. Possible answers are shown.

5.

6.

Common Errors
Items 3–6
Children may draw unequal shares. Engage children in discussions to determine whether the error is a result of misunderstanding of the concept or because children lack the fine-motor skills to draw the lines accurately. If children simply struggled with drawing skills, ask them to use toothpicks to show how they meant to divide the shapes.

Teaching Tips
Items 3–6
Encourage children to use a straightedge to draw the lines on the shapes. Each possible line in problems 3, 4, and 6 must pass through the center of the shapes. In problem 5, at least one of the lines must pass through the center.

Unit 4 ■ Focus on Geometry **237**

Digital Connection

Fractions Games Use available electronic games or a Web browser to have children practice identifying equal shares, halves, and fourths. Although children do not learn the term *fraction* or notation for fractions in grade 1, using *fraction* as a key word in a search will result in several suggestions that are appropriate for reviewing these earliest concepts of equal shares.

Independent Practice

Teaching Tips

Item 8
Ask children to justify their reasoning for their answer. The rectangle is cut into four parts, but because all the parts are not the same size, they do not show equal shares.

Item 9
Ask children how many quarters are in rectangle B. Listen for children to reason that there are no quarters in rectangle B because the shape is not cut into equal shares.

Item 11
One rectangle is divided horizontally and the other vertically, so children must use visual reasoning to estimate and solve the problem. Prompt logical thinking as an alternative approach by asking children whether folding the rectangle one time or two times will make it smaller.

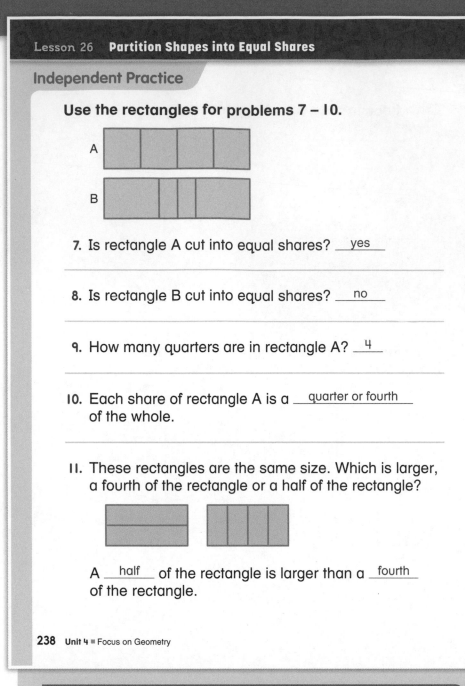

Independent Practice

Use the rectangles for problems 7 – 10.

A

B

7. Is rectangle A cut into equal shares? __yes__

8. Is rectangle B cut into equal shares? __no__

9. How many quarters are in rectangle A? __4__

10. Each share of rectangle A is a __quarter or fourth__ of the whole.

11. These rectangles are the same size. Which is larger, a fourth of the rectangle or a half of the rectangle?

A __half__ of the rectangle is larger than a __fourth__ of the rectangle.

238   Unit 4 ■ Focus on Geometry

Math-to-Math Connection

Money and Time Ask children to describe other math concepts that use the term *quarter.* Most children know that a quarter is a coin, and some may know there are four quarters in one whole dollar. Quarters get their name from the fact that one of those coins is one fourth, or one quarter, of one whole dollar. Children in Grade 1 learn about time to the hour and half hour, but some may have heard time expressed as a quarter after or a quarter till the hour. Give each child a paper analog clock circle. Have them fold the clock face in half vertically and horizontally. After children unfold the clock face, direct them to circle the numbers at the folds: 12, 3, 6, and 9. Have children discuss how these numbers can be used to divide one hour into quarters.

MORE ONLINE sadlierconnect.com

Lesson 26

Independent Practice

MP1 **12.** You can cut other shapes into equal shares. Draw lines to cut each shape into halves.

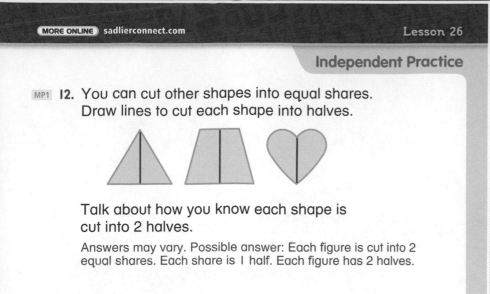

Talk about how you know each shape is cut into 2 halves.

Answers may vary. Possible answer: Each figure is cut into 2 equal shares. Each share is 1 half. Each figure has 2 halves.

MP6 **13.** Show 2 different ways to cut these rectangles into quarters.

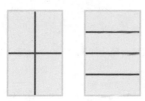

Talk about how you know each rectangle is cut into quarters.

Answers may vary. Possible answer: The 4 parts in the first rectangle are all the same size. Each part is 1 quarter. The 4 parts of the second rectangle are the same size. Each part is 1 quarter. Both rectangles have 4 quarters.

Common Errors

Item 12

Some children may draw horizontal lines, reasoning that the lines pass through the center of the shapes. Ask children whether each part is the same shape. At this level, if the parts are not the same shape, they are not equal.

Teaching Tips

Item 12

Children are most likely to draw a vertical line to divide each of the given shapes because a fold along that line is easy to visualize. A line from any corner to the middle of the opposite side will also divide the triangle in half.

Item 13

Lines that are spaced to show approximately equal fourths should be accepted if children can adequately justify the reasoning behind their drawings.

Return to the

Progress Check

Remind children to return to the Progress Check self-assessment, page 205, to check off additional items they have mastered during the unit.

Mathematical Practices

MP1	**Make sense of problems and persevere in solving them.**
Item 12: Children use pictures to conceptualize and solve a problem.	
MP6	**Attend to precision.**
Item 13: Children give carefully formulated explanations to justify their reasoning.	

Unit 4 Review

The Unit 4 Review covers all the standards presented in the unit. Use it to assess your students' mastery of the unit's concepts and skills.

Depth of Knowledge

The depth of knowledge is a ranking of the content complexity of assessment items based on Webb's Depth of Knowledge (DOK) levels. The levels increase in complexity as shown below.

Level 1: Recall and Reproduction
Level 2: Basic Skills and Concepts
Level 3: Strategic Reasoning and Thinking
Level 4: Extended Thinking

Item	DOK
1	2
2	2
3	3
4	3
5	1
6	1
7	1
8	2
9	3
10	4

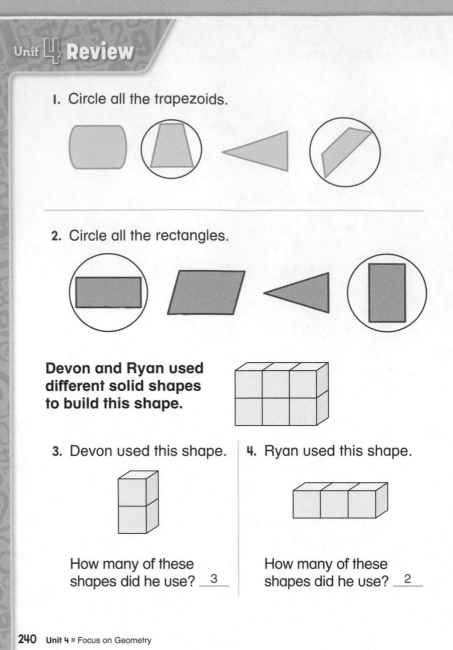

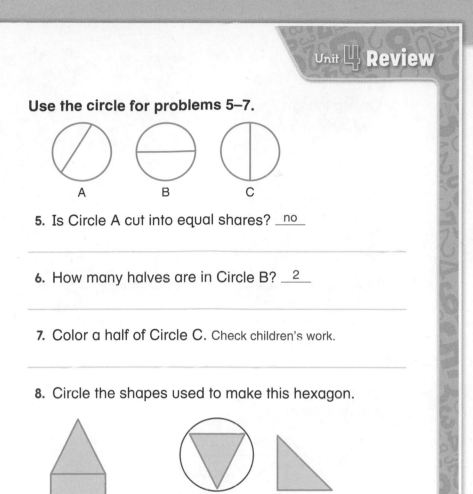

Use the circle for problems 5–7.

A   B   C

5. Is Circle A cut into equal shares? __no__

6. How many halves are in Circle B? __2__

7. Color a half of Circle C. Check children's work.

8. Circle the shapes used to make this hexagon.

This chart correlates the Unit 4 Review items with the lessons in which the concepts and skills are presented.

Item	Lesson
1	23
2	23
3	25
4	25
5	26
6	26
7	26
8	24
9	23
10	26

Talking About Math

Direct students to respond to the Unit 4 Essential Question. (This can also be found on page 207.)

Essential Question:
What shapes do you see?

Possible responses:
- I see triangles, circles, squares, and rectangles.
- I can identify flat shapes and solid shapes in patterns, designs, and other real-world objects.
- I can combine shapes to make bigger shapes. I can also cut shapes apart to show equal halves, thirds, and fourths.

Unit Assessment

- Unit 4 Review, *pp. 240–242*
- Unit 4 Performance Task (ONLINE)

Additional Assessment Options

- Performance Task 2, *pp. 243–246*
  (ALSO ONLINE)

Optional Purchase:

- iProgress Monitor (ONLINE)
- Progress Monitor Student Benchmark Assessment Booklet

Unit 4 **Review**

MP7 **9.** Draw a triangle.
Check children's drawings.

Mia also drew a triangle.
What <u>must</u> be true about your triangle and Mia's triangle?

Both triangles must have 3 straight sides and 3 corners.

What could be different about your triangle and Mia's triangle?

Answers may vary. Possible answer: They could be different sizes or different colors.

MP6 **10.** Show two different ways to cut these squares into quarters.

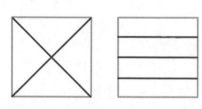

Check children's drawings. Sample drawings shown. Children might also draw 4 vertical lines or one horizontal and one vertical line to cut the squares into fourths.

Explain how you know each square is cut into quarters.

Answers may vary. Possible answer: Each whole is four fourths. In each square, the four parts are all the same size, so each part is 1 quarter of the square.

Mathematical Practices
MP6   **Attend to precision.**
Item 10: Children are careful to draw with appropriate accuracy to show equal shares in more than one way.
MP7   **Look for and make use of structure.**
Item 9: Children analyze triangles by the number of sides and discern similarities and differences of different triangles.

Performance Task 2

Performance Tasks

Performance Tasks show your understanding of the math that you have learned.

Beginning This Task

This is the beginning of a Performance Task. The next three pages have problems for you to solve.

As you work, you will:

1. Show that you can use math skills and concepts.

2. Decide how to solve a problem.

3. Use different ways to model and solve real-world problems.

Tips to help you!

- Read each problem carefully.
- Plan how you will solve the problem.
- Check your work.
- Be ready to show your work or explain your thinking.

Performance Task 2 **243**

ONLINE Customize Performance Task 2

Performance Task 2 in *Progress Mathematics* also provides children with additional practice. You can use the online items of Performance Task 2 to customize the amount and kind of performance task practice based on your ongoing evaluation of your children. You may choose to challenge some children, to give extra experience with a particular kind of task for other children, or to extend exposure to performance assessment for the entire class.

Go to **sadlierconnect.com** to download the following resources for Performance Task 2.

- Additional Items
- Additional Teacher Support
- Additional Scoring Rubrics

Performance Task 2 Overview

Performance Task 2 in *Progress Mathematics* provides children with practice for the types of items that may be found on standardized performance assessments.

Various item formats, including short- and extended-response items and technology-enhanced items, are included in the tasks. All items connect mathematical content correlated to the Mathematical Practices.

Items in Performance Task 2 are based on three primary types of tasks:

Type I Mastery of mathematical concepts, skills, and procedures

Type II Using and explaining mathematical reasoning

Type III Modeling problem situations in a real-world context

Performance Task 2 begins with a collection of three self-contained items in the Student Book and continues with additional items online at **sadlierconnect.com**.

Introduce Performance Task 2 Read page 243 to the children. Explain that Performance Task 2 may cover any of the math they have learned in Units 3 and 4. Orient children to each item and communicate helpful reminders that will enable children to approach each item successfully. Once children have completed each item, go over the correct responses with them.

Recommended Pacing Administer Performance Task 2 on Student Book pages 244–246 over three 15-minute sessions.

Teacher Resources For each task, the teacher materials include:

- Item types and purposes
- Correlations to Standards for Mathematical Practice, and Depth of Knowledge (DOK) levels
- Suggested administration procedure
- Scoring Rubric

Item 1: Art Class

Item	Type	Purpose
1.a.	III	Draw 3 worms of different lengths.
1.b.	I	Order lengths shortest to longest.

Item	MP	DOK
1.a.	1	Level 3
1.b.	6	Level 1

Administering Item 1 (Pacing: 15 minutes)

Ask a volunteer to read the introductory paragraph. Have others describe the situation in their own words.

Item 1.a. (10 minutes)

Guide children to align the left end of each worm with the yellow vertical line that is given. To help children who have difficulty with this task, provide them with connecting cubes to help them model and trace around three different lengths.

Item 1.b. (5 minutes)

Children need to write a color name in each blank. Point out that the color of the shortest worm should be first and the color of the longest worm should be last. The color of the worm that is between these two lengths should be in the middle blank.

Performance Task 2

Art Class

1. Art class is today. Everybody will make a drawing. How about drawing some worms?

   a. Draw a blue worm, a red worm, and a green worm. Make each one a different length.
   Check children's drawings.

   blue worm

   red worm

   green worm

   b. Order your worms from shortest to longest.

   _____ worm, _____ worm, _____ worm
   Compare children's drawings with order below.

244 Performance Task 2

Scoring Rubric

Item	Points	Student Responses
1.a.	2	Draws 3 different lengths, left-aligned.
	1	Draws only 2 worms or makes more than 1 worm the same length.
	0	Draws 1 or 0 worms.
1.b.	2	Orders colors shortest to longest.
	1	Correctly orders 2 of 3 colors.
	0	Does not order the colors or attempt the problem.

2. Tina cuts out these clay shapes.

She makes a table to show the shapes and how many of each shape she cut out.

a. Complete the table.

Shape	Number Cut Out
△	ЖĦ III
◯	IIII
▢	ЖĦ I

b. How many shapes did Tina cut out in all? Write an equation to find how many shapes she cut out in all.

$$\underline{8} + \underline{4} + \underline{6} = \underline{18}$$

Tina cut out __18__ shapes in all.

Performance Task 2 **245**

Scoring Rubric

Item	Points	Student Responses
2.a.	2	Correctly draws 4 and 6 tallies.
	1	Correctly tallies circles or squares.
	0	Does not complete the table.
2.b.	2	Correctly writes equation and sum.
	1	Correctly writes equation or sum.
	0	Does not write equation or sum.

Item 2

Item	Type	Purpose
2.a.	I	Sort, count, and tally shapes.
2.b.	II	Add numbers of all 3 shapes.

Item	MP	DOK
2.a.	1	Level 2
2.b.	2	Level 3

Administering Item 2 (Pacing: 15 minutes)

Ask a volunteer to read the introductory paragraph. Have others describe the situation in their own words.

Item 2.a. (9 minutes)

Guide children to see that they need to count the number of circles and the number of squares and then enter the numbers as tally marks in the table. Make sure children understand how to show a group of five tally marks.

Item 2.b. (6 minutes)

In this problem, children need to write an equation that has three addends. They then need to write the sum in the equation and in the sentence. To help children who have difficulty with this task, suggest the use of an addition strategy, such as making ten.

Item 3

Item	Type	Purpose
3.a.	II	Model fourths in a circle.
3.b.	II	Model fourths in a square.
3.c.	II	Model fourths in a rectangle.
3.d.	III	Explain the relationship between halves and fourths.

Item	MP	DOK
3.a.	6	Level 2
3.b.	6	Level 2
3.c.	6	Level 2
3.d.	3	Level 3

Administering Item 3 (Pacing: 15 minutes)

Ask a volunteer to read the introductory paragraph. Have others describe the situation in their own words.

Item 3.a. (3 minutes)

Guide children to see that the problem can be solved by drawing a circle and then drawing lines inside the circle to show 4 equal shares. To help children who have difficulty with this task, provide them with a circle manipulative and a straightedge to trace and divide the shape.

Item 3.b. (3 minutes)

Make sure children understand that they can show fourths of a square in more than one way. Provide a square manipulative and a straightedge for children who need them.

Item 3.c. (3 minutes)

Make sure children understand how a square and a rectangle are the same or different. Encourage them to divide the square and rectangle in different ways to show fourths.

Item 3.d. (6 minutes)

Have children focus on one of the shapes that they drew rather than comparing the sizes of shares between the models. Make sure they understand that comparing halves and fourths refers to the same whole. Children should be able to explain that the more equal shares, the smaller each share will be.

---

3. Dan is making a wooden puzzle. He wants to cut the puzzle into fourths. Draw three different models of a puzzle Dan could make.

a. Make one model a circle. Answers may vary. Sample puzzles shown.

b. Make one model a square.

c. Make one model a rectangle.

d. If Dan had cut his puzzle into halves, would the equal shares be larger or smaller than the fourths he made? Talk about how you know.

_____ larger; Answers may vary. Possible answer: The more equal shares you make, the smaller each share is. Halves mean 2 equal parts and fourths mean 4 equal parts. 4 is more than 2. So, if the wholes are the same size, fourths are smaller and halves are larger.

Scoring Rubric

Item	Points	Student Responses
3.a.	2	Correctly draws a circle in fourths.
	1	Draws a circle in 4 unequal shares.
	0	Does not divide a circle in 4 parts.
3.b.	2	Correctly draws a square in fourths.
	1	Draws a square in 4 unequal shares.
	0	Does not divide a square in 4 parts.
3.c.	2	Correctly draws rectangle in fourths.
	1	Draws rectangle in 4 unequal shares.
	0	Does not divide rectangle in 4 parts.
3.d.	2	Shows understanding of comparison.
	1	Shows partial understanding.
	0	Shows no understanding.

Foundational Skills Handbook

Number Names and Counting

	❄	❄❄	❄❄❄	❄❄❄❄	❄❄❄❄❄
0	I	2	3	4	5
zero	one	two	three	four	five

❄❄❄ ❄❄❄	❄❄❄❄ ❄❄❄	❄❄❄❄ ❄❄❄❄	❄❄❄❄❄ ❄❄❄❄	❄❄❄❄❄ ❄❄❄❄❄
6	7	8	9	10
six	seven	eight	nine	ten

Match.

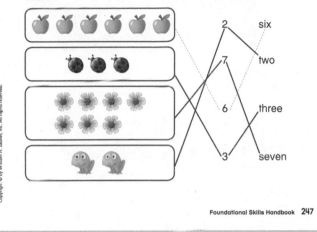

Foundational Skills Handbook **247**

The Foundational Skills Handbook: provides review of prerequisite content and skills needed for Grade 1.

Number Names and Counting

Explain to children that for each group of snowflakes, both the number and the number name below it tell how many are in the group.

For the first matching problem, help children understand why the blue lines match the group of apples to the *6* and *six*. Ensure that they understand that the last number they say as they count also tells how many are in the group. Have children match each group with its number and number name.

Foundational Skills Handbook Contents

Comparing Numbers

Children can use a matching strategy to compare numbers in groups. Have children look at the rows of flowers and ask them to use their own words to explain how the picture shows comparing numbers. Read aloud the sentences under the flowers and explain the meanings of *greater than* and *less than*.

To begin problems 1 and 2, make sure children know that they will draw lines from a picture in the first row to a picture that is directly under it in the second row. Point out that some pictures will not have a match.

If children struggle to remember whether to circle the greater or lesser number in each problem, have them mask the page to show only one problem at a time and draw a line under the second direction line. Children may use a counting strategy to check their answers.

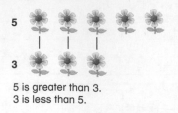

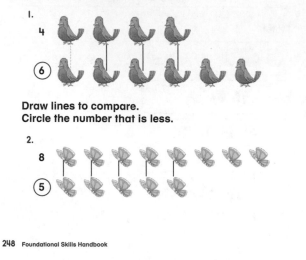

Comparing Numbers

5

3

5 is greater than 3.
3 is less than 5.

Draw lines to compare.
Circle the number that is greater.

1.

4

⑥

Draw lines to compare.
Circle the number that is less.

2.

8

⑤

248   Foundational Skills Handbook

Addition

There are 2 fish.
Then 1 more fish comes.
How many fish are there now?

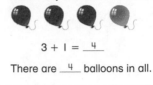

2 + 1 = 3

There are 3 fish now.

Add.

1. There are 3 red balloons and 1 blue balloon.
   How many balloons are there in all?

   3 + 1 = __4__

   There are __4__ balloons in all.

2. There are 4 birds in the yard.
   Then 3 more birds come.
   How many birds are there now?

   4 + 3 = __7__

   There are __7__ birds now.

Addition

Read the sample problem aloud and have children discuss the ways they might find a solution. Then have children look at the page and discuss how the picture of the fish models the problem.

To solve problem 1, children interpret a row of balloons in two colors to count the number in all. They can check their solutions by drawing 4 balloons and then coloring 3 red and 1 blue. Use this problem to review addition as a way to interpret one group that has two parts.

The solution to problem 2 involves the joining of two groups. Help children understand that they can start with the group of 4 birds and then count on to add 3 more birds. Children can check their solutions by counting all of the birds in the combined group.

Subtraction

Ask children to look at the picture and describe what they see. Be sure that children understand that there are 4 birds in all and that the bird that is crossed out is being taken away.

Children should see that problem 1 shows subtraction. Encourage children to cross out the two butterflies that are leaving. Make sure children understand that they need to solve the equation as well as complete the sentence.

For problem 2, explain that the total number of flowers is shown as one group. Have children count the total number of flowers in the drawing. Then, they can count the flowers that are not crossed out to solve the problem.

Subtraction

There are 4 birds. Then 1 flies away.
How many birds are there now?

$$4 - 1 = 3$$

There are 3 birds now.

Subtract.

1. There are 4 butterflies. Then 2 fly away.
   How many butterflies are there now?

$$4 - 2 = \underline{2}$$

There are _2_ butterflies now.

2. There are 7 flowers in the garden.
   Raj picks 4 flowers. How many flowers are left?

$$7 - 4 = \underline{3}$$

There are _3_ flowers left.

Make Names for Numbers

In kindergarten, children learned to decompose numbers in more than one way. The sample problem shows how to use objects or drawings to take apart 3 in four different ways. Make sure children understand that each way to show 3 is a name for 3: 3 + 0, 2 + 1, 1 + 2, and 0 + 3.

Explain to children that there is more than one way to solve problems 1 and 2. Have children work independently to color the circles as they choose and write the numbers that match their art. Allow children to share their solutions with the class. Record their responses on the board, and discuss why there can be several possible answers for each problem.

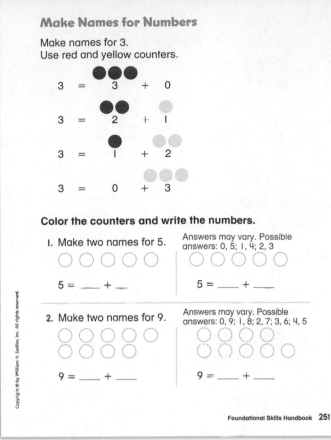

Make Names for Numbers

Make names for 3.
Use red and yellow counters.

3 = 3 + 0

3 = 2 + 1

3 = 1 + 2

3 = 0 + 3

Color the counters and write the numbers.

1. Make two names for 5.

5 = ___ + ___

Answers may vary. Possible answers: 0, 5; 1, 4; 2, 3

5 = ___ + ___

2. Make two names for 9.

9 = ___ + ___

Answers may vary. Possible answers: 0, 9; 1, 8; 2, 7; 3, 6; 4, 5

9 = ___ + ___

Make a Ten

Explain to children that they will use 10-frames to find missing addends that make 10. If available, display 8 red counters and 2 yellow counters to model the sample problem. Lead a discussion on how changing the addends does not change the sum.

For problems 1–4, children may use other strategies as they work with 10-frames. They may count on from the first addend, use a related subtraction fact, or count the number of blank spaces in the 10-frames. Make sure children can show their work by using drawings or hands-on counters and recording the results.

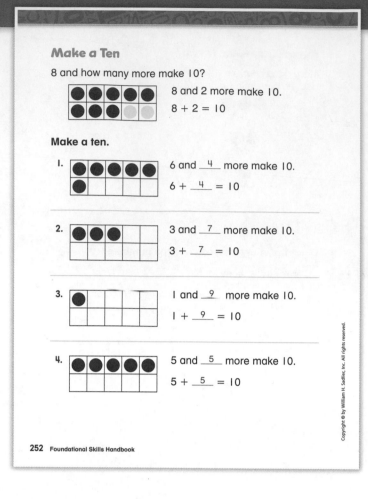

Make a Ten

8 and how many more make 10?

8 and 2 more make 10.

$8 + 2 = 10$

Make a ten.

1. 6 and _4_ more make 10.

   $6 + 4 = 10$

2. 3 and _7_ more make 10.

   $3 + 7 = 10$

3. 1 and _9_ more make 10.

   $1 + 9 = 10$

4. 5 and _5_ more make 10.

   $5 + 5 = 10$

Facts to 5

$1 + 1 = 2$ $3 - 1 = 2$

Add or subtract.

1. $3 + 1 = \underline{4}$

2. $3 + 2 = \underline{5}$

3. $4 - 1 = \underline{3}$

4. $5 - 0 = \underline{5}$

5. $1 + 2 = \underline{3}$

6. $3 - 3 = \underline{0}$

7. $5 - 3 = \underline{2}$

8. $1 + 4 = \underline{5}$

9.
$$\begin{array}{r} 2 \\ +2 \\ \hline 4 \end{array}$$

10.
$$\begin{array}{r} 2 \\ -1 \\ \hline 1 \end{array}$$

11.
$$\begin{array}{r} 2 \\ +3 \\ \hline 5 \end{array}$$

12.
$$\begin{array}{r} 4 \\ -3 \\ \hline 1 \end{array}$$

Facts to 5

In kindergarten children will demonstrate fluency using addition and subtraction facts to 5. Explain to children that the sample problems at the top of the page use pictures to show addition and subtraction. Ask volunteers to explain each picture and its math fact.

For problems 1–12, children should be able to demonstrate fluency by using mental math or addition and subtraction strategies. If children hesitate when approaching the problems, suggest specific strategies to prompt thinking, such as count on, doubles, or related facts. If children need additional help, encourage them to use pictures or objects to find solutions or to check their work.

Numbers 11–19

Explain to children that on this page they will review numbers that show 10 ones and some more ones. Lead a discussion on how the sample problem shows 10 ones and 1 more. Build understanding by having children take turns reading the sample problem aloud.

Children should see that ten ones are already shown in a full 10-frame in problems 1 and 2. Lead them to draw the additional ones that are needed before they complete the problems. Make sure children are able to name and identify numbers 11 to 19 as 10 ones and some more ones.

Numbers 11–19

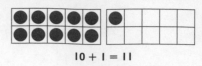

$$10 + 1 = 11$$

10 and 1 more make 11.

How many do you add to 10 to make each number?

1. Make 14.

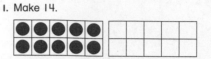

10 and __4__ more make 14.

$$10 + \underline{4} = 14$$

2. Make 19.

10 and __9__ more make 19.

$$10 + \underline{9} = 19$$

Measurement

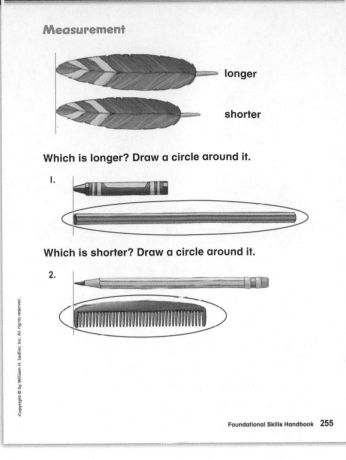

longer

shorter

Which is longer? Draw a circle around it.

1.

Which is shorter? Draw a circle around it.

2.

Measurement

Children need to be able to compare measureable attributes of two objects and describe them with terms such as taller/shorter, larger/smaller, and longer/shorter. In Grade 1, the standards focus on length. Use the sample problem to review the terms and meanings of *longer* and *shorter*. Point out to children the importance of lining up each pair of objects, as shown by the green lines in the problems.

If children struggle recognizing the terms accurately, suggest that they refer to the sample problem. Encourage them to underline the term *longer* and circle the term *shorter* in the sample problem. Then have them find the same terms in the problems and apply the same treatment.

Geometry and Data

Focus children on the sample boxes at the top of the page. Ask children to describe how they know that there are circles in the one box and triangles in the other. Have them describe how the circles and triangles in each group are alike and how they are different. Tell children to count the number of shapes in each box and read the sentences below the boxes.

In problem 1, help children understand that the blue line shows that the first triangle has 3 sides. Ensure that children understand to complete the problem by drawing lines from each shape to the appropriate box.

To complete problems 2 and 3, make sure children understand that they are counting the sorted shapes, not writing the number of sides in the blanks.

Geometry and Data

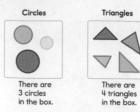

Circles

Triangles

There are 3 circles in the box.

There are 4 triangles in the box.

1. Match each shape to the correct box.

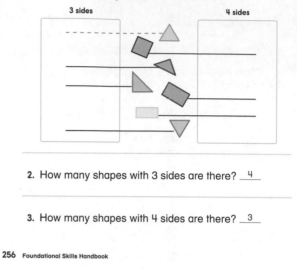

3 sides

4 sides

2. How many shapes with 3 sides are there? __4__

3. How many shapes with 4 sides are there? __3__

Problem-Solving Model

You can use this model to solve problems.

Read

Read the problem.
- What facts do you know?
- What do you need to find?

Plan

Plan how to solve the problem.
- Will you add or subtract?
- Will you draw a picture?
- Is the problem a one-step or two-step problem?

Solve

Use your plan to solve the problem.
- Did you answer the question?
- Did you label your answer?

Check

Make sure your answer makes sense.
- How can you solve the problem a different way?
- Is the answer the same?

Problem-Solving Model **257**

Introducing the Problem-Solving Model

You can use the Problem-Solving Model pages to encourage children to think problems through and solve them successfully.

The Problem-Solving Model is just one way to help children master the art of problem solving. Many children intuitively will see alternative methods or solutions. Their intuitive grasp of the problem situation should not be impeded or slowed by having to use the model. Children should be asked only to demonstrate that they solved a problem using some logical plan, and not necessarily this specific model. Children should be able to explain the method they have used.

A Shell Problem

Models and drawings provide children with a sense of the size of quantities and the relationship between those quantities. To find the missing addend in A Shell Problem, children refer to the drawing to perceive how the missing addend relates to the given addend and to the sum. They use the related subtraction fact to solve the problem and apply the count-on strategy to check the answer.

A Shell Problem

> Tina has some shells.
> Her friend gives her 9 more shells.
> Then Tina has 17 shells in all.
> How many shells did Tina have at the start?

Read

What facts do you know?
Tina's friend gives her 9 shells.
Tina has 17 shells in all.

What do you need to find?
How many shells Tina had at the start

Plan

Make a drawing. The number in all is 17.
One addend is 9. Find the missing addend.

17	
?	9

$$\blacksquare + 9 = 17$$

shells Tina has   shells Tina's   shells Tina
at the start   friend gives her has in all

Solve

Use the related subtraction fact. $17 - 9 = 8$

➤ Tina had __8__ shells at the start.

Check

Start with your answer, 8, and count on 9.
8 ⟶ 9, 10, 11, 12, 13, 14, 15, 16, 17
The answer is correct.

A Saving Quarters Problem

As children learn to add and subtract to solve problems, they begin to use the equation format to record their computations. In A Saving Quarters Problem, children subtract by comparing the two numbers in an equation in order to find an unknown difference. They use the related addition equation to check their subtraction.

A Saving Quarters Problem

> Lily saved 15 quarters.
> Jay saved 4 fewer quarters than Lily.
> How many quarters did Jay save?

Read

What facts do you know?
Lily saved 15 quarters.
Jay saved 4 fewer than Lily.

What do you need to find?
How many quarters Jay saved

Plan

The word *fewer* means not as many.
Write a subtraction sentence.

$$15 - 4 = \blacksquare$$

number of   difference between number of
quarters   Lily's number and   quarters
Lily saved   Jay's number   Jay saved

Solve

$15 - 4 = 11$ __11__ is 4 fewer than 15.

➤ Jay saved __11__ quarters.

Check

Use the related addition sentence. $11 + 4 = 15$
The answer is correct.

Standards for Mathematical Practice

The Standards for Mathematical Practice, identified here, are an important part of learning mathematics. They are covered in every lesson in this book.

MP1 Make sense of problems and persevere in solving them.

- Analyze and plan a solution
- Relate to a similar problem
- Assess progress
- Use concrete objects or pictures
- Check solutions

MP2 Reason abstractly and quantitatively.

- Pay attention to all mathematical language
- Represent problems using symbols
- Consider units in problem solving
- Use properties of operations and objects

MP3 Construct viable arguments and critique the reasoning of others.

- Analyze a problem situation
- Share reasoning with others
- Explain an approach to a problem
- Construct arguments by using drawings or concrete objects

MP4 Model with mathematics.

- Relate mathematics to everyday problems
- Make assumptions and estimations
- Explain the relationship of quantities
- Use concrete tools to explain operations
- Interpret the solution in the context of a situation

MP5 Use appropriate tools strategically.

- Consider the range of available tools (e.g., place-value charts, graphs, clocks, etc.)
- Decide on appropriate tools to use for each situation
- Use tools carefully and strategically

MP6 Attend to precision.

- Communicate with precision
- Identify the meaning of symbols
- Use measurement units appropriately
- Calculate accurately
- Carefully formulate full explanations

MP7 Look for and make use of structure.

- Search for patterns or structure
- Evaluate the structure or design of a problem
- Discuss geometric shapes in terms of their similarities and differences

MP8 Look for and express regularity in repeated reasoning.

- Make generalizations in computation
- Obtain fluency using patterns
- Look for patterns with shapes and designs
- Use patterns to relate operations
- Evaluate reasonableness of answers

Key: MP = Mathematical Practice

Glossary

add to find how many in all

2	+	3	= 5

---

addends the numbers you add

$$4 + 1 = 5$$

addends

$$\begin{array}{r} 3 \\ +7 \\ \hline 10 \end{array}$$ addends

C

cent a unit used for money

3 cents

5 cents

---

clock

column

column

1	2	3	4	5	6	7	8	9	10
11	12	13	14	15	16	17	18	19	20
21	22	23	24	25	26	27	28	29	30
31	32	33	34	35	36	37	38	39	40
41	42	43	44	45	46	47	48	49	50
51	52	53	54	55	56	57	58	59	60
61	62	63	64	65	66	67	68	69	70
71	72	73	74	75	76	77	78	79	80
81	82	83	84	85	86	87	88	89	90
91	92	93	94	95	96	97	98	99	100

corner

corner

corner

count on start at one number and count in order

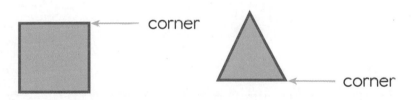

$$4 \longrightarrow 5 \quad 6 \quad 7$$

$$4 + 3 = 7$$

cube

digits 1, 2, 3, 4, 5, 6, 7, 8, 9, 0 are used to write numbers

2 4
↑ ↑
digits

---

dime a coin worth 10 cents, or 10¢

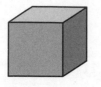

10 cents

---

doubles

3 + 3 = 6

doubles plus 1

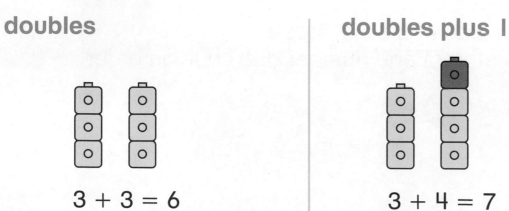

3 + 4 = 7

equal share

Each rectangle shows 4 equal shares.

---

equal sign (=) is equal to

$$1 + 1 = 2$$

↑
is equal to

---

equation a number sentence with an equal sign

$$5 + 6 = 11 \qquad 8 - 6 = 2$$

F

face a flat side of a solid shape

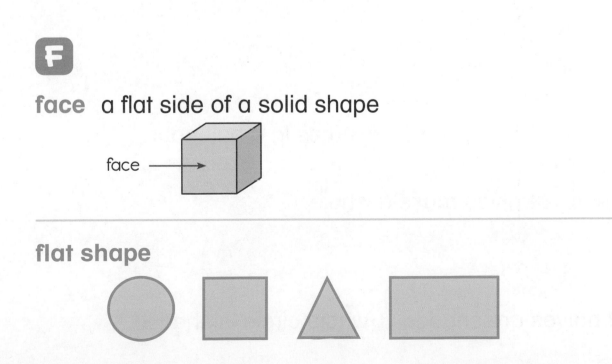

flat shape

fourth The rectangle is in fourths.

I fourth, or I quarter, is shaded.

greater than (>) is greater than

13 is greater than 12

13   >   12

half The rectangle is cut in half.

I half is shaded.

half hour There are 30 minutes in a half hour.

halves 2 halves make a whole

2 halves are shaded. I whole circle is shaded.

hexagon a flat shape with 6 sides and 6 corners

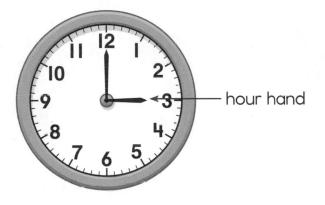

---

hour There are 60 minutes in 1 hour.

---

hour hand the shorter hand on a clock, shows the hour

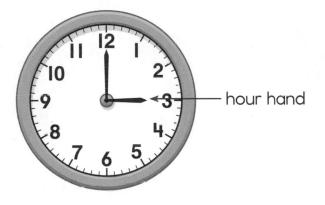

hour hand

length how long an object is

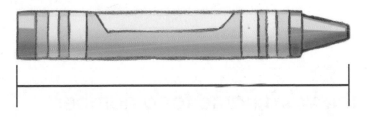

---

less than (<) is less than

13 is less than 22
13 < 22

minute There are 60 minutes in 1 hour.

minute hand the longer hand on a clock, shows the minutes

minute hand

nickel a coin worth 5 cents, or 5¢

5 cents

number names the word name for a number

26

twenty-six ← number name

ones

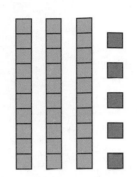

35 has 5 ones.

penny a coin worth 1 cent, or 1¢

1 cent

place-value chart a chart that shows the value of each digit

tens	ones
6	4

64 is 6 tens and 4 ones.

quarter   a coin worth 25 cents, or 25¢

25 cents

rectangle   a flat shape with 4 sides and 4 corners

rectangular prism

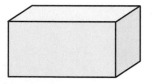

related facts   facts that have the same numbers

$7 + 6 = 13$ $13 - 6 = 7$

$6 + 7 = 13$ $13 - 7 = 6$

These four facts are related facts.

row

1	2	3	4	5	6	7	8	9	10
11	12	13	14	15	16	17	18	19	20
21	22	23	24	25	26	27	28	29	30
31	32	33	34	35	36	37	38	39	40
41	42	43	44	45	46	47	48	49	50
51	52	53	54	55	56	57	58	59	60
61	62	63	64	65	66	67	68	69	70
71	72	73	74	75	76	77	78	79	80
81	82	83	84	85	86	87	88	89	90
91	92	93	94	95	96	97	98	99	100

row →

side

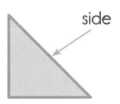

side

solid shape

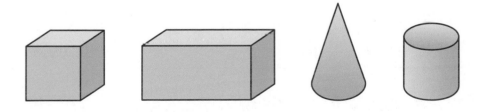

square a flat shape with 4 equal sides and 4 corners

subtract to find how many are left

$$5 - 2 = 3$$

sum the answer in addition

$$4 + 3 = 7 \longleftarrow \text{sum}$$

table

Favorite Sport	Number of Children
Soccer	⁙⁙⁙
Basketball	|||
Baseball	⁙⁙⁙ |||

tally mark marks used to show how many

| means 1   ⁙⁙⁙ means 5

tens

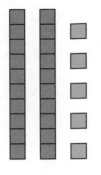

25 has 2 tens.

---

trapezoid

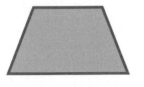

---

triangle   flat shape that has 3 sides and 3 corners

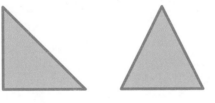

---

unit   used to measure length

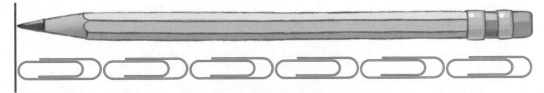

The pencil is 6 paper-clip units long.

Notes